# Making Gluten-Free Living Easy!

## Cecelia's Marketplace

Kalamazoo, Michigan

www.CeceliasMarketplace.com

# Gluten-Free

## GROCERY SHOPPING GUIDE

2009 / 2010 EDITION

## Dr. Mara Matison
## Dainis Matison

*khP*

Kal-Haven Publishing

# Cecelia's Marketplace
# Gluten-Free Grocery Shopping Guide

by Dr. Mara Matison & Dainis Matison

## khP

Kal-Haven Publishing
P.O. Box 20383
Kalamazoo, MI 49019 U.S.A.

ISBN  978-0-9794094-4-8

2009 / 2010 Edition

Printed in the United States of America
Cover illustration: Lilita Austrins

# CONTENTS

# About the Authors

The co-author of this book, Dr. Mara Matison, received her Doctor of Dental Surgery degree from University of Detroit Mercy, and her Bachelor of Arts degree in Psychology from Villanova University. Her husband and co-author, Dainis Matison, received his Master of Science degree in Information Technology and Bachelor of Arts degree in Finance from Ball State University. They are both members of Celiac Disease Foundation, Celiac Sprue Association, Gluten Intolerance Group, and Talk About Curing Autism. These are nationwide organizations that support people with celiac disease, gluten intolerance, gluten sensitivitiy and autism.

Cecelia's Marketplace was established by both Mara and Dainis in 2006, soon after Mara was diagnosed with celiac disease. The couple struggled with Mara's huge lifestyle change, which included adhering to a strict gluten-free diet. Shopping trips to the grocery store were very frustrating. Spending time calling food manufacturers to find out if products were gluten-free seemed like a daily routine. They knew there had to be an easier way, so they decided to compile a gluten-free grocery shopping guide. Since then, Mara has also been diagnosed with a casein and soy intolerance, which brought about the need for the *Gluten/Casein-Free Grocery Shopping Guide* and the *Gluten/Casein/Soy-Free Grocery Shopping Guide*.

Thanks to all three of Cecelia's Marketplace Grocery Shopping Guides, grocery shopping now has become easier for not only the authors, but also their families, friends and thousands of grocery shoppers nationwide.

# Preface - Note to the Reader

*Cecelia's Marketplace Gluten-Free Grocery Shopping Guide* has been written to help people that are in search of gluten-free products. Whether you are on a gluten-free diet, prepare gluten-free meals for yourself or others, or just enjoy eating gluten-free foods, this book is for you. It will help guide you to easy grocery shopping and eliminate the frustration and headaches that you've experienced trying to find gluten-free products. This guide is also great for restaurant owners, chefs, dieticians, family members, husbands, wives, friends, and others that shop for, or prepare gluten-free foods. For those that are not familiar with gluten-free cooking, we have included two special sections in the front of the book: What is Gluten and Gluten-Free Kitchen Tips.

We have alphabetized our Gluten-Free Grocery Shopping Guide to help you quickly find brand names of the products you are looking for. The guide is easy to use: just pick a product, look it up, and you'll have gluten-free brands at your fingertips. The book is small enough so that it can be carried with you to the grocery store when searching for products. Use it anytime, anywhere. In addition to the Gluten-Free Grocery Shopping Guide, there is a section in the back of the book that lists gluten-free over the counter (OTC) medications. Gluten-free shopping has never been easier. Treasure this book and enjoy all the gluten-free foods that are available!

Due to periodic changes in ingredients and new products, *Cecelia's Marketplace Gluten-Free Grocery Shopping Guide* will be updated annually.

A percentage of our proceeds are donated to nationwide nonprofit organizations that support people with celiac disease, gluten intolerance and other gluten sensitivities.

Dr. Mara Matison
Dainis Matison

# Acknowledgments

There are many people that have contributed to the creation of this book. The support from our family and friends has made this journey more enjoyable. Lilita A. for editing, cover illustration, and all the gluten-free meals that kept us going; Mik for editing, critiquing and successful business strategies; Ray for editing, all the reference materials and guidance to becoming successful entrepreneurs; Ligita for editing, supporting us and all the delicious gluten-free recipes along the way; Lija for data collection, packaging, and shipping; Ryan for data entry; Lilita M. for showing us 'The Secret'; Liana, Lauma, Velta and Ilga for believing in us; Annette Hensley and Leah Gorske for data collection; Jonnie Bryant for all the publishing advice and knowledge; Dr. Heidi Gjersoe for the diagnosis and support; Larisa Kins for book page layout & cover design; Jeff Matson at Creative Group for logo design; Natural Health Center for the wonderful gluten-free book signing events; Dr. Arnis Pone, Dr. Jason Ham, Kal-Haven Publishing, McNaughton & Gunn, and all our fellow "celiacs" for all the support.

# Warning - Disclaimer

This book has been prepared for the gluten-free consumer in order to make gluten-free grocery shopping easier.

This book should be used as an aide to guide the gluten-free consumer in the right direction when trying to find gluten-free products. The content of this book is not medical advice nor is it the advice of medical professionals. The authors, Cecelia's Marketplace, and Kal-Haven Publishing shall have neither liability, nor responsibility to any person or entity with respect to gluten ingestion or any health consequence.

Every effort has been made to make this gluten-free product guide as complete and accurate as possible. However, there may be errors, both typographical and in content. Therefore this text should be used only as a general guide, not as the ultimate source for gluten-free information. Food companies and manufacturers indicate that product ingredients may change periodically; therefore, the consumer needs to always check the ingredients on the manufacturers' labels before consuming their products. For specific questions or further information on celiac disease, please consult your physician.

If you do not wish to be bound by the above, you may return this book to the publisher within 30 days of purchase for a full refund (minus any shipping fees).

# What is Gluten?

Gluten is a special type of protein that is most commonly found in wheat, rye, and barley. It is comprised of two main protein groups: gliadins, and gluteins. People that have celiac disease, gluten intolerance, or gluten sensitivity may suffer from chronic digestive problems when ingesting foods that contain gluten. Gluten is found in most cereals, breads, pastas, soups, and pizza crusts. It may also be hidden in foods such as seasonings, salad dressings, sauces, additives and natural flavors. Maintaining a strict gluten-free diet is the only treatment. If these conditions are left untreated, it may lead to serious health complications. After gluten is eliminated from the diet, the digestive tract begins to heal and the symptoms normally start to disappear after a few weeks.

Celiac disease, gluten intolerance and gluten sensitivity are diagnosed using various testing methods. These can include a blood test, a biopsy of the small intestine lining and/or a stool sample.

Approximately 3 million Americans are affected by celiac disease (1 in 133 people).[1]

[1]University of Maryland Medical Center, Dr. Alessio Fasano, 2003 *Archives of Internal Medicine*

# Gluten-Free Kitchen Tips

It is very important prior to preparing a gluten-free meal, to clean the surrounding area including, pots, pans, utensils and any other items being used. Bread crumbs, flour particles or other gluten containing foods left in the cooking area can potentially contaminate a gluten-free meal.

Here are some tips to help prevent gluten contamination:

- Use an uncontaminated sponge to wash all working surfaces with soap and water.
- Clean and inspect pots, pans, utensils, cutting boards and other kitchenware for gluten residue.
- Use clean kitchen hand towels.
- If grilling, place aluminum foil over the grilling area.
- Use squeeze bottle mayonnaise, mustard, ketchup, peanut butter, jelly/jam, butter/margarine or other condiments to prevent cross-contamination.
- Avoid using wooden utensils. Gluten residue can stay embedded in wooden utensils and cutting boards.
- Use a separate toaster for gluten-free bread, rice cakes, etc..
- In commerical kitchens, if using latex/rubber gloves, make sure the gloves are not coated with powder (starch).
- Do not deep fry foods in contaminated oil (i.e. from breaded chicken wings, breaded chicken tenders, mozzarella sticks).

# Gluten-Free Dining Out

Nationwide restaurant chains offering gluten-free menus:

Austin Grill
Biaggi's Ristorante
Bonefish Grill
Bugaboo Creek Steakhouse
Carino's Italian Grill
Carraba's Italian Grill
Charlie Brown's Steakhouse
Cheeseburger In Paradise
Chili's Grill & Bar
Claim Jumper Restaurants
Fleming's Prime Steakhouse & Wine Bar
Legal Sea Foods
Romano's Macaroni Grill
Ninety Nine Restaurant
Old Spaghetti Factory
On The Border Mexican Grill
Outback Steakhouse
P.F. Chang's China Bistro
Pasta Pomadoro
Pei Wei Asian Diner
Pizza Fusion
Uno Chicago Grill
Weber Grill Restaurant
Wildfire Restaurants
Z. Tejas Southwestern Grill

# Other Products Available
## by Cecelia's Marketplace

### Grocery Shopping Guides:
*Gluten/Casein Free*
*Gluten/Casein/Soy Free*


### Other Products:
*GF Dining Out Cards*
*Gluten-Free Safety Labels*


### *FREE* Email Sign-Up
*Gluten-Free Product of the Day*


For **Product Alerts** or more information about our products please visit us online:

## www.CeceliasMarketplace.com

# Our Data Collection

The product information in this book was collected between May 2009 - August 2009. The information was received from product manufacturers and major supermarkets via internet, e-mail, phone, mail, or product labels.

The Food and Drug Administration (FDA) has proposed to define the term "gluten-free" as containing less than 20 parts per million (ppm) gluten. This regulation was scheduled to be issued in 2008. Some food manufacturers have begun testing their products for the presence of gluten. Those products that have not passed this test have been excluded from this book. Currently, not all companies test their products, therefore, we cannot guarantee that all the products listed in our book are less than 20 ppm gluten.

Those products that have been manufactured in the same facility as gluten, but indicate that they thoroughly wash their lines between products have been included. We have tried our best not to include products from manufacturers that do not take measures to prevent cross-contamination.

For more information on our data collection and up to date product alerts, please visit our website www.CeceliasMarketplace.com.

# Symbols

## Certified/Tested Gluten-Free Products

## &

## Gluten-Free Facilities

There are some companies that manufacture their products in a dedicated gluten-free facility or environment. Some products also go through strict guidelines and vigorous testing by either the Celiac Sprue Association (CSA) Recognition Seal Program or the Gluten Intolerance Group (GIG) Gluten-Free Certification Organization to be verified as gluten-free. In this guide we have marked these manufacturers and products with the following symbols:

- ▲ - manufactured in a dedicated gluten-free facility or environment

- ● - verfied, tested, or certified gluten-free by either the CSA Recognition Seal Program or the GIG Gluten-Free Certification Organization

Celiac Sprue Association ®

## This book is dedicated to:

All those in search of gluten-free products.

# Gluten-Free
# Grocery Shopping Guide (A-Z)

# ▲ A

**Alfredo Sauce**
  **Bertolli** - Mushroom, Regular
  **Classico** - Alfredo Sauce (All Varieties)
  **Full Flavor Foods▲** - Alfredo Sauce Mix●
  **Mayacamas** - Chicken Fettuccine, Regular
  **Safeway Select** - Regular, Roasted Garlic, Sundried Tomato
**Almond Beverage...see Nut Beverage**
**Almonds... see Nuts**
**Amaranth**
  **Arrowhead Mills** - Whole Grain
  **Bob's Red Mill▲** - Organic Flour
  **Nu-World Foods** -
    Amaranth Side Serve (Garlic Herb●, Savory Herb●, Spanish Tomato●)
    Bread Crumbs●
    Flour●
    Pre Gel Powder●
    Puffed●
    Seed●
    Starch●
    Toasted Bran Flour●
**Anchovies**
  **Crown Prince** - Natural (In Olive Oil, Paste), Regular (Flat In Olive Oil,
    Rolled w/Capers In Olive Oil)
**Angel Hair Pasta... see Pasta**
**Animal Crackers...see Cookies**
**Apple Butter**
  **Apple Time**
  **Bramley's**
  **Eden** - Apple, Apple Cherry, Cherry
  **Fischer & Wieser** - Texas Pecan (Apple, Peach)

**A**

Lucky Leaf
Manischewitz
Musselman's

**Apple Cider... see Cider**

**Apple Cider Vinegar... see Vinegar**

**Apple Rings**

Lucky Leaf - Spiced

Musselman's - Spiced

**Apples...** *All Fresh Fruits & Vegetables Are Gluten-Free*

Lucky Leaf - Fried, Sliced

Musselman's - Sliced

**Applesauce**

Albertsons - Cinnamon, Natural, Original

Appletime - Natural

Baxters - Bramley Apple Sauce

Beech Nut Baby Food - Applesauce (Stage I Fruits, Stage 2 Fruits)

Eden - Organic Apple (Cherry, Cinnamon, Regular, Strawberry)

Food Club Brand - Applesauce (Chunky, Cinnamon, Mixed Berry, Natural, Original, Strawberry, Unsweetened)

Full Circle - Organic (Cinnamon, Sweetened, Unsweetened)

Great Value Brand (Wal-Mart) -

Applesauce Glass Jar (Cinnamon, Regular, Unsweetened)

Applesauce Plastic Cups (Cinnamon, Natural, No Sugar Added, Regular)

Canned Applesauce Regular

Home Harvest Brand - Natural, Regular

Hy-Vee - Applesauce, Cinnamon, Light (w/Mixed Berry, w/Strawberry), Natural

Kroger Brand - Flavored, Plain

Lucky Leaf - Cherry Fruit 'N Sauce, Cinnamon, Natural, Regular, Strawberry Fruit 'N Sauce

**A**

**Meijer Brand -** Chunky, Cinnamon, Mixed Berry, Natural, Organic (Cinnamon, Sweetened, Unsweetened), Original, Regular, Strawberry

**Midwest Country Fare -** Home Style, Natural, w/(Cinnamon, Peaches, Raspberries, Strawberries)

**Momma's Old-Fashioned Applesauce -** Original Flavor

**Mott's -** All Varieties

**Musselman's -** Chunky, Cinnamon (Lite, Regular), Golden Delicious, Granny Smith, Healthy Picks (Blueberry Pomegranate, Cupucacu Key Lime, Raspberry Acai), Homestyle (Cinnamon, Regular), Lite Fruit 'N Sauce (Cherry, Grape, Orange Mango, Peach, Raspberry, Strawberry), McIntosh Apple, Organic (Regular, Unsweetened), Regular, Sesame Street (Cherry), Totally Fruit (Apple, Peach, Strawberry), Unsweetened

**Nature's Goodness Baby Food -** Applesauce (Stage 1, Stage 2)

**O Organics**

**Publix -** Chunky, Cinnamon, GreenWise (Organic Unsweetened Apple Sauce), Old Fashioned, Unsweetened

**Safeway Brand -** Cups, Natural, Sweetened

**Spartan Brand -** Cinnamon, Natural, Peach, Raspberry, Regular, Strawberry

**Stop & Shop Brand -** Applesauce (Chunky, Cinnamon, Mixed Berry, Natural, Strawberry)

**Trader Joe's -** Chunky Spiced Apples

**Wegmans Brand -**

Applesauce (Chunky, Cinnamon, McIntosh, Mixed Berry, No Sugar Added, Peach Mango, Regular)

Natural Applesauce No Sugar Added

Sweetened Applesauce

**Winn Dixie -** Cinnamon, Sweetened, Unsweetened

**Woodstock Farms -** Organic Applesauce (Apricot, Blueberry, Cinnamon, Mango, Raspberry, Regular)

**Apricots...** *All **Fresh** Fruits & Vegetables Are **Gluten-Free***

**Albertsons -** Canned

**A**

**Del Monte -**
  Canned/Jarred Fruit (All Varieties)
  Fruit Snack Cups (Metal, Plastic)

**Food Club Brand** - Canned Unpeeled Apricot Halves

**Hy-Vee** - Unpeeled Halves

**Meijer Brand** - Halves Unpeeled In Pear Juice

**Publix** - Canned Halves (In Heavy Syrup, Water & Artificial Sweetener)

**S&W** - All Canned/Jarred Fruits

**Stop & Shop Brand** - Heavy Syrup, Island Apricots In Light Syrup, Splenda

**Winn Dixie -** Unpeeled Halves In Heavy Syrup

Artichokes... *All **Fresh** Fruits & Vegetables Are **Gluten-Free***

  **Birds Eye** - All Plain Frozen Vegetables *(Except With Sauce)*

  **Cara Mia** - Marinated, Packed In Water, Salad

  **Native Forest** - Artichoke Hearts (Marinated, Quartered, Whole)

  **Reese** - Artichokes (Marinated, Regular)

  **S&W** - All Canned Vegetables

  **Safeway Select -** Marinated Artichokes

  **Spartan Brand -** Artichoke Hearts (Marinated, Regular)

  **Trader Joe's** - Artichoke Antipasto, Artichoke Hearts In Water, Artichoke Red Pepper Tapenade,

  **Wegmans Brand** - Artichoke Hearts (Halves & Quarters, In Brine, Marinated Quartered), Marinated Long Stemmed

Asparagus... *All **Fresh** Fruits & Vegetables Are **Gluten-Free***

  **Albertsons -** Cuts & Tips, No Salt Spears, Whole Spears

  **Birds Eye** - All Plain Frozen Vegetables *(Except With Sauce)*

  **Cara Mia** - Marinated Green

  **Cascadian Farm** - Organic Frozen Asparagus Cuts

  **Del Monte** - All Canned Varieties

  **Food Club Brand** - Canned Whole Asparagus

**A**

**B**

**Great Value Brand (Wal-Mart) -**
   Canned (All Green Asparagus Spears, Cuts & Tips, Extra Long)
   Frozen (Whole Spear Asparagus)
**Green Giant -** Canned Spears, Cut Asparagus
**Hannaford Brand -** Cuts & Tips, Whole Tall
**Hy-Vee -** Cut Spears
**Kroger Brand -** All Plain Vegetables (Canned, Frozen)
**Laura Lynn -** Cut Asparagus
**Meijer Brand -** Canned Cuts & Tips
**Native Forest -** Green (Cuts & Tips, Spears), White
**Nature's Promise -** Organic Asparagus Spears
**S&W -** All Canned Vegetables
**Safeway Brand -** Canned Cut
**Spartan Brand -** Cut
**Stop & Shop Brand -** Asparagus (Spears, Tips & Cuts)
**Trader Joe's -** All Plain Vegetables (Frozen)
**Wegmans Brand -** Cleaned And Cut Tips, Cut Spears & Tips
**Woodstock Farms -** Organic Frozen Whole Baby Asparagus
Avocado... *All **Fresh** Fruits & Vegetables Are **Gluten-Free***
Avocado Dip... see Guacamole and/or Dip/Dip Mix

# B

**Baby Food**
 **Beech-Nut -**
   Cereals (DHA Plus Rice, Rice)
   Cereals Good Evening (Whole Grain Brown Rice)
   Stage 1 Fruits (Applesauce, Chiquita Bananas, Peaches, Pears, Prunes)
   Stage 1 Meats (Beef & Beef Broth, Chicken & Chicken Broth, Turkey & Turkey Broth)
   Stage 1 Vegetables (Butternut Squash, Tender Golden Sweet Potatoes, Tender Sweet Carrots, Tender Sweet Peas, Tender Young Green Beans)

## baby food

**B**

Stage 2 Desserts (Banana Apple Yogurt, DHA Plus Apple Delight)

Stage 2 Dinners (Apples & Chicken, Chicken & Rice, Chicken Noodle, Homestyle Chicken Soup, Macaroni & Beef w/Vegetables, Pineapple Glazed Ham, Sweet Potatoes & Chicken, Turkey & Rice, Vegetables & Beef, Vegetables & Chicken)

Stage 2 Dinners Good Evening (Creamy Chicken Noodle, Ham & Pineapple & Rice, Hearty Vegetable Stew, Sweet Potato & Turkey, Turkey Tetrazzini)

Stage 2 Fruits (Apples & Bananas, Apples & Blueberries, Apples & Cherries, Apples w/Mango & Kiwi, Apples w/Pears & Bananas, Applesauce, Apricots w/Pears & Apples, Chiquita Bananas, Chiquita Bananas & Strawberries, DHA Plus Apple Delight, DHA Plus Apple w/Pomegranate Juice, DHA Plus Banana Supreme, Guava, Mango, Papaya, Peaches, Peaches & Bananas, Pears, Pears & Pineapples, Pears & Raspberries, Plums w/Apples & Pears)

Stage 2 Rice Cereal (Apples w/Cinnamon)

Stage 2 Vegetables (Butternut Squash, Carrots & Peas, Corn & Sweet Potatoes, Country Garden Vegetables, DHA Plus Butternut Squash w/Corn, DHA Plus Garden Vegetable, DHA Plus Sweet Potatoes, Mixed Vegetables, Sweet Corn Casserole, Sweet Potatoes & Apples, Tender Golden Sweet Potatoes, Tender (Sweet Carrots, Sweet Peas, Young Green Beans))

Stage 3 Dinners (Country Vegetables & Chicken)

Stage 3 Fruits (Apples & Bananas, Chiquita Bananas, Homestyle Apples Cherries Plums, Homestyle Cinnamon Raisins & Pears, Homestyle Peaches Apples & Bananas, Homestyle Pears & Blueberries)

Stage 3 Rice Cereal & Pears

Stage 3 Turkey Rice Dinner

Stage 3 Vegetables (Green Beans & Corn & Rice, Sweet Potatoes)

**Bright Beginnings** - Pediatric Drink (Chocolate, Vanilla)

**Earth's Best Organic Baby Food** -

1st Beginner First Foods (Apples, Bananas, Carrots, Peas, Pears, Sweet Potatoes)

**B**

2nd Fruits (Apples, Apples & Apricots, Apples & Bananas, Apples & Blueberries, Apples & Plums, Bananas, Bananas & Peaches & Raspberries, Pears, Pears & Mangos, Pears & Raspberries, Plum Banana Brown Rice Fruit & Whole Grain Combinations)

2nd Vegetables (Carrots, Corn & Butternut Squash, Garden Vegetables, Green Beans & Rice, Peas & Brown Rice, Sweet Potatoes, Winter Squash)

3rd Dinners (Vegetable Beef Pilaf)

3rd Fruits (Banana & Strawberries, Chunky Orchard Fruit)

Whole Grain Rice Cereal

**Ella's Kitchen** - Organic Baby Food (Apples & Bananas, Broccoli Pears & Peas, Carrot Apple & Parsnip, Peaches & Bananas, Strawberries & Apples, Sweet Potato Pumpkin Apple & Bluberries)

**Gerber Baby Food-**

1st Foods Fruits & Vegetables (Applesauce, Bananas, Carrots, Green Beans, Peaches, Pears, Peas, Prunes, Squash, Sweet Potatoes)

2nd Foods Desserts (Banana Yogurt, Fruit Medley)

2nd Foods Dinners (Apples & Chicken, Beef & Beef Gravy, Chicken & Chicken Gravy, Chicken & Rice, Ham & Ham Gravy, Pears & Chicken, Sweet Potatoes & Turkey, Turkey & Turkey Gravy, Veal & Veal Gravy, Vegetable Beef, Vegetable Chicken)

2nd Foods Fruits & Vegetables (Apple Blueberry, Apple Strawberry Banana, Apples & Cherries, Applesauce, Apricots w/Mixed Fruit, Banana Mixed Berry, Banana Orange Medley, Banana Plum Grape, Banana w/Apples & Pears, Bananas, Carrot Apple Mango, Carrots, Garden Vegetable, Green Beans, Mango, Mixed Vegetables, Peaches, Pear Pineapples, Pears, Peas, Prunes w/Apples, Smoothies (Hawaiian Delight, Peach Cobbler), Squash, Sweet Potatoes, Sweet Potatoes & Corn)

3rd Foods Desserts (Fruit Medley Dessert)

3rd Foods Dinners Vegetable (Beef, Chicken, Turkey)

3rd Foods Fruits & Vegetables (Applesauce, Banana Strawberry, Bananas, Broccoli & Carrots w/Cheese, Carrots, Green Beans w/Rice, Peaches, Pears, Squash, Sweet Potatoes)

DHA (Apple Blackberry, Apples & Summer Peaches, Banana Mango, Banana Pineapple Orange Medley, Butternut Squash & Harvest Apples, Farmers Market Vegetable Blend, Spring Vegetable Risotto w/Cheese Dinner)

Graduates Finger Foods (Apple Wagon Wheels, Carrot Wagon Wheels)

Graduates For Toddlers (Lil' Sides Mashed Sweet Potatoes & Glazed Carrots, White Turkey Stew w/Rice & Vegetables)

Graduates Fruit (Diced Apples, Diced Peaches)

Graduates Fruit Strips (Apple, Strawberry, Wildberry)

Graduates Fruit Twists (Apple & Strawberry, Strawberry & Grape)

Graduates Healthy Meals For Preschoolers (Chicken & Black Beans, Chicken & Rice, Mixed Vegetables, Southwestern Style Rice)

Graduates Juice Treats (Fruit Medley, Tropical)

Graduate Lil' Sticks (Chicken, Chicken & Carrot, Meat, Turkey)

Graduate Smart Sips (Mild Strawberry, Mild Vanilla, Plain)

Graduates Yogurt Melts (Peach, Mixed Strawberry, Strawberry)

Rice Cereal (DHA, DHA Brain & Eye Development, Single Grain, w/Apples, w/Mixed Fruit)

Rice Single Grain Cereal

**Gerber Organic Baby Food** -

1st Foods (Applesauce, Bananas, Carrots, Pears, Sweet Peas, Sweet Potatoes)

2nd Foods (Apple Strawberry, Applesauce, Bananas, Butternut Squash & Carrots, Carrots, Chicken & Wild Rice, Chicken w/Country Vegetables, Corn, Green Beans, Pear & Wildberry, Squash Corn & Chicken, Sweet Potatoes)

3rd Foods (Tender Harvest Savory Carrots Potatoes Beef)

Brown Rice Whole Grain Cereal

Mini Fruits - Apple, Banana Pineapple, Banana Strawberry

**B** **Homemade Baby** - Baby Tex Mex●, Just (Apples●, Green Beans●, Pears●, Peas●, Squash●, Sweet Potatoes●), Piwi●, Squapples●, Yummy Yammies●

**Meijer Brand** -

DND (Chocolate, Strawberry, Vanilla)

Gluco Burst (Arctic Cherry, Chocolate Diabetic Nutritional Drink, Strawberry DND, Vanilla DND)

Little Fruit (Apple, Strawberry/Banana)

Little Veggies Corn

PND (Bright Beginnings Vanilla Soy, Chocolate, Strawberry, Vanilla Soy, Vanilla w/Fiber)

Term Formula (Regular, Soy)

Vanilla Pediatric Nutritional Drink

w/DHA (Follow On, Gentle Protein, Lactose Free, Milk, Soy)

**Nature's Goodness Baby Food**

Stage 1 Fruits & Vegetables (Applesauce, Bananas, Carrots, Green Beans, Peaches, Pears, Peas, Prunes, Squash, Sweet Potatoes)

Stage 2 Desserts (Banana Pudding, Cherry Vanilla Pudding, Dutch Apple, Fruit Dessert, Mango Fruit, Papaya Fruit, Tutti Frutti)

Stage 2 Dinners (Apples & Chicken, Apples & Ham, Beef & Beef Gravy, Broccoli & Chicken, Chicken & Chicken Gravy, Green Beans & Turkey, Sweet Potatoes & Turkey, Turkey & Turkey Gravy, Turkey Rice Dinner, Vegetable Dinner (Bacon, Beef, Chicken, Ham)

Stage 2 Fruits & Vegetables (Applesauce, Apples & Blueberries, Apples & Pears, Apples Strawberries & Bananas, Apples w/Squash, Apricots w/Pears & Apples, Bananas, Bananas w/Apples & Pears, Bananas w/Mixed Berries, Carrots, Corn & Sweet Potatoes, Green Beans, Mixed Vegetables, Peaches, Pears, Plums w/Apples, Prunes w/Pears, Pumpkins w/Pears, Squash, Sweet Peas, Sweet Potatoes, Sweet Potatoe Casserole)

Stage 2 Rice Cereal (& Peaches, w/Applesauce)

Stage 3 Desserts (Bananas & Strawberry w/Tapioca, Bananas w/Tapioca)

**B**

Stage 3 Dinners (Green Beans & Rice, Turkey Rice)

Stage 3 Vegetable Sweet Potatoes

## O Organics -

Stage 1 (Applesauce, Bananas, Carrots, Peas, Sweet Potatoes)

Stage 2 (Apple Apricot, Apple Banana, Apple Wild Blueberry, Applesauce, Bananas, Carrots, Mixed Vegetables, Peach Rice Banana, Pear Raspberry, Pears, Peas and Brown Rice, Prunes, Squash, Sweet Potatoes, Summer Vegetables)

Stage 3 (Sweet Potato Chicken Dinner, Vegetable Beef Dinner, Vegetable Lentil Dinner)

## Baby Formula

### Bright Beginnings -

Baby Formulas (Follow On, Gentle Baby, Organic Baby, Original, Soy)

**Earth's Best** - Organic Infant Formula w/DHA & ARA *(Except Soy Infant Formula)*

**Enfamil** - All Varieties

**Hy-Vee -** Baby Formula (Formula, Gentle, Milk Based, Soy), Pediatric Electrolyte (Fruit, Grape, Regular)

**Neocate -** Infant (DHA & ARA, Regular), Junior (Chocolate, Tropical, Unflavored), Nutra, One +

### Nestle Good Start -

2 For Older Babies

Gental (Gental 2, Gental Plus, Protect Plus, Soy Plus 2)

Soy DHA & ARA

Supreme (DHA & ARA w/Iron, 2 DHA & ARA w/Calcium & Iron)

**Nutramigen** - All Varieties

**Pregestimil** - All Varieties

**Publix -** Infant Formula (Milk, Soy)

**Similac** - All Varieties

## Bacon

**Applegate Farms -** Natural (Canadian, Dry Cured, Peppered, Sunday, Turkey), Organic (Sunday, Turkey)

**B**

Black Label

**Butcher's Cut** - All Varieties *(Must Have EST 1331)*

**Butterball** - Turkey (Lower Sodium, Regular, Thin & Crispy)

**Dietz & Watson** - Canadian Style, Premium Imported

**Dorothy Lane Market** - All Varieties (Uncured)

**Farmer John** - Center Cut, Dry Salt Pork, Ends And Pieces, Maple Ends And Pieces, Old Fashion Maple Table Brand, Premium (Cracked Peppercorn, Low Sodium, Old Fashioned Maple, Regular Smoked, Thick Sliced), Quick Serve Fully Cooked, Table Brand, Thick Smoked

**Five Star Brand** - Canadian

**Garrett County Farms** - Classic Sliced (Dry Rubbed, Turkey), Sliced (Applewood, Canadian Style), Thick Sliced Dry Rubbed, Turkey Peppered

**Global Gourmet** - Irish Bacon

**Great Value Brand (Wal-Mart)** - Hickory Smoked, Peppered

**Honeysuckle White** - Smoked Turkey Bacon

**Hormel** - Canadian Style, Fully Cooked, Microwave, Natural Choice (Canadian, Original)

**Hy-Vee** - Applewood, Double Smoked, Hickory, Hickory Smoked Fully Cooked, Lower Sodium, Maple, Peppered, Sweet Smoked

**Jennie-O** - Bacon (Extra Lean Turkey, Turkey)

**Jimmy Dean** - Fully Cooked Slices (Hickory Smoked, Maple), Premium Bacon (Hardwood Smoked Turkey, Lower Sodium, Original, Thick Slice)

**Jones Dairy Farm** - Canadian●, Old Fashioned Slab●, Sliced (Cherrywood Smoked●, Regular●, Thick●)

**Kroger Brand** - Plain

**Lowes Foods Brand** - Center Cut Sliced, Fully Cooked, Lower Sodium, Sliced

**Marsh Brand** - Bacon

**Meijer Brand** - Lower Sodium, Regular

**Old Smokehouse** - Applewood, Maple Peppered, Original

## bacon bits

**B**

**Organic Prairie** -
Fresh Organic (Hardwood Smoked Bacon 8 oz., Hardwood Smoked Turkey Bacon 8 oz., Sliced Canadian Bacon 6 oz.)
Frozen Organic Hardwood Smoked 8 oz. (Bacon, Turkey Bacon)

**Oscar Mayer** - America's Favorite, Center Cut, Hearty Thick Cut, Lower Sodium, Natural Smoked Uncured, Ready To Serve (Bacon, Thick Cut)

**Publix** - All Varieties

**Range Brand**

**Safeway Brand** - Hickory Smoked, Lower Sodium, Regular

**Shelton's** - Turkey Breakfast Strips

**Smithfield** - Brown Sugar, Center Cut 40% Lower Fat, Cracked Peppercorn, Maple, Natural Hickory Smoked, Natural Hickory Smoked Thick Sliced

**Stop & Shop Brand** - Bacon (Center Cut Sliced, Lower Sodium, Maple Flavored, Regular Sliced)

**Trader Joe's** - Turkey, Uncured

**Ukrop's** - Sliced, Thick

**Wegmans** - Fully Cooked Natural Smoked, Uncured Applewood Smoked

**Wellshire Farms** - Bacon (Bulk Maple, Classic Sliced Dry Rubbed, Classic Sliced Turkey, Dry Rubbed Center Cut, Fully Cooked Hickory Smoked, Natural, PA Pork Applewood Smoked, Sliced Beef, Sliced Canadian Brand Turkey, Sliced Canadian Style, Sliced Dry Rubbed, Sliced Maple, Sliced Panchetta, Sliced Peppered Dry Rubbed, Sliced Peppered Turkey, Thick Sliced Dry Rubbed, Whole Panchetta)

**Wellshire Organic** - Organic Bacon (Dry Rubbed, Turkey)

**Winn Dixie** - Hickory Sweet Sliced Bacon (Lower Sodium, Regular, Thick, Thin)

## Bacon Bits

**Garret County Farms** - Salt Cured Bacon Bits

**Hormel** - Bacon (Crumbles, Bits, Pieces)

**Laura Lynn** - Bacon Chips

**Oscar Mayer** - Real Bacon Bits

**B**

**Publix** - 100% Real Bacon Pieces

**Wellshire Farms** - Salt Cured Bacon Bits

**Winn Dixie** - Bak'n Bits, Imitation Bacon Bits

**Bagels**

**Enjoy Life▲** - Bagels (Cinnamon Raisin●, Classic Original●)

**Gluten-Free Creations▲** - Berry●, Cinnamon Raisin●, Everything●, Jalapeno Cheese●, Onion●, Plain●

**Glutino▲** - Premium (Cinnamon 'n Raisin, Plain, Poppy Seed, Sesame)

**Kinnikinnick▲** - Tapioca Rice (Cinnamon Raisin, New York Style Plain, Sesame)

**Trader Joe's** - Gluten Free Bagels

**Baguettes... see Bread**

**Baked Apples**

**Lucky Leaf** - Dutch

**Musselman's** - Dutch

**Baking Bars**

**Baker's** - Bittersweet, German's Sweet, Select (Bittersweet, Semi Sweet), Semi Sweet, Unsweetened, White

**Dagoba** - Semisweet, Unsweetened

**Trader Joe's** - Unsweetened Belgium Baking Chocolate

**Baking Chips**

**Andes** - Crème de Menthe, Peppermint Crunch

**Ener-G ▲** - Chocolate Chips

**Enjoy Life▲** - Semi Sweet Chocolate Chips●

**Food Club Brand** - Baking Chips (Butterscotch, Peanut Butter, Milk Chocolate, Semi Sweet, Vanilla)

**Ghirardelli** - Chocolate Chips (60% Bittersweet, Milk Chocolate, Semi Sweet)

**Hannaford Brand** - Semi Sweet Chocolate Chips

**Hershey** - Chocolate Chips (Milk, Semi Sweet, Special Dark), Cinnamon Chips

**Home Harvest Brand** - Chocolate Flavor Chips

## baking cocoa

**B**

**Hy-Vee** - Chips (Butterscotch, Milk Chocolate, Mini Semi Sweet, Peanut Butter, Semi Sweet Chocolate, Vanilla Flavored White)

**Kroger Brand** - Butterscotch Morsels, Chips (Milk Chocolate, Peanut Butter, Semi Sweet), Chocolate Chunks

**Lecour's** - Real Chocolate Chips

**Manischewitz** - Chocolate Morsels

**Meijer Brand** - Butterscotch Chips, Chocolate Chips Semi Sweet, Milk Chocolate Chips, Peanut Butter Chips, White Baking Chips

**Midwest Country Fare** - Chocolate Flavored Chips

**Nestle** - Milk Chocolate & Peanut Butter Swirled Morsels, Milk Chocolate Morsels, Peanut Butter & Milk Chocolate Morsels, Premier White Morsels, Semi Sweet Chocolate (& Premier White Swirled Morsels, Chunks, Mini Morsels, Morsels)

**Nonuttin' Foods ▲** - Mini Chocolate Chips

**Publix** - Morsels (Butterscotch, Milk Chocolate, Semi Sweet Chocolate)

**Safeway Select** - Butterscotch Chips, Milk Chocolate Chips

**Spartan Brand** - Baking Chips (Butterscotch, Chocolate Semi Sweet, Milk Chocolate, White Chocolate)

**Stop & Shop Brand** - Semi Sweet Chocolate Chips

**Trader Joe's** - Chocolate Chips (Milk, White), Milk Chocolate Peanut Butter Chips

**Tropical Source** - Semi Sweet Chocolate Chips

**Wegmans Brand** - Chocolate Morsels Semi Sweet

**Woodstock Farms** - Organic Dark Chocolate Chips w/Evaporated Cane Juice

## Baking Cocoa

**Dagoba** - Organic

**Hy-Vee**

**Kroger Brand**

**Spartan Brand** - Cocoa Baking Chocolate

**Stop & Shop Brand**

**Watkins**

**B** Baking Decorations & Frostings

Betty Crocker▲ -

Brownie Topper (Cream Cheese, Dark Chocolate)

Cookie Icing (Chocolate, Cream Cheese, Red, White)

Cupcake Icing (Cloud White)

Decorating Decors (Chocolate Sprinkles, Nonpareils, Rainbow Mix Sprinkles, Red White & Blue Sprinkles, Stars, Sugars)

Decorating Gels (All Colors)

Decorating Icing (All Colors)

Easy Flow Icing (All Colors)

Pooh Decors

Princess Decors

Select Sugar Decors

Select Sugars

**Cake Mate** - Decorating Gels (All Colors), Decorating Icing (All Colors)

**Cherrybrook Kitchen** - Gluten Free Frosting (Chocolate, Vanilla) *(Box Must Say Gluten-Free)*, Ready To Spread Vanilla Frosting

**Dagoba** - All Varieties

**Duncan Hines** -

Frosting

Caramel

Chocolate Buttercream

Classic (Chocolate, Vanilla)

Coconut Supreme *(Coconut Pecan is NOT Gluten-Free)*

Cream Cheese

Dark Chocolate Fudge

French Vanilla

Lemon Supreme

Milk Chocolate

Strawberries 'N Cream

Vanilla Buttercream

**B**

Whipped (Chocolate, Cream Cheese, Fluffy White, Vanilla)
White Chocolate Almond

**Earthly Treats**▲ - Sugar Sprinkles●

**Edward & Sons** - Let's Do...Sprinkelz (Carnival, Chocolatey, Confetti)

**Food-Tek Fast & Fresh** - Dairy Free Chocolate Flavored Icing, Dairy Free Vanilla Flavored Icing

**Ginger Evans** - All Flavors *(Except Coconut Pecan)*

**Gluten-Free Creations**▲ - Frosting Mix (Chocolate●, White●)

**Gluten-Free Essentials**▲ - Frosting Mix (Lemon Glaze●, Supreme Chocolate●, Vanilla Royal●)

**Great Value Brand (Wal-Mart)** - Whipped Topping (Light, Regular)

**Katy Sweet**▲ - Crumbles (Praline●, Toffee●)

**Kinnikinnick**▲ - Icing Sugar

**Kroger Brand** - Sugar Sprinkles, White & Chocolate Bark Coating

**Laura Lynn** - Sprinkles Toppings (Chocolate, Rainbow)

**Manischewitz** - Dairy Free Rich & Creamy (Chocolate, Vanilla)

**Namaste Foods**▲ - Chocolate Fudge, Toffee Vanilla

**Pamela's Products**▲ - Frosting Mix (Chocolate Chunk, Confetti, Dark Chocolate, Vanilla)

Baking Mix... see Bread Mix

Baking Powder

Barkat

Bob's Red Mill▲

Clabber Girl

Davis

Durkee

Ener-G ▲ - Double Acting, Regular

Food Club Brand

Glutino▲

Great Value Brand (Wal-Mart)

Hain Pure Foods

**B**

Hannaford Brand
Hearth Club
Hilltop Mills
Hy-Vee - Double Acting
KC
Kinnikinnick▲ - KinnActive
Kraft - Calumet
Kroger Brand
Laura Lynn
Royal
Rumford
Safeway Brand
Spartan Brand
Spice Islands
Tone's
Watkins
Wegmans Brand - Double Acting

Baking Soda
Albertsons
Arm & Hammer
Bob's Red Mill▲
Durkee
Ener-G ▲ - Calcium Carbonate (Baking Soda Substitute)
Food Club Brand
Great Value Brand (Wal-Mart)
Hannaford Brand
Hilltop Mills
Hy-Vee
Kroger Brand
Laura Lynn
Lowes Foods Brand

## barbeque sauce

**B**

Meijer Brand
Spartan Brand
Spice Islands
Tone's

## Banana Chips

**Brothers All Natural▲** - Crisps (Banana, Strawberry Banana)

**Woodstock Farms** - Banana Chips (Regular, Sweetened)

## Bananas... *All Fresh Fruits & Vegetables Are Gluten-Free*

Chiquita

Dole

**Woodstock Farms** - Organic Frozen Bananas

## Barbeque Sauce

**Annie's Naturals** - Organic (Hot Chipotle, Original, Smokey Maple, Sweet & Spicy)

**Bone Suckin' Sauce** - Habanero, Original

**Cattleman's** - All Varieties *(Except Honey)*

**Daddy Sam's** - Bar B Que Sawce (Medium Ginger Jalapeno, Original)

**Dorothy Lane Market** - Original

**Fischer & Wieser** - Elly May's Wild Mountain Honey, Plum Chipotle BBQ, Southern Style

**Food Club Brand** - BBQ Sauce (Hickory, Honey, Traditional)

**Great Value Brand (Wal-Mart)** - Hickory, Honey, Original

**Hannaford Brand** - Honey, Kansas City Style, Original, Sweet & Zesty

**Heinz** - Chicken & Rib, Garlic, Honey Garlic, Original

**Homestyle Meals** - Original, Smoked Chipotle

**Hy-Vee** - Hickory, Honey Smoke, Original

**Isaly's** - All Varieties

**Jack Daniels** - Hickory Brown Sugar, Honey Smokehouse, Original No.7 Recipe, Spicy Original

**Lowes Foods Brand** - Hickory, Honey, Regular

**Marsh Brand** - Texas Style BBQ Sauce w/(Beef, Chicken, Pork)

**B**

**Midwest Country Fare** - Hickory, Honey, Original

**Mr. Spice Organic** - Honey BBQ

**Mrs. Renfro's** - Barbecue Sauce

**Organicville** - Organic BBQ Sauce (Original, Tangy)

**Publix** - Deli BBQ, Hickory, Honey, Original

**Safeway Select** - Hickory Smoked, Honey (Mustard, Smoked), Original

**San-J** - Gluten Free Asian BBQ●

**Saz's** - Original, Sassy, Vidalia Onion

**Spartan Brand** - Hickory & Brown Sugar, Honey, Original

**Sweet Baby Ray's** - Hickory & Brown Sugar, Honey, Honey Chipotle, Hot 'N Spicy, Original, Sweet Vadalia Onion

**Trader Joe's** - Kansas City, Original

**Ukrop's** - Honey, Tomato

**Walden Farms** - Hickory Smoked, Honey, Original, Thick & Spicy

**Wegmans Brand** - Memphis Style, Tropical

**Wild Thymes** - Spicy Island BBQ Sauce

**Winn Dixie** - Hickory, Honey, Original

## Bars... (includes Breakfast, Energy, Fruit, Protein, etc.)

**1-2-3 Gluten Free▲** - Sweet Goodness Pan Bars●

**Activ8** - Blueberry/Acai, Cherry/Vanilla, Peanut/Chocolate Chip, Pomegranate/Goji

**Aller Energy Bars** - Apple Cinnamon, Cherry Blossom, Chocolate Swirl, Wild Berry

**Alpsnack** - Apricots & Cranberries, Coconut/Mango & Pineapple, Fair Trade (Dark Chocolate, Espresso Chocolate), Plums & Currants

**Arico** - Cookie Bars (Almond Cranberry, Chocolate Chip, Double Chocolate, Lemon Ginger, Peanut Butter)

**Bakery On Main** - Gluten Free Granola Bars (Cranberry Maple Nut, Extreme Trail Mix, Peanut Butter Chocolate Chip)

**Boomi Bar** - Almond Protein Plus, Apricot Cashew, Cashew (Almond, Protein Plus), Cranberry Apple, Fruit & Nut, Healthy Hazel, Macadamia Paradise, Maple Pecan, Perfect Pumpkin, Pineapple Ginger, Pistachio Pineapple, Walnut Date

**bars**

**B**

**Bumble Bar** - Awesome Apricot, Chai w/Almonds, Cherry Chocolate, Chocolate Crisp, Chunky Cherry, Lushus Lemon, Original Flavor, Original Flavor w/(Almonds, Cashews, Hazelnuts, Mixed Nuts), Tasty Tropical

**Carb Safe** - Sugar Free Chocolate Bars (Dark, Milk)

**Clif Nectar** - Organic (Cherry Pomegranate, Cranberry Apricot Almond, Dark Chocolate Walnut, Lemon Vanilla Cashew)

**Crispy Cat** - Candy Bars (Chocolate Sundae, Mint Coconut, Toasted Almond)

**Dagoba** - All Chocolate Bars

**Eat Natural** -

100% Organic Brazils Hazelnuts & Sultans

Almonds Apricots & Yoghurt Coating

Blackcurrants Walnuts Mango & Dark Chocolate

Brazils Sultanas Almonds & Hazelnuts

Cranberry Macadamia & Dark Chocolate

Dates Walnuts & Pumpkin Seeds

Macadamias Brazils & Apricots

Peanuts Almonds & Hazelnuts

Peanuts Cranberries Pistachios & Milk Chocolate

**Ener-G** ▲ - Snack Bar (Chocolate Chip, Crispy Rice, Dark Chocolate, Rice Milk)

**Enjoy Life** ▲ - Boom Chocol Boom (Crispy Rice●, Dark Chocolate●, Milk●), Caramel Apple●, Cocoa Loco●, Sunbutter Crunch●, Very Berry●

**George Delights** - Just Fruit Bar (Apple, Apple Blueberry, Apple Cherry, Apple Raspberry, Blueberry Pear, Pear, Pear Cranberry, Pear Strawberry)

**Glutino** ▲ - Breakfast Bars (Apple, Blueberry, Chocolate, Cranberry), Candy Bars (Chocolate Peanut Butter, Dark Chocolate, Milk Chocolate), Organic Bars (Chocolate Banana, Chocolate Peanut Butter, Wildberry)

**Gopal's** - Adam & Eve, Apple Delicious, Ayurvedic, Carob Quinoa, Happy Herb w/Maca, Pineapple Nut, Pumpkin Agave, Sesame Mango

**B**

**Goraw** - Bar (Banana Bread Flax●, Live Pumpkin●, Live Granola●, Real Live Flax●, Spirulina Energy●

**Ian's** - Wheat Free Gluten Free Go Bars (Apple Pie, Cinnamon Bun)

**Jennies** - Omega 3 Energy Bar (Coconut, Coconut Almond, Coconut Chocolate)

**Jungle Grub** - Berry Bamboozle●, Chocolate Chip Cookie Dough●, Peanut Butter Groove●

**Larabar** - Apple Pie●, Banana Cookie●, Cashew Cookie●, Cherry Pie●, Chocolate Coconut●, Cinnamon Roll●, Cocoa Mole●, Coconut Cream Pie●, Ginger Snap●, Jocalat (Chocolate Cherry●, Chocolate Hazelnut●, Chocolate Coffee●, Chocolate●, Chocolate Mint●, Chocolate Orange●, German Chocolate Cake●), Key Lime Pie●, Lemon Bar●, Peanut Butter & Jelly●, Peanut Butter Cookie●, Pecan Pie●, Pistachio●, Tropical Fruit Tart●

**Manischewitz** - Raspberry Jell Bars

**Meijer Brand** - Xtreme Snack Bars

**Mixes From The Heartland▲** - Coffee Bars (Apple Cinnamon●, Cinnamon●, Cranberry●, Tropical●)

**Mrs. May's Naturals** - Trio (Blueberry●, Cranberry●, Strawberry●, Tropical●)

**Nature's Path Organic** - Crispy Rice Bars (Cheetah Berry, Fruity Burst, Koala Chocolate, Lemur Peanut Choco Drizzle, Peanut Butter)

**Necco** - Clark Bar, Skybar

**Nonuttin' Foods▲** - Granola Bars (Apple Cinnamon, Chocolate Chip, Double Chocolate Chunk, Raisin)

**NuGO Free** - Gluten Free Bars (Carrot Cake●, Dark Chocolate Crunch●, Dark Chocolate Trail Mix●)

**Nutiva Bars** - Organic (Flax Chocolate, Flax & Raisin, Hempseed)

**Omega Smart Bars▲** - Banana Chocolate Chip, Organic (Apricot Almond, Carrot Cake, Chocolate Nut, Cinnamon Apple, Raisin Spice), Pomegranate Strawberry Colada, Pumpkin Spice, Youth In A Bar (Dark Chocolate Cherry, Organic Almond Macaroon, Organic Wild Blueberry w/Orange Essence, Yummy Cherry Berry)

**Organic Food Bar** -

Organic Food Bar (Active Greens, Active Greens Chocolate,

Chocolate Chip, Cranberry, Omega 3 Flax, Original, Protein, Vegan, Wild Blueberry)

Organic Food Bar Kids (Oooatmeal Apple Pie, Oohmega Cherry Pie, Keerunch Chocolate Brownie Crunch)

Raw Organic Food Bar (Chocolate Coconut, Chocolatey Chocolate Chip, Cinnamon Raisin, Fiber Chocolate Delite)

**Orgran▲** - Fruit Bars (Fruit Medley), Fruit Filled Bar (Apricot, Blueberry)

**Oskri Organics** -

Coconut Bar (Almond, Cherry, Mango, Original, Pineapple, Strawberry)

Date Fruit

Fig Fruit

Honey Bar (Cashew, Desert Date, Flaxseed, Granola, Mixed Nuts, Muesli, Turkish Delight)

Jalow (Almond Cranberry, Cashew Cranberry, Pecan Raisin)

Sesame Bar (Black Sesame, Date Syrup & (Black Cumin, Fennel, Regular), Molasses & (Black Cumin, Fennel, Regular), Quinoa)

**Prana** - Apricot Goji, Apricot Pumpkin, Cashew Almond, Cinnamon Apple, Coconut Acai, Pear Ginseng

**PURE Bar** - Organic (Apple Cinnamon, Cherry Cashew, ChocChip Trailmix, Chocolate Brownie, Cranberry Orange, Wild Blueberry)

**Ruth's Hemp Power** - Cranberry Trail HempPower, CranNut Flax Power, Ginger Almond MacaPower, VeryBerry Flax Power, Vote Hemp/Blueberry Bar

**Seitenbacher** - Banana Cranberry, Choco Apricot, Energy, Fitness, Natural (Energizer, Sports), Sweet Romance, Xtra Fiber

**Shakti Bar** - Organic (Blueberry Chia, Goldenberry Goji, Mango Maca)

**Taste Of Nature** -

Exotics (Caribbean Ginger Island●, Chilean Blueberry Fields●, Himalayan Goji Summit●, Persian Pomegranate Garden●)

Regular (Argentina Peanut Plains●, Brazilian Nut Fiesta●, California Almond Valley●, Niagara Apple Country●, Quebec Cranberry Carnival●)

**B**

**thinkFruit** - Apple Noni Nourish, Cashew Acai Protect, Chocolate Pomegranate Power, Peanut Goji Glow)

**thinkGreen** - Blueberry Noni, Peanut Butter Chocolate

**thinkOrganic** - Cashew Pecan

**thinkThin** - Brownie Crunch, Chocolate (Fudge, Mudslide), Dark Chocolate, Peanut Butter (Chunky, Creamy), White Chocolate Chip

**thinkThin bites**- Chocolate Toffee Nut, Cookies and Cream, White Chocolate Raspberry

**Tiger's Milk** - Peanut Butter, Peanut Butter & Honey, Protein Rich

**Trader Joe's** - Fiberful Fruit

**Wegmans Brand** - Fruit Flats (Cherry, Grape, Raspberry, Strawberry)

**Basmati Rice... see Rice**

**Bean Dip... see Dip/Dip Mix**

**Beans...** *All **Fresh** Fruits & Vegetables Are **Gluten-Free***

**Albertsons** - Fat Free, Pork & Beans, Refried Beans (Regular), Spicy, Vegetarian

**Amy's -** Light In Sodium (Black, Traditional), Organic Refried Beans (Black, Traditional, w/Green Chiles), Vegetarian Baked

**Arrowhead Mills** - Adzuki, Anasazi, Garbanzo (Chickpeas), Green Split Peas, Lentils (Green, Red), Pinto, Soybeans

**B&M Baked Beans** - All Varieties

**Birds Eye** - All Plain Frozen Vegetables *(Except With Sauce)*

**Bush's Best** -

Baked Beans (Bold & Spicy, Boston Recipe, Country Style, Homestyle, Honey, Maple Cured Bacon, Onion, Original, Vegetarian)

Black

Butter (Baby, Large, Speckled)

Cannellini

~~Chili Magic (Texas Recipe, Traditional Recipe)~~

Garbanzo

Great Northern

Grillin' Beans (Bourbon And Brown Sugar, Smokehouse Tradition, Southern Pit Barbecue, Steakhouse Recipe)

**B**

Kidney (Dark Red, Light Red)

Microwaveable Cup Original

Navy

Pinto (Regular, w/Pork)

Red

Refried Beans Traditional

**C & W** - All Plain Frozen Vegetables

**C R Darbell's** - Pork & Beans

**Cascadian Farm** - Organic Frozen (Cut Green Beans, French Cut Green Beans w/Toasted Almonds, Petite Whole Green Beans)

**Del Monte -**

All Canned Vegetables

Harvest Selections Heat & Eat (Chili & Beans, Santa Fe Style Rice & Beans)

**Eden -**

Organic (Aduki, Baked w/Sorghum & Mustard, Black, Black Eyed Peas, Black Soybeans, Butter, Cannellini, Caribbean Black, Garbanzo, Great Northern, Kidney, Navy, Pinto, Small Red)

Organic Dried (Aduki, Black, Black Soybeans, Garbanzo, Green (Lentils, Split Peas), Kidney, Navy, Pinto, Small Red)

Refried (Black, Black Soy & Black, Kidney, Pinto, Spicy Black, Spicy Pinto)

Rice & (Cajun Small Red, Caribbean Black, Garbanzo, Kidney, Lentils, Pinto)

**Fantastic World Foods** - Hummus Original, Instant (Black, Refried)

**Food Club Brand -**

Canned (Baked Homestyle, Baked Onion, Baked Original, Baked Vegetarian, Chili, Cut Green, Cut Green No Salt Added, Dark Red Kidney, French Style Green, French Style Green No Salt Added, Great Northern, Navy, Pinot, Pork & Beans, Red),

Frozen (Baby Lima, Cut Green, French Style Green, Whole Green)

Refried Beans (Authentic, Fat Free)

**B**

**Freshlike** - Frozen Plain Vegetables *(Except Pasta Combos & Seasoned Blends)*

**Full Circle -** Canned Organic (Baked Beans, Baked Beans Maple & Onion, Black, Dried (Kidney, Lentil, Navy, Pinto), Garbanzo, Green Cut, Red Kiney, Refried (Black, Fat Free, Green Chile & Lime, Vegetarian), Organic Frozen Cut Beans

**Grand Selections** - Fancy (Cut Green, Whole Green), Frozen Whole Green

**Great Value Brand (Wal-Mart)** -

Beans & Weiners

Canned Beans (Baked, Black, Chili, Cut Green, Dark Red Kidney, Fat Free Refried, French Style Green, Great Northern, Light Red Kidney, No Salt Added (Cut Green, French Style Green), Pinto, Pork & Beans, Red, Whole Green)

Dried Beans (Baby Lima, Black, Garbanzo, Great Northern, Large Lima, Light Red Kidney, Navy, Pinto, Small Red)

Dried Lentils

Dried Peas (Blackeye, Chick, Green Split)

Frozen (Baby Lima, Cut Green, French Style Green)

Microwavable Plastic Cups Cut Green Beans

**Green Giant** -

Canned

Cut Green (50% Less Sodium, Regular)

French Style Green

Kitchen Sliced Green

Three Bean Salad

Frozen

Baby Lima

Cut Green

Green Beans & Almonds

Select w/No Sauce Whole Green

Simply Steam (Baby Lima, Green Beans & Almonds)

Steamers (Cut Green, Roasted Red Potatoes Green Beans & Rosemary Butter Sauce)

**Halstead Acres -** Butter, Chili Hot, Dark Kidney, Great & White Lima, Great Northern, Light Kidney, Pinto, Pork & Beans

**Hannaford Brand -** Black, Cannellini, Cut Green, Cut Wax, Dark Red Kidney, French Green, Great Northern, Light Red Kidney, No Salt (Cut, French), Pinto, Whole Green

**Hargis House -** Beans & Franks

**Health Market -** Organic (Black, Cut Green, Dark Red Kidney, French Cut Green, Garbanzo, Pinto, Refried)

**Heinz -** Vegetarian Beans

**Home Harvest Brand -** Canned Green (Cut, French Cut)

**Hy-Vee -**

    Black (Refried, Regular)

    Blue Lake (Cut Green, French Style Green, Whole Green)

    Butter

    Chili (Style, Beans)

    Country Style Baked

    Dark Red Kidney

    Diced Baby Lima

    Dried (Large Lima, Lentils, Mixed Soup, Navy)

    Fat Free Refried

    Frozen (Cut Green, French Cut Green)

    Garbanzo Beans Chick Peas

    Great Northern (Dried, Regular)

    Home Style Baked

    Large Lima

    Lentils

    Light Red Kidney

    Maple Cured Bacon Baked

    Navy

    Onion Baked

**B**

Original Baked
Pinto (Dried, Regular)
Pork & Beans
Red (Dried, Kidney, Regular)
Spicy Refried
Steam In A Bag Frozen Beans
Traditional Refried
Vegetarian Refried

**Joan of Arc** - Black, Butter, Dark Red Kidney, Garbanzo, Great Northern, Light Red Kidney, Pinto, Red

**Kid's Kitchen** - Beans & Wieners

**Kroger Brand** - All Plain Vegetables (Canned, Frozen), Unseasoned (Canned, Dry)

**Laura Lynn** - All Dried Beans, Beans & Franks, Canned (Kidney, Lima), Chili, Cut Green, Fat Free Refried, French Style Green, No Salt Cut Green, Polo, Pork & Beans, Refried

**Lowes Foods Brand** -

Canned (Baked, Black, Chili, Cut Green No Salt, French, Garbanzo, Great Northern, Green (Cut, French Style, Whole), Lima, Pinto (Regular, w/Pork), Pork & Beans, Red Kidney Beans (Dark, Light), Refried (Fat Free, Regular), Whole Green)

Dry (Baby Lima, Black Eyed Peas, Great Northern, Lentil, Lima, Mixed, Navy, Pinto)

Frozen (Deluxe Whole Green, Green (Cut, French Cut, Regular), Lima (Baby, Deluxe Tiny, Regular), Speckled Butter)

**Meijer Brand** -

Baked Beans - Organic

Canned Beans (Black (Regular, Organic), Butter, Garbanzo (Organic, Regular), Great Northern, Lima, Mexican Style, Pinto (Organic, Regular), Red Kidney (Dark, Dark Organic, Light, Regular), Refried (Fat Free, Regular, Vegetarian), Refried Organic (Black Bean, Black Bean/Jalapeno, Roasted Chili/Lime, Traditional), Wax Cut)

**B**

Canned Green Beans Cut (Blue Lake, French Style (Blue Lake, No Salt, Organic, Veri Green), No Salt, Organic, Veri Green)

Canned Green Beans Whole

Dry Beans (Black, Blackeye, Frozen Edamame (Soybeans), Frozen Green Beans (Cut, French Cut, Italian Cut), Frozen Lima Beans (Baby, Fordhook), Great Northern, Green Split Beans & Peas, Lentil, Lima Large, Navy, Pinto, Pork Beans, Red Kidney)

**Midwest Country Fare** - Chili Style, Cut Green, French Style Green, Pork & Beans

**Nielsen-Massey** - Madagascar Bourbon Pure Vanilla Bean Paste●, Whole Vanilla Beans●

**O Organics** - Canned (Black, Cut Green, Garbanzo, Kidney, Pinto), Frozen Whole Green

**Old El Paso** - Refried Beans (Fat Free, Spicy Fat Free, Traditional, Vegetarian, w/Green Chiles)

**Ortega** - Refried (Fat Free, Regular)

**Pictsweet** - All Plain Vegetables (Frozen)

**Publix** -

Canned (Baked, Black Beans (Frijoles Negros, In Seasoned Sauce), Garbanzo, Great Northern, Green (French Cut, French Style, Italian Cut, Lima, No Salt Added, Original, Veggi Green, Whole), Kidney (Dark, Light), Pinto, Pork & Beans, Vegetarian)

Dry (Baby Lima, Black, Blackeye, Garbanzo, Great Northern, Green Split Peas, Large Lima, Lentils, Light Red Kidney, Navy, Pinto, Small Red)

Frozen (Butter, Green (Cut, French Cut, Pole), Lima (Baby, Fordhook), Spec. Butter)

**Publix GreenWise Market** - Organic Canned (Black, Dark Red Kidney, Garbanzo, Green, Pinto, Soy)

**S&W** - All Canned Vegetables

**Safeway Brand** -

Canned (Black (Eyed, Regular), Chick, Dark Kidney, Green (Cut, Cut No Salt, French Style, Whole), Light Kidney, Lima, Pinto, Pork & Beans)

**B**

Dried (Baby Lima, Black (Eyed, Regular), Great Northern, Green Split, Large Lima, Lentils, Light Red Kidney, Navy, Pink, Pinto, Small (Red, White),

Frozen (Baby Lima, Cut, Fordbook Lima, French Style, Whole)

Refried Beans (Fat Free, Traditional, Vegetarian)

**Sierra Miguel -** Black, Refried

**Spartan Brand -**

Canned (Baked (Regular, w/Bacon & Maple Flavor, w/Onions), Black, Butter, Chili Beans, Dark Red Kidney, Garbanzo, Great Northern, Green (Cut, French Cut French Style), Homestyle Baked, Light Red Kidney, Pinto, Pork & Beans, Red, Lima, Refried (Fat Free, Regular), Wax, Whole Green)

Dried (Black, Black Eyed, Great Northern, Kidney, Lentil, Lima (Baby, Large), Navy, Pinto)

Frozen (Baby Lima, Cut Green, Fordhook Lima, French Cut Green, Speckled Butter, Whole Green)

**Stop & Shop Brand -** Baby Lima, Beans, Black, Brown Sugar & Bacon Baked, Dark Red Kidney, Fordhook Lima, Garbanzo, Golden Cut Wax, Green Beans (& Wax, Cut, French, Italian, No Added Salt, w/Garlic, Whole), Homestyle Baked, Italian, Kidney Light, Lima, Organic Green, Pink, Pinto, Red, Romano, Vegetarian Baked

**Thrifty Maid -** Frozen Green Beans

**Trader Joe's -** All Varieties, Marinated Bean Salad

**Wegmans Brand -**

Baby Lima

Baked Beans (Homestyle, Original, Vegetarian, w/Brown Sugar & Bacon)

Black

Butter

Canned (Baked, Black, Chili, Dark Red Kidney, Great Northern, Light Red Kidney, Pinto, Pork & Beans, Red)

Cannellini Beans Italian Classics

Cut Green Beans (No Salt, Regular)

**B**

Dark Kidney

French Style Green Beans (No Salt, Regular)

Garbanzo Beans Italian Classics

Great Northern

Green (Cut, French Style, Italian Cut, Regular, Whole)

Light Kidney

Lima

Pinto

Pork & Beans In Tomato Sauce

Seasoned Chili

Wax Cut

**Winn Dixie -**

Canned Beans (Baby White Lima, Baked, Baked w/Bacon & Onion, Dark Red Kidney, Garbanzo, Great Northern, Green & White Lima, Green Cut, Green French Style Sliced, Green Lima, Green No Salt Added, Green Whole, Light Red Kidney, Mexican Style Chili, Navy, Veggi Green

Frozen Green Beans (Butter Speckled, Cut, French Style Sliced, Italian, Organic Cut, Whole)

Frozen Lima Beans (Baby, Fordhook, Petite, Speckled)

Steamable Green Beans Cut

**Woodstock Farms -** Dried Green Beans, Organic Frozen (Baby French Beans, Cut Green Beans, Lima)

**Wylwood -** Butter, Dark Kidney, Great & White Lima, Great Northern, Light Kidney

**Beef...** *All Fresh Meat Is **Gluten-Free (Non-Marinated, Unseasoned)***

**Always Tender -** Flavored Fresh Beef (Non Flavored, Peppercorn)

**Applegate Farms -**

Natural (Beef Hot Dogs, Roast Beef)

Organic (Frozen Beef Burger, Roast Beef)

**Boar's Head -** All Varieties

**Butcher's Cut -** Beef Burgers, Bulk Wrapped Corned Beef Brisket, Corned Beef, Corned Beef Brisket

**B**

**Dietz & Watson** -
    Corned Beef Brisket
    Corned Beef Flat (Extra Lean)
    Pastrami (Brisket, Spiced Beef)
    Roast Beef (Black Bear Choice, Cap Off ½, Italian, London Broil, Natural Angus, Oven Roasted All Natural Rare Whole)

**Five Star Brand** - Corned Beef, Jumbo Beef Wieners, Roast Beef, SC Beef Wieners

**Full Circle** - All Natural Frozen 80% Lean Beef Patties

**Garrett County Farms** -
    Beef Franks (4XL Big, Old Fashioned, Premium)
    Corned Beef Brisket (Half, Whole)
    Sliced (Beef Bologna, Beef Salami, Corned Beef, Roast Beef)
    Whole Roast Beef

**Great Value Brand (Wal-Mart)** -
    Frozen (100% Pure Beef Patties, Thinly Sliced Beef Philly Steak)

**Hillshire Farms** - Deli Select Thin Sliced (Corned Beef, Roast Beef), Deli Select Ultra Thin Roast Beef

**Homestyle Farms** - Shredded Beef In BBQ Sauce

**Hormel** - Corned Beef, Corned Beef Hash, Deli Sliced Cooked Corned Beef, Deli Sliced Seasoned Roast Beef, Dried Beef, Fully Cooked Entrees (Beef Roast Au Jus, Italian Style Beef Roast), Natural Choice Roast Beef

**Hy-Vee** - Quarter Pounders, Thin Sliced (Corned Beef, Regular)

**Isaly's** - All Deli Meat

**John Soules Foods** - Fully Cooked Fajitas (Angus Beef, Beef), Ready To Cook (Beef For Fajitas)

**Kayem** - Roast Beef

**Lloyd's** - Beef Ribs w/Original BBQ Sauce, Shredded Beef In Original BBQ Sauce

**Meijer Brand** - Ground Beef (Chuck Fine, Fine), Sliced Chipped Meat

**Nature's Basket** - Seasoned Roast Beef

**B**

### Organic Prairie

Fresh Organic

Ground Beef 1 lb. (85% Lean, 90% Lean)

Sliced Roast Beef 6 oz.

Frozen Organic

Beef Liver Steak 12 oz.

Ground Beef 12 oz.

Ground Beef Patties 10.6 oz.

New York Strip Steak 8 oz.

Ribeye Steak 8 oz.

**Oscar Mayer** - Shaved Deli Fresh (French Dip Roast Beef, Slow Roasted Roast Beef)

**Primo Taglio -** Cooked Corned Beef, Roast Beef (Caramel Color Added, Coated w/Seasonings)

**Publix** - Beef Pot Roast w/Home Style Gravy Fully Cooked, Deli (Choice Cooked Beef Bottom Round Roast, Corned Beef), Premium Certified Beef

### Publix GreenWise Market -

Beef (Cubed Steak, For Stew)

Beef Back Ribs

Bottom Round (Regular, Steak)

Brisket Flat

Chuck (Eye Steak, Roast Boneless, Short Rib Boneless, Short Ribs, Steak Boneless)

Eye Round (Regular, Steak)

Flank Steak

Flap Meat

Flat Iron Steak

Ground (Chuck, Chuck For Chili, Chuck Patties, Round, Round Patties)

Porterhouse Steak

Rib Eye (Roast Boneless, Steak Bone In, Steak Boneless)

**B**

Rib Roast

Round Cubes

Rump Roast

Shoulder (Roast Boneless, Steak)

Sirloin (Flap Meat, For Kabobs, For Stir Fry, Tip Roast, Tip Side Steak, Tip Steak)

Skirt Steak (Inside, Outside)

Strip Steak Boneless

T Bone Steak

Tenderloin (Roast, Steak)

Top Blade (Roast Boneless, Steak)

Top Round (For Stir Fry, London Broil, Regular, Steak, Steak Thin Sliced)

Top Sirloin (Filet Steak, Steak Boneless)

Tri Tip (Roast, Steak)

**Spartan Brand** - Corned Beef Hash

**Thumann's** - All Varieties●

**Trader Joe's** - Fully Cooked & Seasoned Prime Rib of Beef, Shepherds Pie (Beef)

**Ukrop's** -

All Natural Beef Tenderloin Steak Supreme (Au Poivre, Cut, Cut Wrapped In Bacon)

All Natural Frozen Ground Beef Patties

All Natural New York Strip Steak (Au Poivre, w/Montreal Steak Seasoning)

All Natural Rib Eye Steak (Au Poivre, w/Montreal Steak Seasoning)

Angus New York Strip (Au Poivre, w/Montreal Steak Seasoning)

Angus Rib Eye Steak (Au Poivre, w/Montreal Steak Seasoning)

Beef Top Round For Stir Fry

Burgundy Seasoning Beef Kabob w/Vegetables

Flank Steak (w/Cilantro Pesto Parmesan, w/Portobella Bacon Bleu Cheese)

Sirloin Kabob

## beets

**B**

    **Wellshire Farms** - Roast Beef (Sliced Top Round, Whole)
    **Wellshire Organic** - Organic Beef Franks
**Beef Jerky... see Jerky/Beef Sticks**
**Beef Sticks... see Jerky/Beef Sticks**
**Beer**
  **AMERICAN**
      **Anheuser-Busch** - Redbridge Beer
      **Bard's Tale Beer** - Dragon's Gold Gluten Free Lager
      **Lakefront Brewery** - New Grist Beer
      **Old Hat Brewery** - Bees Knees
      **Ramapo Valley Brewery** - Passover Honey Lager

  **IMPORTED**
      **Bi-Aglut** - Special 76 Lager (Italy)
      **Brauerei Grieskirchen AG** - Beer Up Glutenfrei Pale Ale (Austria)
      **Carlsberg Brewery** - Saxon Premium Lager (Finland)
      **Fine Ale Club** - Against The Grain (England)
      **Glutaner** - Glutenfrei Pils (Belgium)
      **Green's** - Discovery, Explorer, Herald, Pioneer, Trailblazer (England)
      **Hambleton Ales** - GFA, GFL (England)
      **Koff** - Lager, Taytelainen Kevytolut (Finland)
      **Laitilan** - Kukko Pils III Lager, Kukko Tumma III Dark Lager (Finland)
      **Les Bieres de la Nouvelle France** - La Messagere Pale Ale (Canada)
      **Liebhart's Privatbrauerai** - Bio Reis (Gold, Gold Dunkel) (Germany)
      **O'Brien** - Bown Ale, Pale Ale, Premium Lager (Australia)
      **Schnitzer Brau** - Glutenfrei Bier (Germany)
      **Silly Yaks** - Aztec Gold (Australia)
      **St. Peter's Brewery -** G Free (England)
**Beets...** *All Fresh Fruits & Vegetables Are **Gluten-Free***
  **Del Monte** - All Canned Vegetables
  **Food Club Brand** - Canned (Pickled, Sliced, Whole)

**B**

**Great Value Brand (Wal-Mart)** - Canned (Sliced, Sliced Pickled)

**Hannaford Brand** - Cut, Sliced, Whole

**Hy-Vee** - Fancy (Diced, Sliced)

**Laura Lynn** - Cut, Sliced

**Lowes Foods Brand** - Cut, Whole

**Meijer Brand** - Harvard Sweet Sour, Sliced (No Salt, Pickled, Regular), Whole (Medium, Pickled)

**Publix** - Canned

**S&W** - Pickled

**Safeway Brand** - Canned (Sliced, Whole)

**Spartan Brand** - Diced, Sliced, Whole

**Stop & Shop Brand** - Sliced No Salt Added

**Trader Joe's** - Steamed

**Wegmans Brand** - Harvard, Sliced (No Salt, Pickled, Regular), Whole (Pickled, Regular)

Berries... *All **Fresh** Fruits & Vegetables Are **Gluten-Free***

**Cascadian Farm** - Organic Frozen Harvest Berries

**Del Monte** -

Canned/Jarred Fruit (All Varieties)

Fruit Snack Cups (Metal, Plastic)

**Great Value Brand (Wal-Mart)** - Frozen

**Meijer Brand** - Frozen Berry Medley, Frozen Triple Berry Blend

**Publix** - Frozen Mixed Berries

**Spartan Brand** - Frozen Berry Medley

**Stop & Shop Brand** - Frozen Berry Medley

**Wegmans Brand** - Berry Medley

**Woodstock Farms** - Organic Frozen Mixed Berries

Beverages... see Drinks/Juice

Biscotti

**Ener-G ▲** - Chocolate Chip

**Foods By George▲** - Currants & Nuts

**Orgran▲** - Amaretti, Classic Chocolate

## blackberries

**B**

**Pamela's Products**▲ - Almond Anise, Chocolate Walnut, Lemon Almond

**Simply Organic**▲ - Cocoa Biscotti Mix●

**Sorella Bakery**▲ - Biscottines (Chocolate Almond, Chocolate Chip, Cinnamon Swirl, Hazelnut, Vanilla)

## Biscuits

**1-2-3 Gluten Free**▲ - Southern Glory Biscuits●

**3 Fellers Bakery**▲ - Buttermilk Biscuits Dough

**Bob's Red Mill**▲ - Wheat Free Biscuit & Baking Mix

**Cause You're Special**▲ - Hearty Gluten Free Biscuit Mix

**Food-Tek Fast & Fresh** - Quick Bake Biscuit Mix (Homestyle)

**Mixes From The Heartland**▲ - Biscuit Mix (Country●, Dilly●, Garlic Roasted Pepper●, Sun Dried Tomato●)

**Namaste Foods**▲ - Biscuits Piecrust & More Mix

**Really Great Food Company**▲ - Biscuit Mix (Loaf, Old Time, Spinach & Cheese)

**Whole Foods Market Gluten Free Bakehouse** ▲- Cheddar Biscuits, Cream Biscuits

Black Eyed Peas... see Peas

Blackberries... *All **Fresh** Fruits & Vegetables Are **Gluten-Free***

**Albertsons** - All Plain Frozen Fruit

**Cascadian Farm** - Organic Frozen

**Food Club Brand**

**Great Value Brand (Wal-Mart)** - Frozen

**Meijer Brand** - Frozen

**Publix -** Frozen

**Safeway Brand** - Frozen

**Spartan Brand** - Frozen

**Stop & Shop Brand** - Frozen

**Trader Joe's** - Plain Frozen

**Wegmans Brand**

**Winn Dixie -** Frozen

**Woodstock Farms** - Organic Frozen

**B** Blueberries... *All **Fresh** Fruits & Vegetables Are **Gluten-Free***

    **Albertsons** - All Frozen Fruit

    **Cascadian Farm** - Organic Frozen

    **Food Club Brand** - Frozen

    **Full Circle** - Organic

    **Great Value Brand (Wal-Mart)** - Frozen

    **Hy-Vee** - Frozen

    **Kroger Brand** - Plain Frozen Fruit

    **Meijer Brand** - Frozen (Organic, Regular)

    **Publix** - Frozen

    **Safeway Brand** - Frozen

    **Spartan Brand** - Frozen

    **Trader Joe's** - Plain Frozen

    **Wegmans Brand**

    **Winn Dixie** - Frozen

    **Woodstock Farms** - Organic Frozen Wild

Bok Choy... *All **Fresh** Fruits & Vegetables Are **Gluten-Free***

Bologna

    **Applegate Farms** - Turkey Bologna

    **Boar's Head** - All Varieties

    **Dietz & Watson** - Beef, German Brand, Original, Ring

    **Five Star Brand** - Beef, Leona, Natural Casing, Pork & Beef

    **Honeysuckle White** - Turkey

    **Hy-Vee** - Beef, Garlic, German Brand, Regular Bologna, Thick, Thin

    **Midwest Country Fare** - Sliced, Thick Sliced

    **Perdue** - Deli Turkey Bologna

    **Publix** - Deli Pre Pack Sliced Lunch Meat (Beef Bologna, German Bologna)

    **Shelton's** - Uncured Turkey

    **Thumann's** - All Varieties●

    **Wellshire Farms** - Sliced Beef Bologna

**B**

### Bouillon/Bouillon Cubes

**Better Than Bouillon** - All Varieties *(Except Reduced Sodium Beef, Reduced Sodium Vegetable)*

**Celifibr** - Bouillon Cubes (Vegetable Medley, Vegetarian Beef, Vegetarian Chicken), Bouillon Soup Base (French Onion, Vegetable Medley, Vegetarian Beef, Vegetarian Chicken)

**Edward & Sons -** Garden Veggie, Low Sodium Veggie, Not Beef, Not Chick'n

**Harvest Sun** - Organic Bouillon Cubes (All Flavors)

**Herb-Ox** - Beef, Chicken, Garlic Chicken, Low Sodium (Beef, Chicken), Vegetable

**Hy-Vee** - Bouillon Cubes (Beef, Chicken), Instant Bouillon (Beef, Chicken)

**Kum Chun** - Chicken Bouillon Powder

**Lee Kum Kee** - Chicken Bouillon Powder

**Marigold -** Swiss Vegetable, Vegan Reduced Salt

**Massel** - Ultracubes (Beef, Chicken, Vegetable)

**Spartan Brand** - Soup Beef Bouillon (Cube, Granular), Soup Chicken Bouillon (Cube, Granular)

**Stop & Shop Brand** - Beef Flavored Bouillon Cubes (Instant, Regular)

### Bourbon... *All Distilled Alcohol Is Gluten-Free* [2]

### Bowls

**Amy's -**

Baked Ziti Bowl

Brown Rice & Vegetable Bowl (Light In Sodium, Regular)

Brown Rice w/Black Eyed Peas & Veggies Bowl

Cream Of Rice Hot Cereal

Mexican Casserole Bowl (Light In Sodium)

Santa Fe Enchilada Bowl

Teriyaki Bowl

Tortilla Casserole Bowl

**Chi-Chi's** - Fiesta Plates (Creamy Chipotle, Salsa, Savory Garlic)

**B**   **Del Monte** - Harvest Selections Heat & Eat (Chili & Beans, Santa Fe Style Rice & Beans)

**Lundberg**▲ - Organic Brown Rice Bowls (Country Wild, Long Grain, Short Grain)

**Simply Asia** - Rice Noodle Soup Bowl (Garlic Sesame, Sesame Chicken, Spring Vegetable)

**Thai Kitchen** - Rice Noodle Soup Bowls (Lemongrass & Chili, Mushroom, Roasted Garlic, Spring Onion, Thai Ginger)

**Trader Joe's** - Chicken Tandoori Rice Bowl

**Bratwurst... see Sausage**

**Bread... (includes Rolls)**

**Aleia's**▲ - Cinnamon Raisin●, Farmhouse White●

**Andrea's Fine Foods**▲ - Buns (Hamburger, Hot Dog), Focaccia, Loaf (Casein Free Sandwich, White Sandwich), Rolls (Cinnamon, Dairy Free Dinner, White)

**Apple's Bakery**▲ - Loaf (Olive Oil, Seeded Sandwich)

**Aunt Gussie's**▲ - Focaccia, Kalamata Garlic Bread

**Barkat** - Home Fresh Bread Rolls

**Celiac Specialties**▲ -

Bread (Apple Cinnamon, Cheddar Herb, Cheesy Flat, Cinnamon Raisin, Dill, Flat, Flaxseed, Multigrain, Multigrain Flat, Navy Bean, Light White, Parmesan Flat, Sun Dried Tomato, White)

Buns (Hamburger, Hot Dog, Sub)

Rolls (Cinnamon, Onion Poppy)

**Cybros Inc** - 100% Rice Bread & Rolls & Nuggets, Mock Rye & Rolls, Rice & Raisin, Tapioca Almond

**Deerfields Bakery**▲ - Mini Baguette, Rice Bran Artisan Roll, Stuffing Cubes

**El Peto**▲ - Bread (Brown Rice, Cheese, Flax Seed Loaf, Gourmet, Italian Style, Millet, Multi Grain, Potato, Raisin, Supreme Italian Style, Tapioca, White Rice)

**Ener-G** ▲ -

Sliced Breads

Brown Rice

**B**

    Cinnamon Rolls

    Corn

    Egg Free Raisin

    Four Flour

    Hi Fiber

    Light (Brown Rice, Tapioca, White Rice, White Rice Flax)

    Papas

    Raisin Loaf w/Eggs

    Rice Starch

    Seattle Brown

    Tapioca Loaf (Dinner Rolls, Regular Sliced, Thin Sliced)

    White (Regular, Rice Flax)

    Yeast Free (Brown Rice, Sweet, White Rice)

  Specialty Breads

    Bread Crumbs

    Broken Melba Toast

    Communion Wafers

    Plain Croutons

**Everybody Eats ▲** - Bagels, Baguette, Banana Bread, Dairy Free Deli Rolls, Deli Rolls, Dinner Rolls, Egg Challah, White Bread

**Food For Life** - Almond Rice, Bhutanese Red Rice, Brown Rice, Multi Seed Rice, Raisin Pecan, Rice Pecan, White Rice

**French Meadow Bakery** - Gluten Free (Cinnamon Raisin Bread●, Italian Rolls●, Sandwich Bread●)

**Gillian's Foods ▲** - Carmalized Onion Rolls, Cinnamon Raisin (Loaf, Rolls), Crostini, English Muffins, Everything Dinner Rolls, French (Bread, Rolls), Garlic Bread, Poppyseed Rolls, Rye No Rye Loaf, Sandwich Loaf, Sesame Seed Rolls, Sundried Tomato & Roasted Garlic Loaf

**Glutano ▲** - Multi Grain, Three Grain, White

**Gluten Free Life ▲** - Country Brown Pure, Multi Grain Pure, Pumpernickle

**B** **Gluten-Free Creations**▲ - Almond Flax●, Banana Tea Bread●, Cheddar Cheese●, Cinnamon Rolls●, Herb Baguettes●, Herb Loaf Bread●, Herb Rolls●, Honey Oat●, Hot Dog Buns●, Pecan Sticky Rolls●, Rye Bread w/Caraway Seeds●, Sandwich●, Seeded Multigrain●, White●, Whole Grain●, Wild Rice●

**Glutino**▲ -

Premium

    Cinnamon & Raisin Bread

    Corn Bread

    English Muffins

    Fiber Bread

    Flax Seed Bread

**Good Juju Bakery** ▲-

Award Winning Banana Bread

Dinner Rolls

Exceptional English Muffins

**Josef's** ▲- All Varieties

**Katz Gluten Free**▲ - Bread (Sliced Challah, White, Whole Grain), Chocolate (Cup Cake, Rugelech, Strip), Cinnamon (Rugelech, Strip), Cookies (Chocolate Chip, Chocolate Dipped, Colored Sprinkle, Sugar Free Vanilla, Vanilla), Cup Cakes, Farfel, Honey Loaf, Kiska Kugel, Marble Cake, Rolls (Large Callah, Sandwich, Small Challah), Sugar Free Blueberry Muffins

**Kinnikinnick**▲ -

Brown Sandwich

Candida Yeast Free Multigrain Rice

Festive

Many Wonder Multigrain Rice

Robins Honey Brown Rice

Sunflower Flax Rice

Tapioca Rice (Cheese, Italian, Raisin, Regular, Yeast Free)

Tru Fibre Multigrain Rice

White Sandwich

## bread mix

**B**

**Laurel's Sweet Treats** ▲ - Banzo Bread, Dinner Rolls, Freshly Baked Cheese Buns, Freshly Baked Sandwich Rolls

**Madwoman Foods** ▲ - Flatbread

**Miller's Gluten Free Bread Co.** ▲ - Asiago Cheese Bread, Cinnamon Streusel Bread, Deli Rolls, Garlic Knots, White Sandwich Bread

**Namaste Foods** ▲ - Bread Mix

**Nu-World Foods** - Flatbread Amaranth (Buckwheat●, Garbanzo●, Sorghum●)

**O'Doughs Bakery** ▲ - Buns (Breakfast, Flax, White), Loaf (Flax, Flax Half, White, White Half)

**Orgran** ▲ - Crisp Bites (Balsamic Herb, Corn, Onion & Chives), Crisp Bread (Corn, Rice, Rice & Cracked Pepper, Rice & Garden Herb, Salsa)

**Rose's Bakery** ▲ - All Varieties ●

**Schar** ▲ - Bread (Classic White, Multi Grain), Rolls (Classic White)

**Trader Joe's** - Gluten Free (Bagels, French Rolls), Ryeless "Rye" Bread

**Whole Foods Market Gluten Free Bakehouse** ▲ -

Bread (Banana, Cinnamon Raisin, Cornbread, Honey Oat Bread, Prairie, Sandwich, Sundried Tomato & Garlic)

Cream Biscuits

Hamburger Buns

## Bread Mix... (includes Baking Mix, Roll Mix)

**1-2-3 Gluten Free** ▲ - Aaron's Favorite Rolls ●

**365 Everyday Value** - Gluten Free (All Purpose Baking Mix, Cornbread & Muffin Mix, Muffin Mix, Sandwich Bread Mix)

**AgVantage Naturals** ▲ - Multi Grain Bread Mix ●

**Arrowhead Mills** - All Purpose Baking Mix

**Authentic Foods** ▲ - Bread Mix Homestyle, Cinnamon Bread Mix

**Bob's Red Mill** ▲ - Bread Mix (Cinnamon Raisin, Hearty Whole Grain, Homemade Wonderful)

**Breads From Anna** ▲ - Bread Mix (Banana, Classic Herb, Gluten Free, Gluten & Yeast Free All Purpose, Original, Pumpkin)

**Cause You're Special** ▲ - Bread Mix (Homestyle White, Traditional French)

**B** Chebe▲ -

Bread Mix (All Purpose●, Cinnamon Rolls●, Focaccia Italian Flatbread●, Pizza Crust●)

Frozen Dough (Bread Sticks●, Pizza Crust●, Rolls●, Sandwich Buns●, Tomato Basil Bread Sticks●)

Garlic Onion Breadsticks Mix●

**Ener-G ▲** Mix (Corn, Potato, Rice)

**Fearn** - Baking Mix (Brown Rice, Rice)

**Food-Tek Fast & Fresh** - Bread Mix (White)

**Gillian's Foods▲** - All Purpose Baking Mix, Cinnamon Bread Mix, French Bread Mix

**Gluten-Free Creations▲** - Bread Mix (Almond Flax●, Cinnamon Raisin●, Honey Oat●, Sandwich●, Seeded Multigrain●)

**Gluten-Free Essentials▲** - All Purpose Baking Mix●, Holiday Gingerbread●, Lemon Poppy Seed●, Multi Grain (Cinnamon Spice●, Meatloaf Starter●, Original●, Zesty Italian●)

**Gluten-Free Pantry▲** - Favorite Sandwich Bread Mix, French Bread & Pizza Mix, Quick Mix, Toms Light Gluten Free Bread, Whole Grain Bread Mix, Yankee Cornbread Mix

**Hodgson Mill▲** - Gluten Free Bread Mix, Multi Purpose Baking Mix

**Kinnikinnick▲** -

All Purpose Mix

Candida Yeast Free Rice

Cornbread & Muffin Mix

Kinni Kwik Bread & Bun Mix

Kinni Kwik Sunflower Flax Bread & Bun Mix

Tapioca Rice

White Rice

**Meister's Gluten Free Mixtures▲** - Bread Mix●

**Mixes From The Heartland▲** - Bread Machine Mix (Garden Veggie●, Garlic Roasted Pepper●, Plain●), Sweet Bread Mix (Banana●, Blueberry●, Cranberry●, Zuchini●)

**Namaste Foods▲** - Bread Mix

## breakfast

**B**

**Orgran**▲ - Bread Mix (Alternative Grain Wholemeal, Easy Bake)

**Pamela's Products**▲ - Amazing Bread Mix

**Really Great Food Company**▲ - Bread Mix (Brown Rice, Dark European, French/Country Farm, Home Style Cornbread, Irish Soda, Old Fashioned Cinnamon, Original White, Rye Style)

**Schar**▲ - Classic White Bread Mix

**Simply Organic**▲ - Banana Bread Mix●. Chai Spice Scone Mix●

**Sylvan Border Farm** - Bread Mix (Classic Dark, Non Dairy, White)

**Tastefully Gluten Free**▲ - Bread & Roll Mix

**Toro**▲ - White Bread Mix, Whole Meal White Bread Mix

Breadcrumbs... see Coating

Breadsticks

**Chebe**▲ - Garlic & Onion Breadsticks Mix, Original Frozen Dough, Tomato Basil Frozen Dough

**Glutino**▲ - Pizza Breadsticks, Sesame Breadsticks

**Schar**▲ - Italian Breadsticks

Breakfast

**Amy's** - Mexican, Tofu Scramble

**Farmer John** - Breakfast Sausage Links & Patties (Firehouse Hot Roll, Firehouse Hot Skinless Links, Old Fashined Maple Skinless, Original Roll, Original Skinless, Premium Original Chorizo, Premium PC Links Lower Fat, Premium Sausage Patties Lower Fat, Premium SC Links, Premium Spicy Hot Chorizo, Premium Traditional Chorizo, Quick Serve Fully Cooked)

**Garrett County Farms** - Frozen Breakfast Links (Chicken Apple, Original, Surprise Maple, Turkey Maple)

**Honeysuckle White** - Breakfast Sausage (Links, Patties, Roll)

**Ian's** - Wheat Free Gluten Free Recipe French Toast Sticks, Wheat Free Gluten Free Wafflewiches (Egg & Maple Cheddar, Maple Sausage & Egg)

**Jennie-O Turkey Store** -
  Breakfast Lover's Turkey Sausage

**B**

Fresh Breakfast Sausage (Maple Links, Mild Links, Mild Patties)

Frozen Fully Cooked Sausage (Links, Patties)

## Jimmy Dean -

Breakfast Bowls

Bacon Eggs Potatoes Cheddar Cheese

Ham Egs Potatoes Cheddar Cheese

Sausage Eggs Potatoes Cheddar Cheese

Breakfast Entrees

Scrambled Eggs w/Bacon & Cheese w/Diced Apples & Seasoned Hash Browns

Scrambled Eggs w/Sausage & Cheese w/Diced Apples & Seasoned Hash Browns

Breakfast Skillet (Bacon, Ham, Sausage, Smoked Sausage, Southwest Style)

## Johnsonville -

Original (Breakfast (Links, Patties)

Vermont Maple Syrup (Links, Patties)

## Jones Dairy Farm

All Natural

Hearty Pork Sausage Links●

Light Pork Sausage and Rice Links●

Little Link Pork Sausage●

Maple Sausage Patties●

Original Pork Roll Sausage●

Pork Sausage Patties●

All Natural Golden Brown Cooked & Browned Sausage Patties (Maple Fully●, Mild Fully●)

**Only Oats** - Breakfast Blend (Apple & Cinnamon●, Maple & Roasted Flax●)

**Sunshine Burger -** Organic Breakfast Patty

**Van's -** Wheat Free French Toast Sticks

**Broccoli...** *All **Fresh** Fruits & Vegetables Are **Gluten-Free***

**Albertsons** - Canned & Frozen

**B**

**Birds Eye** - All Plain Frozen Vegetables *(Except With Sauce)*

**C & W** - All Plain Frozen Vegetables

**Cascadian Farm** - Organic Frozen (Broccoli Cuts, Broccoli Florets), Purely Steam Organic Frozen Broccoli & Carrots

**Food Club Brand** - Frozen (Chopped, Cut)

**Freshlike** - Frozen Plain Vegetables *(Except Pasta Combos & Seasoned Blends)*

**Great Value Brand (Wal-Mart)** - Frozen (Broccoli & Cauliflower, Broccoli Florets, Cut Broccoli)

**Green Giant**

Frozen

Broccoli & Carrots w/Garlic & Herbs Seasoned

Broccoli & Cheese Sauce

Broccoli Spears & Butter Sauce

Chopped

Immunity Blend

Steamers (Broccoli & Cheese Sauce, Broccoli Cauliflower Carrots & Cheese Sauce, Cheesy Rice & Broccoli)

**Home Harvest Brand** - Cuts

**Hy-Vee** - Frozen (Chopped, Cuts, Florets)

**Kroger Brand** - All Plain Vegetables (Canned, Frozen)

**Lowes Foods Brand** - Frozen (Chopped, Cuts, Deluxe Baby Florets, Deluxe Florets, Spears)

**Meijer Brand** - Frozen (Chopped, Cuts, Spears)

**Midwest Country Fare** - Frozen (Chopped, Cuts)

**Nature's Promise** - Organic Broccoli Mini Spears

**Pictsweet** - All Plain Vegetables (Frozen)

**Publix** - Frozen (Chopped, Cuts, Florets, Spears)

**Safeway Brand** - Frozen (Cuts, Florets, Stem In Bag)

**Spartan Brand** - Cuts, Florets, Spears

**Stop & Shop Brand** - Broccoli (Chopped, Cuts, Spears), Broccoli & Cauliflower

**Trader Joe's** - All Plain Vegetables (Frozen)

**B**

**Wegmans Brand** - Broccoli (Chopped, Cuts), Broccoli Cuts & Cauliflower Florets, Spears

**Winn Dixie** - Frozen (Chopped, Cuts, Florets, Spears), Steamable Broccoli Cut

**Woodstock Farms** - Organic Frozen Broccoli Florets

Broth

**Baxters** - Chicken

**Bowman & Landes** - Chicken, Turkey

**Caskey's** - Beef, Chicken

**College Inn Broth** - Garden Vegetable, Organic Beef, White Wine & Herb Culinary Chicken

**El Peto▲** - Broth Concentrate (Beef, Chicken)

**Food Club Brand** - Beef, Chicken (Fat Free, Reduced Sodium) *(Box Only)*

**Great Value Brand (Wal-Mart)** - Chicken *(Box Only, Not Canned)*

**Hannaford Brand** - Chicken *(Only In Resealable Box)*

**Health Valley** -

Fat Free (Beef Flavored (No Salt Added, Regular), Chicken, Vegetable)

Low Fat Chicken (No Salt Added, Regular)

**Hy-Vee** - Chicken

**Imagine** - Free Range Chicken (Low Sodium, Regular), No Chicken, Organic (Beef (Low Sodium, Regular), Vegetable (Low Sodium, Regular))

**Kaskey's** - Beef, Chicken

**Lipton** - Recipe Secrets Onion Soup & Dip Mix

**Lowes Foods Brand** - Beef, Chicken (Low Sodium, Regular)

**Manischewitz** - Clear Chicken Consomme

**Meijer Brand** - Chicken

**Midwest Country Fare** - Chicken

**Nature's Promise** - All Natural Beef Broth, Organic Chicken Broth, Organic Vegetable Broth

**Pacific Natural Foods** - Beef Broth, Free Range Chicken, Organic (Beef, Free Range Chicken, Low Sodium Chicken, Low Sodium Vegetable, Mushroom, Vegetable Broth)

**Safeway Brand** - 99% Fat Free, Beef, Chicken, Fat Free Reduced Sodium, Regular

**Shelton's** -

Chicken (Fat Free Low Sodium, Regular)

Organic (Chicken, Chicken Fat Free Low Sodium)

**Spartan Brand** - Beef, Chicken

**Stop & Shop Brand** - Beef, Chicken, Ready To Serve Chicken Broth

**Swanson** -

Chicken Broth (Canned, Carton)

Chicken Broth w/Garlic (Canned)

Natural Goodness Chicken Broth (Canned, Carton)

Vegetarian Broth (Canned)

**Sweet Sue** - 99% Fat Free (Chicken)

**Trader Joe's** - Organic (Free Range Chicken, Hearty Vegetablev, Low Sodium Chicken), Savory Broth Concentrates (Reduced Sodium)

## Brown Sugar... see Sugar

## Brownies/Brownie Mix

**1-2-3 Gluten Free▲** - Devilishly Decadent Brownies●, Divinely Decadent Brownies●

**365 Everyday Value** - Gluten Free Chocolate Brownie Mix

**Andrea's Fine Foods▲** - Brownies

**Arrowhead Mills** - Gluten Free Brownie Mix

**Betty Crocker▲** - Gluten Free Chocolate Brownie Mix

**Bob's Red Mill▲** - Gluten Free Brownie Mix

**Celiac Specialties▲** - Gluten Free Brownie (Round, Tray)

**Cherrybrook Kitchen** - Gluten Free Fudge Brownie Mix *(Box Must Say Gluten-Free)*

**Choices Rice Bakery ▲** - Brownie Mix

**Crave Bakery▲** - Brownies (Dark Chocolate, Toasted Pecan)

**Ener-G ▲** - Brownies

**B**

Everybody Eats▲ - Fudge Brownies Dairy Free

Food-Tek Fast & Fresh - Minute Gooey Brownie Decadence

Foods By George▲ - Brownies

Frankly Natural Bakers - Carob Almondine, Cherry Berry, Java Jive, Misty Mint, Wacky Walnut

French Meadow Bakery - Gluten Free (Frozen Fudge Brownies●, Fudge Brownie Bites●, Fudge Brownies●)

Gillian's Foods▲ - Brownie Mix, Brownies, Chocolate Cherry Brownies

Gluten Free Life▲ - Brownies, The Ultimate Gluten Free Cake Muffin & Brownie Mix

Gluten-Free Creations▲ - Rich Brownie Mix●

Gluten-Free Essentials▲ - Brownie Mix (Chocolate Mint Fudge●, Decadent Chocolate Fudge●, Speedy Bake Fudge●

Gluten Free & Fabulous▲ - Brownie Bites●

Gluten-Free Pantry▲ - Chocolate Truffle Brownie Mix

Hol Grain - Chocolate Brownie Mix

Kinnikinnick▲ - JB Brownie Squares

Laurel's Sweet Treats ▲ - Chocolate Dream Brownie Mix

Maggie's Gluten Free Goodies ▲ - Oh So Chocolatey Brownie Mix

Mixes From The Heartland▲ - Sweet Potato Brownie Mix●

Namaste Foods▲ - Brownie Mix

Pamela's Products▲ - Chocolate Brownie Mix

Really Great Food Company▲ - Aunt Tootsie's Brownie Mix

Rose's Bakery▲ - All Varieties●

Tastefully Gluten Free ▲ - Brownie Mix

The Cravings Place ▲ - Ooey Gooey Chocolatey Chewy Brownie Mix

Trader Joe's - Gluten Free Brownie Mix

WOW Baking Company▲ - Chocolate Brownie●

Bruschetta

Classico - All Varieties

Santa Barbara

Tassos - Mediterranean, Olivara

**B**

**Trader Joe's** - Bruschetta Sauce (Refrigerated), Grilled Vegetable, Mixed Olive, Sun Dried Tomato

**Ukrop's**

**Brussel Sprouts...** *All Fresh Fruits & Vegetables Are **Gluten-Free***

**Birds Eye** - All Plain Frozen Vegetables *(Except With Sauce)*

**C & W** - All Plain Frozen Vegetables

**Food Club Brand** - Frozen

**Green Giant** - Frozen Baby Brussels Sprouts & Butter Sauce

**Hy-Vee** - Frozen

**Lowes Brands Foods** - Frozen (Deluxe Baby, Regular)

**Meijer Brand** - Frozen

**Midwest Country Fare** - Frozen

**Pictsweet** - All Plain Vegetables (Frozen)

**Publix** - Frozen

**Stop & Shop Brand**

**Spartan Brand** - Frozen

**Trader Joe's** - All Plain Vegetables (Frozen)

**Wegmans Brand** - Frozen (In Butter Sauce, Regular)

**Winn Dixie** - Frozen

**Buckwheat**

**Arrowhead Mills**

**Arzu** - Chai●, Original●, Southwest●

**Bob's Red Mill▲** - Organic Buckwheat (Groats, Kasha)

**Pocono** - Buckwheat Flour (Light, Whole), Cream Of Buckwheat

**Buckwheat Bread... see Bread**

**Buckwheat Groats**

**Arrowhead Mills**

**Wolff's** - Whole

**Buffalo Meat**

**Trader Joe's** - Classic Buffalo Burger, Flame Grilled Buffalo Patties

**Buffalo Wing Sauce... see Wing Sauce**

**Buffalo Wings... see Wings**

**B** Buns

    **Celiac Specialties▲** - Buns (Hamburger, Hot Dog, Sub)

    **Chebe▲** - Sandwich Buns (Frozen Dough)

    **Cybro's** - Gluten Free Rice Rolls

    **Ener-G ▲** -

        Hamburger Buns (Brown Rice, Seattle Brown, Tapioca, White Rice)

        Hot Dog Buns (Seattle Brown, Tapioca)

    **Food-Tek Fast & Fresh** - Minute Hamburger Bun Mix

    **Gluten-Free Creations▲** - Hamburger Buns (Regular●, White●), Hot Dog Buns●

    **Kinnikinnick▲** - Tapioca Rice Buns (Cinnamon, Hamburger Buns, Hot Cross, Hot Dog, Multigrain Seed & Fibre, Tray)

    **Quejos** - Buns (Cheese Quejos, Dairy Free Quejos, Soya Quejos)

    **Rose's Bakery▲** - All Varieties●

    **Schar▲** - Classic White Rolls

    **Whole Foods Market Gluten Free Bakehouse ▲** - Hamburger Buns

    Burgers... *All Fresh Ground Meat Is **Gluten-Free (Non-Marinated, Unseasoned)***

    **Amy's** - Bistro Burger

    **Applegate Farms** - Organic (Beef, Turkey)

    **Butcher's Cut -** Beef Burgers

    **Butterball -** Turkey Burgers (All Natural, Seasoned)

    **Full Circle -** All Natural Frozen 80% Lean Beef Patties

    **Great Value Brand (Wal-Mart) -** 100% Frozen Beef Patties

    **Henry & Lisa's -** White Alaskan Salmon Gluten Free Burgers

    **Honeysuckle White** - Fresh Ground Turkey Patties, Frozen Turkey Burgers

    **Jennie-O** - Fresh Lean Turkey Patties, Frozen Turkey Burgers

    **Organic Prairie** - Frozen Organic Ground Beef Patties 10.6 oz.

    **Perdue** - Ground Burgers (Chicken, Turkey)

    **Shelton's** - Turkey

**B**

**Sol Cuisine** - Organic Falafel Burger, Original Burger, Spicy Bean Burger, Vegetable Burger

**Sunshine Burgers -** Organic (Barbecue, Breakfast, Falafel, Garden Herb, Original, South West)

**Trader Joe's -** Chicken Artichoke Patties, Chili Lime Chicken Burgers, Classic Buffalo Burger, Flame Grilled Buffalo Patties, Never Never Angus Beef Burgers, Premium Salmon Patties, Salmon Burger, Tofu Veggie Burger

**Ukrop's -** All Natural Frozen Ground Beef Patties

**Wellshire Farms** - All Natural Frozen (Beef Hamburgers, Turkey Burgers)

**Wild Wood Organics** - Tofu Veggie Burgers (Original, Shiitake, Southwest)

**Winn Dixie -** Frozen Angus Beef Patties (Original, w/Grill Seasoning, w/Sweet Onion)

**Burrito Seasoning Mix... see also Seasonings**

　　**Old El Paso**

**Burritos**

　　**GlutenFreeda▲ -** Breakfast, Chicken & Cheese, Vegetarian & Dairy Free, Vegetarian Bean & Cheese

**Butter... see also Spread**

　　**365 Every Day Value** - Sweet Cream Butter

　　**365 Organic Every Day Value** - Organic (Butter, Unsalted Butter)

　　**Bramley's** - Apple

　　**Cabot** - 83, Salted, Unsalted

　　**Earth Balance -** Natural Buttery Spread (Olive Oil, Original, Soy Free, Soy Garden, Natural Shortening, Organic Buttery Spread (Original Whipped), Vegan Buttery Sticks)

　　**Eden Organic** - Apple, Apple Cherry, Montmorency Tart Cherry

　　**Food Club** - Margarine

　　**Full Circle -** Organic Salted Butter

　　**Great Value Brand (Wal-Mart)** - Margarine, Salted Sweet Cream Butter, Unsalted Sweet Cream Butter

　　**Home Harvest Brand -** 52% Quarters, Spread (48% Crock, Regular)

**B**

**Horizon Organic** - All Varieties

**Hy-Vee** - Best Thing Since Butter, Sweet Cream Butter (Quarters & Solid, Unsalted, Whipped), Unsalted Sweet Quarters

**I Can't Believe It's Not Butter** - All Varieties

**Ian's** - Soy Butter 4 ME

**Kroger Brand** - Butter, Margarine

**Land-O-Lakes** - Butter w/Olive Oil, Fresh Buttery Taste, Garlic Butter, Honey Butter, Margarine, Salted Butter, Spreadable Butter w/Canola Oil, Unsalted Butter, Whipped Salted Butter, Whipped Unsalted Butter,

**Laura Lynn** - Butter, Margarine Spread (Light, Quarters, Squeezeable, Taste Like Butter)

**Lowes Foods Brand** - Butter (Salted, Unsalted), Margarine (Patties, Quarters, Soft Ilb, Spread, Squeeze)

**Lucerne** - Butter (Salted, Unsalted), Whipped

**Manischewitz** - Apple Butter

**Meijer Brand** - Butter (AA CTN Quarters)

**Nature's Promise** - Organic Butter

**O Organics** - Sweet Cream (Salted, Unsalted)

**Odell's** - Clarified Butter, Original Popcorn Butter, Seafood Butter

**Organic Valley** - Cultured Unsalted, European Cultured, Pasture Cultured, Salted, Whipped Salted

**Prairie Farms** - Salted, Unsalted

**Publix** - Finishing Butter (Cajun, Lemon Herb, Sun Dried Tomato), Salted, Sweet Cream (Salted, Unsalted), Unsalted, Whipped (Salted, Unsalted)

**Smart Balance** - All Varieties

**Spartan Brand** - 52% Crock, Butter, Is It Butter (70% Crock, 70% Spread Tub), Margarine (Corn Oil Quarters, Quarters, Soft Sleeve, Soft Tub), Spread (70% Quarters, Regular), Unsalted

**Stop & Shop Brand** - Butter Quarters (Salted, Unsalted)

**Tillamook** - All Varieties

**Trader Joe's** - All Butter

**B**

**C**

**Wegmans Brand** -
  Club Pack (Sweet Cream Butter Sticks)
  Finishing Butter (Bearnaise, Chipotle Lime, Garlic Cheese, Lemon Dill)
  Solid Butter
  Sweet Cream Butter Sticks (Salted, Unsalted)
  Whipped Tub (Salted, Unsalted)
  **Winn Dixie** - Salted, Unsalted, Whipped
  **Woodstock Farms** - Organic Butter (Salted, Unsalted)
**Buttermilk... see Milk**

# C

**Cabbage...** *All Fresh Fruits & Vegetables Are Gluten-Free*
**Cake/Cake Mix**
  **1-2-3 Gluten Free▲** - Delightfully Gratifying Bundt Poundcake●, Peri's Perfect Chocolate Bundt Poundcake●, Yummy Yellow Cake Mix●
  **365 Everyday Value** - Gluten Free Cake Mix (Chocolate, White)
  **Andrea's Fine Foods▲** - Blueberry, Brownie, Carrot Spice, Chocolate, Chocolate Chunk, Coffeecake, German Chocolate, German Chocolate Layer, Gooey Butter, Pinwheel Roll, Red Velvet, Strawberry Cream, Yellow
  **Apple's Bakery▲** - White Layer Cake Kit
  **Arrowhead Mills** - Gluten Free Vanilla Cake Mix
  **Authentic Foods▲** - Cake Mix (Chocolate, Lemon, Vanilla)
  **Betty Crocker▲** - Gluten Free Cake Mix (Devil's Food, Yellow)
  **Bob's Red Mill▲** - Chocolate Cake Mix
  **Cause You're Special▲** - Golden Pound, Moist (Lemon, Yellow), Rich Chocolate
  **Cherrybrook Kitchen** - Gluten Free Chocolate Cake Mix *(Box Must Say Gluten-Free)*

**C**

**Crave Bakery▲** - Mama Z's Chocolate Cake, Chocolate Cupcake

**Deerfields Bakery▲ -** Cheesecake, Coffeecakes (Blueberry Cream Cheese, Pecan Sour Cream), Decorated Cakes (Flourless Chocolate Cake, Special Occasion Cakes), Mini Chocolate Cupcakes

**Dowd & Rogers▲** - Cake Mix (Dark Vanilla, Dutch Chocolate, Golden Lemon)

**El Peto▲** - Cake Mix (Chocolate, Lemon, Marble, White)

**El Torito** - Sweet Corn Cake Mix

**Ener-G ▲** - Poundcake

**Everybody Eats▲** - Poundcake

**Food-Tek Fast & Fresh** - Cake Mix (Dairy Free Minute (Chocolate, Cinnamon Coffee, White Cake, Yellow Cake), Double Chocolate)

**Foods By George▲** - Cake (Crumb, Pound)

**Gluten Free Life▲** - The Ultimate Gluten Free Cake Muffin & Brownie Mix

**Gluten-Free Creations▲** - Carrot Picnic Cake●, Chocolate Cake●, Chocolate Cupcakes●, Cinnamon Coffee Cake●, Yellow Cake●, Yellow Cupcakes●, Winkies●

**Gluten-Free Essentials▲** -

Mix (Extreme Chocolate Cake●, Holiday Gingerbread●, Spice Cake & Muffin●, Yellow Velvet Cake●)

Speedy Bake Mix (Chocolate Mud●, Spice Is Nice●, Yella Vanilla●)

**Gluten-Free Pantry▲** -

Chocolate Chip Cookie & Cake Mix

Coffee Cake Mix

Decadent Chocolate Cake Mix

Old Fashioned Cake & Cookie Mix

Spice Cake & Gingerbread Mix

**Glutino▲** - Sans Gluten Free Cake Mix (Chocolate, White)

**Good Juju Bakery ▲** - Cup Cakes (Chocolate, Vanilla)

**Hodgson Mill▲** - Multi Purpose Baking Mix

**Josef's▲** - Brownie Roll, Jelly Roll

**C**

**Kinnikinnick▲** - Angel Food, Chocolate, Fruit, Sponge, White

**Laurel's Sweet Treats ▲**- Cake Mix (Cinnamon Spice, Mom's Chocolate, Vanilla)

**Madwoman Foods▲** - Tea Cakes (Banana Chocolate, Banana Cinnamon, Blueberry, Chocolate Cherry, Cocoa Mocha, Lemon Poppyseed, Orange Chocolate, Orange Cranberry, Pecan Cocoa Mocha)

**Maggie's Gluten Free Goodies▲**- Scrumptious Chocolate Cake Mix

**Mixes From The Heartland▲** - Cake Mix (Chocolate Angel Food●, Chocolate Poundcake●, Cinnamon Orange●, Lime Poundcake●, Raspberry Poundcake●, Strawberry Angel Food●, Strawberry Poundcake●, Upside Down●, Vanilla Angel Food●, Vanilla Poundcake●)

**Namaste Foods▲** - Cake Mix (Chocolate, Spice, Vanilla)

**New Harvest Naturals** - Classic GF Pound Cake, Raisin Pound Cake

**O'Doughs Bakery▲** - Cake (Banana, Carrot, Chocolate)

**Pamela's Products▲** - Cake Mix (Chocolate, Classic Vanilla)

**Really Great Food Company▲** - Cake Mix (Angle Food, Devil's Food, Banana Bread, Chocolate, Chocolate Cupcake, Colonial Spice, Gingerbread, Golden, Grandma's Pound, Lemon Poppy, Orange, Pineapple, Pumpkin Bread, Pumpkin Spice, White, Yellow)

**Ruby Range** - Gluten Free Baking Mix (Chocolate Truffle Cake & Cupcakes●, Spice Cake & Cupcakes●)

**Simply Organic** - Mix (Carrot Cake●, Cocoa Cayenne Cupcake●)

**Skye Foods** - Heart Cake●, Spice Cake●

**Sofella** - Gluten Free Chocolate Cake Mix & Frosting Mix●

**Sylvan Border Farm** - Cake Mix (Chocolate, Lemon)

**Tastefully Gluten Free▲** - Chocolate Cake Mix

**The Cravings Place▲** - Cake & Cookie Mix, Cinnamon Crumble Coffeecake Mix, Dutch Chocolate Cake Mix

**The Lite-Ful Cheesecake ▲**- Cheesecake (Amaretto Almond●, Blueberry●, Chocolate Bliss●, Chocolate Swirl●, Cinnamon, Grand ●, Kahlua●, Lemon●, Mandarin●, Mocha●, Plain Vanilla●, Peanut Butter●, Pumpkin●, Strawberry●)

**C**

Toro▲ - Sponge Cake Mix

Trader Joe's - Flourless Chocolate Cake

Whole Foods Market Gluten Free Bakehouse ▲ - Carrot Cake, Chocolate Cupcakes, Vanilla Cupcakes

## Candy/Candy Bars

Altoids - Curiously Strong Mints Large Tins (Creme De Menthe, Peppermint, Wintergreen) *(Smalls Contain Gluten)*

Amanda's Own - All Varieties

Andes - Thins (Cherry Jubilee, Crème de Menthe, Mint Parfait, Toffee Crunch), Crème de Menthe Sugar Free

Benecol - Smart Chews

Candy Tree

Licorice

Black Licorice (Bites, Laces, Vines)

Cherry (Bites, Laces, Vines)

Raspberry (Bites, Laces, Vines)

Strawberry (Bites, Laces, Vines)

Candytree Gourmet Lollipops - All Varieties

Caramel Apple Pops

Carb Safe - Sugar Free Chocolate Bars (Dark, Milk)

Cella's - Chocolate Covered Cherries (Dark, Milk)

Charleston Chew - Chocolate, Mini Vanilla, Strawberry, Vanilla

Charms - Blow Pops (Bubblegum, Minis, Regular), Candy Carnival, Flat Pops, Sweet Pops

Cherry Mash - Cherry Flavored Candy Bar

Coffee Rio's

Cry Baby - Candy, Gumballs, Twist Gum

Dots - Crows, Fruit Flavors, Regular, Tropical

Fluff Stuff - Cotton Candy, Tear Jerkers

Food Club Brand - Butter Toffee

Frooties - Fruit Flavored Chewy Candy

Gimbal's Fine Candies ▲ All Varieties

**Glutino ▲** - Candy Bars (Chocolate Peanut Butter, Dark Chocolate, Milk Chocolate)

**Goelitz** - Candy Corn

**Great Value Brand (Wal-Mart)** -

Butterscotch Discs

Candy Corn

Cinnamon Discs

Fruit Slices

Gummy (Bears, Worms)

Orange Slices

Spearmint Starlight Mints

Spice Drops

Starlight Mints

**Haribo** -

Alphabet Letters

Brixx

Build A Burger

Centipedes

Clown Fish

Fizzy Cola

Frogs

Fruit Salad

Fruity Pasta

Gold Bears

Grapefruit

Gummi Apples

Happy Cola

Mini Rainbow Frogs

Peaches

Pink Grapefruit

Raspberries

Rattle Snakes

**C**

Roulettes (Mega, Regular)

Sour Cherries

Strawberries (& Cream, Licorice Wheel, Regular, Wheels)

Super Cola

Techno Bears

Twin Cherries

**Hershey's -**

Heath Bar

Jolly Ranchers (Gummies, Hard Candy)

Kisses (Milk Chocolate, Milk Chocolate Meltaways, Milk Chocolate w/Almonds, Milk Chocolate w/Caramel, Milk Chocolate w/Cherry Cordial Crème, Special Dark Chocolate)

Milk Chocolate Bar (Original, w/Almonds)

Mr. Goodbar

PayDay

Reese's Peanut Butter Cups (Original)

Skor

York Peppermint Patty

**Hy-Vee -**

Assorted Gum Balls

Butterscotch Buttons

Chocolate (Caramel Clusters, Covered Raisins, Peanut Clusters, Stars)

Cinnamon Imperials

Circus Peanuts

Dubble Bubble Gum

Dum Dum Suckers

Gum Drops

Gummi (Bears, Peach Rings, Sour Worms, Worms)

Lemon Drops

Milk Chocolate Peanut Butter Cups

Orange Slices

Smarties

Spice Drops

Starlight Mints

Tootsie Flavored Rolls

Tootsie Pops

Wax Bottles

**Jelly Belly** - Jelly Beans (All Varieties)

**Junior Mints -** Deluxe, Inside Out, Junior (Caramels, Mints), Minis

**Kroger Brand** - Hard Candy

**Let's Do...Organic -** All Gummi Bears

**Lifesavers**

**Lowes Foods Brand** - After Dinner Mints, Candy Corn, Chocolate (Peanuts, Raisins), Cinnamon Imperials, Dubble Bubble Gum, Gummi (Bears, Worms, Worms Sour), Kiddie Mix, Laffy Taffy, Orange Slices, Peppermint Twists, Starlight Mints

**M & M's** - All Varieties

**Manischewitz** - Chocolate Frolic Bears, Fruit Slices, Hazelnut Truffles, Mallo Cups, Max's Magic Lollycones, Mini Sour Fruit Slices, Patties (Peppermint, Tender Coconut), Raspberry Gel Bars, Swiss Chocolate Mints

**Maple Grove Farms Of Vermont -** Blended Maple, Pure Maple

**Mars -**

Dove Chocolate - All Varieties

M & M's - All Varieties

Milky Way Products - All Varieties *(Except The Milky Way Bar)*

Munch Bar

Snickers

Snickers Dark Bar

**Munch Bar**

**Necco -**

Banana Split & Mint Julep Chews

Canada Mint & Wintergreen Lozenges

**C**

Candy Eggs (Easter)

Clark Bar

Haviland Peppermint & Wintergreen Patties

Haviland Thin Mints & Candy Stix

Mary Janes (Peanut Butter Kisses, Regular)

Skybar

Squirel Nut (Caramels, Zippers)

Sweethearts Conversation Hearts *(Valentines Only)*

Talking Pumpkins (Halloween)

Ultramints

**Nestle** -

Baby Ruth

Bit o Honey

Butterfinger *(Except Crisp & Stixx)*

Goobers

Milk Chocolate

Nips (Regular, Sugar Free)

Oh Henry!

Raisinets

Sno Caps

Spree

**Newman's Own Organics** - All Chocolate Bars *(Except Crisp Rice)*, All Chocolate Cups

**Nik-L-Nip** - Wax Bottles

**Orgran▲** - Molasses Licorice

**Publix** -

Candy Corn

Chocolate Covered Peanut Brittle

Circus Peanuts

Classic Buttery Peanut Brittle

Double Dipped Chocolate

Fruit Slices

**C**

Gummi (Bears, Worms)

Jelly Beans

Orange Slices

Party Time Mix

Pastel Mints

Smarties Candy

Spearmint Starlight Mints

Spice Drops

Starlight Mints Candy

Sweet Stripes

**Razzles -** Gum (Regular, Sour, Tropical)

**Safeway Brand -** Candy Corn, Dessert Mints, Gummi Bears, Gummi Worms (Regular, Sour), Jelly Beans, Lemon Drops, Orange Slices, Spice Drops, Star Light Mints, Trail Mix w/Candy Pieces

**Seitenbacher -** Cherry Dolphins, Sunhats (Black Currant, Cherry, Passion Fruit, Strawberry), Roses For You, Smooch Lions, Strawberry Alligators, Vampires Lunch

**Sharkies ▲ -** Energy Sports Chews (Berry Blast, Citrus Squeeze, Fruit Splash, Peach Tea Breeze, Watermelon Screem)

**Shaw's Brand -** Gum Drops, Gummi Bears, Jelly Beans

**Sipahh -** Milk Flavoring Straws

**Skittles -** All Varieties

**Snickers -** Almond, Dark, Fudge, Snickers

**Sour Patch Kids -** All Varieties

**Spangler -** Candy Canes, Cane Classics, Dum Dum (Canes, Chewy Pops, Pops), Marshmallow Treats, Saf T Pops, Swirl Saf T Pops

**St. Claire's Organics -** All Candy, Mints, Sour Tarts

**Starburst -** All Varieties

**Stop & Shop Brand -**

Assorted (Fruit Filled Candy, Star Drops, Starlights)

Blue Gummi Sharks

Butter Toffee

Butterscotch Disks

**C**

Canada Wintergreen
Candy Corn
Candy Necklaces
Cinnamon Starlights
Fish
Gum (Balls, Bears, Drops)
Jelly Beans
Kiddie Mix
Lemon Drops
Neon Sour Crawlers
Orange Slices
Pastel Mints
Peach Rings
Pina Colada Coated Cashews
Red Jug Coins Coins
Root Beer Barrels
Royal Mix
Silver Mints
Smarties
Soft Peppermints
Sour Balls
Sour Gummi Worms
Spearmint (Leaves, Starlights)
Spice Drops
Starlight Mints
Strawberry Buds
Watermelon Hard Candy

**Sugar Babies** - Sugar Babies (Caramel Apple, Chocolate Covered, Original)

**Sugar Daddy** - Caramel Pops

**Sugar Mama Caramels**

**Swedish Fish**

## candy/candy bars

C

**Taffy Tree** ▲ - All Varieties

**The Ginger People** - Ginger Chews

**Timothy's Confections** - Sugar Free Chocolate Covered Almonds (Dark, Milk)

**Tootsie Roll** -
 Child's Play Assortment of Favorites
 Tootsie Fruit Rolls
 Tootsie Pops (Bunch Pops, Drop Pops, Miniatures, Original)
 Tootsie Roll (Mini Chews, Regular, Sugar Free)

**Trader Joe's** -
 Almond Clusters
 Black Licorice Scottie Dogs
 Brown Rice Marshmallow Treats
 Chocolate Covered (Blueberries, Orange & Raspberry Sticks)
 Green Tea Mints
 English Toffee
 Lumpy Bumpy Bar
 Milk & Dark Chocolate Covered Almonds
 Milk Chocolate (Clouds, Covered Raisins, Peanut Butter Cups)
 Mini Milk Chocolate Peanut Butter Cups
 Organic Pops
 Pecans Praline
 Yogurt Raisins

**Wack-O-Wax** - Wax Fangs, Wax Lips

**Wonka** -
 Bottlecaps
 Gobstoppers (Chewy, Original)
 Laffy Taff
 Lik M Aid Fun Dip
 Mix-Ups
 Nerds (Rope & Gumballs, Regular)
 Pixy Stix

**C**

Rope & Fruit Tart Chews
Runts (Chewy, Original)
Shockers
Sweet Tarts
**Woodstock Farms** - Vegetarian (Jelly Pebbles, Gummy Cubs)
**Zip-A-Dee** - Mini Pops

**Canned Chicken**
  **Hormel -** Chunk Meats (Breast of Chicken)
  **Meijer Brand** - Chicken Chunk White
  **Member's Mark**
  **Spartan Brand -** Chunk Chicken Breast
  **Sweet Sue -** Boned Chicken Breast

**Canned Ham**
  **Black Label** - Canned Hams
  **Great Value Brand (Wal-Mart)** - Luncheon Meat, Potted Meat
  **Hormel** - Chunk Meats (Ham)
  **SPAM** - Classic, Less Sodium, Lite, Oven Roasted Turkey, Smoke Flavored
  **Underwood** - Deviled Ham

**Canned Salmon... see Fish**

**Canned Tuna... see Tuna**

**Canned Turkey**
  **Hormel** - Chunk Meats (Turkey)
  **SPAM** - Oven Roasted Turkey

**Canola Oil... see Oil**

**Capers**
  **B&G**
  **Safeway Select**
  **Trader Joe's -** Nonpareil
  **Wegmans Brand** - Italian Classics (Capote, Nonpareil)

**Cappuccino...see Coffee**

**Caramel... see Candy/Candy Bars and/or Dip/Dip Mix**

**C**

Carbonated Beverage... see Soda Pop/Carbonated Beverages

Carrots... *All Fresh Fruits & Vegetables Are Gluten-Free*

**Albertsons** - Canned, Frozen

**Birds Eye** - All Plain Frozen Vegetables *(Except With Sauce)*

**C & W** - All Plain Frozen Vegetables

**Del Monte** - All Canned Vegetables

**Food Club Brand** - Canned Sliced, Crinkle Cut, Whole Baby

**Freshlike** - Frozen Plain Vegetables *(Except Pasta Combos & Seasoned Blends)*

**Grand Selections** - Frozen Whole Carrots

**Great Value Brand (Wal-Mart)** - Canned Sliced Carrots, Crinkle Cut, Frozen (Crinkle Cut, Whole Baby), Microwavable Plastic Cup Frozen, Whole Baby

**Hannaford Brand** - Sliced, Whole Baby

**Hy-Vee** - California, Classic Cut & Peeled Baby, Frozen Crinkle Cut, Sliced

**Kroger Brand** - All Plain Vegetables (Canned, Frozen)

**Laura Lynn** - Sliced Carrots, Whole Baby Carrots

**Lowes Foods Brand** - Deluxe Whole Baby, Peas & Carrots, Sliced

**Meijer Brand** - Canned Sliced (No Salt, Regular), Frozen Carrots (Crinkle Cut, Whole Baby)

**Midwest Country Fare** - Sliced Carrots

**Pictsweet** - All Plain Vegetables (Frozen)

**Publix** - Canned (Carrots), Frozen (Crinkle Cut, Peas & Carrots, Whole Baby)

**Publix GreenWise Market** - Organic (Baby, Carrots, Chips, Juicing, Shredds, Snack)

**S&W** - All Canned Vegetables

**Safeway Brand** - Carrots (Sliced)

**Spartan Brand** - Canned (Peas & Sliced Carrots, Sliced), Frozen (Crinkle Cut, Peas & Carrots, Whole Baby)

**Stop & Shop Brand** - Carrots

**Trader Joe's** - All Plain Vegetables (Frozen)

**C** **Wegmans Brand -** Baby Cut, Carrots/Potatoes/Celery & Onions, Crinkle Cut, Organic, Sliced Carrots (No Salt Added, Regular), Whole Style

**Winn Dixie -** Frozen (Crinkle Cut, Whole Baby)

Cashews... see Nuts

Cauliflower... *All **Fresh** Fruits & Vegetables Are **Gluten-Free***

**Albertsons -** Canned & Frozen

**Birds Eye -** All Plain Frozen Vegetables *(Except With Sauce)*

**C & W -** All Plain Frozen Vegetables

**Freshlike -** Frozen Plain Vegetables *(Except Pasta Combos & Seasoned Blends)*

**Great Value Brand (Wal-Mart) -** Frozen (Broccoli & Cauliflower, Cauliflower)

**Green Giant -** Frozen (Cauliflower & Cheese Sauce, Steamers Broccoli Carrots Cauliflower & Cheese Sauce)

**Hy-Vee -** Frozen Cauliflower Florets

**Kroger Brand -** All Plain Vegetables (Canned, Frozen)

**Lowes Foods Brand -** Frozen Cauliflower

**Meijer Brand -** Frozen Cauliflower Florets

**Midwest Country Fare -** Frozen Cauliflower

**Pictsweet -** All Plain Vegetables (Frozen)

**Publix -** Frozen

**Safeway Brand -** Frozen

**Spartan Brand -** Frozen Florets

**Trader Joe's -** All Plain Vegetables (Frozen)

**Wegmans Brand -** Florets

**Winn Dixie -** Frozen

Caviar

**Romanoff -** Black (Lumpfish, Whitefish), Red (Lumpfish, Salmon)

Celery... *All **Fresh** Fruits & Vegetables Are **Gluten-Free***

Celery Salt... see Seasonings

# Cereal

**C**

**Amy's -** Cream Of Rice Hot Cereal Bowl

**Ancient Harvest Quinoa -** Quinoa Flakes

**Bakery On Main -** Gluten Free Granola (Apple Raisin Walnut, Cranberry Orange Cashew, Extreme Fruit & Nut, Nutty Maple Cranberry, Rainforest)

**Barbara's Bakery** - Honey Rice Puffins, Multigrain Puffins, Organic Brown Rice Crisps, Organic Corn Flakes

**Beech-Nut Baby Food** - Cereals (Rice), Cereals Good Evening (Whole Grain Brown Rice)

**Bob's Red Mill▲ -** Creamy Rice Hot Cereal (Organic, Regular), Flaxseed Meal, Gluten Free Mighty Tasty Hot, Organic Creamy Buckwheat

**Earth's Best Organic Baby Food** - Whole Grain Rice Cereal

**Eat Natural -** For Breakfast (Gluten Free Toasted Buckwheat Pumpkin Seeds Raisins & Mango, Gluten Free Raisins Almonds Mixed Seeds & Crispy Rice)

**Eco-Planet -** 7 Whole Grains Hot Cereal (Apples & Cinnamon●, & Cream●, Maple & Brown Sugar, Original●)

**Ener-G ▲** - Rice Bran

**Enjoy Life▲** - Granola Crunch (Cinnamon●, Cranapple●, Very Berry●)

**Erewhon -**

Aztec Crunchy Corn & Amaranth

Brown Rice Cream

Corn Flakes

Crispy Brown Rice (Cocoa, Gluten Free Regular, w/Mixed Berries)

Rice Twice

Strawberry Crisp

**General Mills▲** - Chex (Chocolate, Cinnamon, Corn, Honey Nut, Rice, Strawberry)

**Gerber -**

Boxed Cereal Rice w/(Apples, Mixed Fruit)

**C**

Rice Cereal DHA Brain & Eye Development

Rice Single Grain Cereal

**Gerber Organic Baby Food** - Brown Rice Whole Grain Cereal

**Glutano▲** - Cornflakes, Pops

**Gluten Free Sensations** - Cream Of Brown Rice, Granola (Apple Crisp, Cherry Vanilla Almond, Cranberry Pecan, French Vanilla Almond)

**GlutenFreeda▲** - Instant Oatmeal (Apple, Banana Maple, Cinnamon, Maple Raisin)

**Glutino▲** - Apple & Cinnamon, Honey Nut

**Health Valley** - Blue Corn Flakes, Corn Crunch Ems, Rice CrunchEms

**Kinnikinnick▲** - Kinni Crisp Rice Cereal, Rice Bran

**Lundberg▲** - Hot 'N Creamy Purely Organic Rice

**Meijer Brand** - Grits (Buttered Flavored Intant, Quick)

**Montana Monster Munchies** - Whole Grain Oat Bran●

**Nabisco** - Cream Of Rice Hot Cereal

**Nature's Path** -

Envirokidz Organic

Amazon Frosted Flakes

Gorilla Munch

Koala Crisp

Leapin Lemurs

Peanut Butter Panda Puffs

Nature's Path Organic

Crispy Rice

Corn Flakes

Honey'd Corn Flakes

Mesa Sunrise

Whole O's

**New Morning** - Cocoa Crispy Rice

**Nu-world Foods** -

Amaranth Berry Delicious●

Amaranth O's (Original●, Peach●)

**C**

Cereal Snaps (Cinnamon●, Cocoa●, Original●)

Puffed Amaranth Cereal●

**Only Oats** - Oat Bran●

**Orgran▲** - Multigrain O w/Quinoa, Puffed Amaranth Breakfast Cereal

**Pacific Grain** - Nutty Rice

**Perky's** - Nutty (Flax●, Rice●), O's (Apple Cinnamon●, Frosted●, Original●)

**Pocono** - Cream of Buckwheat

**Seitenbacher** - Whole Grain Cornflakes, Musli #7

**Trader Joe's** - Gluten Free Granola, Golden Roasted (Flaxseed w/ Blueberries, Whole Flaxseed)

**Wegmans Brand** - Fruity Rice Crisps

**Chamomile Tea... see Tea**

**Champagne...** *All Champagne **made in USA** is Gluten-Free[2]

**Cheese**

**A & E Cheese** -

Pre Sliced (American, Colby Jack, Havarti, Mild Cheddar, Mozzarella, Muenster, Pepper Jack, Provolone, Swiss)

Shredded (Colby Jack, Mild Cheddar, Mexican Mix, Mozzarella, Sharp)

**Albertsons** - All (Blocks, Singles, String, Shredded), Ricotta Cheese (Part Skim, Whole)

**Andrew & Everett** - All Varieties

**Applegate Farms** -

Natural (Aged Cheddar, American, Cheddar, Emmentaler Swiss, Havarti, Monterey Jack w/Jalapeno Peppers, Muenster, New York Sharp Aged Cheddar, Provolone

Organic (Cheddar, Jack Muenster)

Probiotic Yogurt Cheese

**Athenos** -

Blue Crumbled

Feta (Basil & Tomato, Black Peppercorn, Garlic & Herb, Lemon Garlic & Oregano, Mild, Packed In Brine, Reduced Fat Tomato &

**C**

Basil, Reduced Fat Traditional, Roasted Red Pepper & Garlic, Traditional)

Gorgonzola Crumbled

**Bakers & Chefs -** Cheddar Cheese Sauce

**Belgioioso -** American Grana, Asiago, Auribella, Burrata, Crescenza Stracchino, Fontina, Fresh Mozzarella, Gorgonzola, Italico, Kasseri, Mascarpone, Parmesan, Pepato, Peperoncino, Provolone, Ricotta con Latte, Romano, Unwrap & Roll, Vegetarian Parmesan

**Boar's Head -** All Varieties

**Borden -** All Varieties *(Except Single Sensations Applewood Bacon Cheddar Singles)*

**Cabot -**

Aged Cheddars (Extra Sharp, Mild, Private Stock, Seriously Sharp, Sharp)

Flavored Cheddars (Chili Lime, Chipotle, Garlic & Herb, Habanero, Horseradish, Sun Dried Tomato Basil, Tuscan Rubbed)

Other Cheeses (All Natural Swiss Slices, American Slices, Colby Jack, Fancy Blend Shredded, Monterey Jack, Mozzarella Shredded, Muenster, Pepper Jack)

Reduced Fat Cheddars (50%, 50% Jalapeno, 50% Pepper Jack, 75%)

Shredded Cheeses (Fancy Blend, Mozzarella, Swiss)

Specialty Cheddars (Classic Vermont, Clothbound Wheel, Mild Reserve, Old School, Private Stock, Vintage Choice)

**Cracker Barrel -** Cheddar (2% Extra Sharp, Extra Sharp, Sharp White)

**Deliano's -** Grated Parmesan

**Dorothy Lane Market -** Mozzarella (All Varieties)

**Eat In The Raw -** Parma Vegan Parmesan (Chipotle Cayenne, Original)

**Fair Oaks Farms -** Emmentaler, Havarti (Regular, w/Dill, w/Pepper), Sweet Swiss

**Finlandia -**

Club Store Products

Deli Slices (Monterey Jack/Colby Jack, Muenster)

Imported Black Label Emmental

**C**

Imported Deli Slices (Light Swiss, Swiss, Thin Sliced Swiss)

Deli Slices Imported (Double Gloucester, Gouda, Havarti, Light Swiss, Muenster, Swiss, Thin Sliced Swiss)

Deli Sticks Imported (Gouda, Havarti, Light Swiss, Muenster, Swiss)

Sliced To Order (Imported Light Swiss, Imported Muenster, Imported Swiss, Lappi)

Specialty Cheeses (Black Label Emmental, Black Label Aged Goat, Black Label Gouda, Black Label Gruyere, Swiss, Oltermanni Baby Muenster, Viola)

**Follow Your Heart** - Vegan Gourmet (Cheddar, Monterey Jack, Mozzarella, Nacho)

**Food Club Brand**

Cheese Bar (Cheddar, Colby Jack, Mozzarella, Pepper Jack)

Cottage Cheese (4%, Low Fat)

Cream Cheese Spreads (Light, Neufchatel, Original, Whipped)

Ricotta Cheese (Low Fat, Part Skim)

Shredded (Cheddar, Mexican Blend, Monterey Jack, Mozzarella, Parmesan, Swiss)

Sliced (American, Colby Jack, Mild Cheddar, Mozzarella, Muenster, Pepper Jack, Swiss, Provolone)

**Friendship** - All Varieties

**Galaxy Nutritional Foods** - All (Rice, Rice Vegan, Vegan, Veggie, Veggy, Wholesome Organic Valley)

**Great Value Brand (Wal-Mart)** - American Slices, All Shredded, Parmesan

**Gopal's** - Rawmesan

**Hannaford Brand -** Cheese Spread, Parmesan Grated, Parmesan Romano

**Home Harvest Brand** - Imitation Cheddar, Imitation Mozzarella, Parmesan

**Horizon Organic** - All Varieties

**Hy-Vee** -

American (Cheese Food, Fat Free Singles, Singles, Singles 2% Milk)

**C**

Cheddar (Extra Sharp, Fancy Shredded Jack, Fancy Shredded Mild 2%, Finely Shredded Mild, Lil' Hunk Mild, Medium, Medium Longhorn, Mild, Mild Cubes, Mild Hunk, Mild Shredded, Mild Slices, Sharp, Sharp Hunk, Sharp Longhorn, Sharp Shredded)

Colby (1 lb, Half Moon Longhorn, Hunk, Longhorn, Slice Singles)

Colby Jack (1 lb, Cubes, Fancy Shredded, Finely Shredded, Half Moon Longhorn, Hunk, Lil' Hunk, Shredded, Slices)

Hot Pepper

Monterey Jack (1 lb, Hunk)

Mozzarella (1 lb, Hunk, Fancy Shredded, Fancy Shredded 2% Milk, Shredded, Sliced Low Moisture Part Skim)

Muenster (1 lb, Slices)

Nacho Cheese

Parmesan (Grated, Shredded)

Pepper Jack Cheese (1 lb, Cubes, Hunk, Singles, Slices)

Provolone Cheese (1 lb, Slices)

Ricotta Cheese (Low Fat, Part Skim)

Shredded Blends (Fancy 4 Italian, Mexican Blend, Pizza, Taco)

Swiss (1 lb, Fat Free Slices, Singles, Slices)

**Kraft** -

Block (Cheddar & Monterey Jack, Colby & Monterey Jack, Extra Sharp Cheddar, Medium Cheddar, Mild Cheddar, Monterey Jack)

Crumbles (Blue Cheese, Colby & Monterey Jack, Feta, Sharp Cheddar, Three Cheese)

Deli Fresh Slices (2% Swiss, Colby Jack, Mild Cheddar, Mozzarella, Pepper Jack Spicy, Provolone, Sharp Cheddar, Swiss)

Easy Cheese (American, Cheddar)

Natural Shredded

2% Milk (Colby & Monterey, Mild Cheddar, Sharp Cheddar)

Cheddar (Cheddar Jack, Mild, Mild Cheddar & Monterey Jack, Mild Finely Shredded, Organic, Sharp Finely Shredded)

Colby & Monterey Jack (Finely Shredded, Regular)

**C**

    Italian Style Five Cheese
    Mexican Cheddar Jack (Regular, w/Jalapenos)
    Mexican Four Cheese
    Monterey Jack
    Mozzarella (Fat Free, Low Moisture Part Skim)
    Pizzeria
    Swiss
  Shredded
    Parmesan
    Parmesan & Romano
    Parmesan Romano & Asiago
    Reduced Fat Parmesan Style Grated
  Singles
    2% Milk (American, Pepperjack, Sharp Cheddar, Swiss)
    Deli Deluxe (2%, American, Sharp Cheddar)
    Fat Free (American, Sharp Cheddar, Swiss)
    Regular (American, Sharp Cheddar)
    Select American
  Snackables
    String Cheese
    Twists 2% Milk
  Velveeta (2% Mild, Regular, Slices)
**Kroger Brand** - Cheese (Bars, Cubes, Shredded, Sliced)
**Land-O-Lakes** -
  Chunk
    American (White, Yellow)
    Cheddar (Extra Sharp, Mild, Medium, Sharp)
    Cheddarella
    Colby
    Monterey Jack
    Mozzarella

**C**

Deli Slices
- American
- Co Jack
- Muenster
- Pepper Jack
- Provolone
- Swiss

Singles (Process American)

Snack 'N Cheese To Go
- Chedarella
- Co Jack (Reduced Fat, Regular)
- Medium Cheddar
- Mild Cheddar (Reduced Fat, Regular)
- Monterey Jack

**Laughing Cow** - All Varieties *(Except Gourmet Cheese & Baguettes)*

**Laura Lynn** - Cheese Chunks, Parmesan, Parmesan & Romano, Ricotta

**Lifetime** - Cheese Bars (All Varieties)

**Lifeway** - All Varieties

**Lisanatti** -

Almond Cheese (Cheddar, Garlic & Herb, Jalapeño Jack, Mozzarella)

Premium Soy Sation (Mozzarella, Pepper Jack)

Rice Cheese (Cheddar, Mozzarella, Pepper Jack)

Senora Lupe (Chipotle, Manchego, Mild Jalapeno, Quesadilla)

**Litehouse** - Bleu Cheese Crumbles, Classic Feta, Heart of Bleu Cheese, Monarch Mountain Gorgonzola Crumbles, Roquefort

**Lowes Foods Brand** -

American Processed Slices

Cheddar (Extra Sharp Bar, Fancy Shredded Mild, Fancy Shredded Sharp, Medium Bar, Medium Chunk, Mild Bar, Mild Chunk, Mild Cube, Mild Shredded, NY Sharp Chunk, Sharp Bar, Sharp Chunk, Sharp Slices, Shredded Sharp, Shredded)

Cheddar Jack (Shredded)

Colby (Chunk)

Colby Jack (Bar, Chunk, Shredded)

Hot Pepper Jack (Chunk)

Monterey Jack (Chunk)

Mozzarella (Bar, Chunk, Fancy Shredded, Shredded, Sliced)

Muenster (Chunk)

Parmesan (Bar, Shredded)

Pepper Jack (Bar, Slices)

Provolone (Sliced)

Ricotta (Low Fat, Whole Milk)

Shredded Blends (Fancy Italian, Fancy Mexican, Fancy Pizza w/Mozzarella & Cheddar, Taco Blend)

String Cheese

Swiss (Chunk, Sliced)

**Lucerne -** Cheese (All Varieties), Ricotta, String

**Meijer Brand -**

Aerosol Cheese (American, Cheddar, Sharp Cheddar)

American Processed (Slices)

Cheddar (Fancy Mild Shredded, Fancy Sharp Shredded, Fancy Shredded, Medium Bar, Midget Horn, Mild Bar, Mild Chunk, Sharp Bar, Sharp Chunk, Sharp Shredded Zipper Pouch, Shredded Zipper Pouch, Sliced Longhorn Half Moon, X Sharp Bar)

Cheddar Marble (C&W Cheddar)

Cheddar/Monterey Jack (Bar, Fancy Shred Zip Pouch)

Cheese Food Individually Wrapped (2% American, 2% Sharp, Fat Free Sharp, Sliced Pepper, Swiss)

Cheezy Does It (Jalapeño, Spread Loaf)

Colby (Bar, Chunk, Fancy Shredded)

Colby Jack (Bar, Fancy Shredded, Longhorn Half Moon, Sliced Shingle)

Colby Longhorn (Full Moon, Half Moon, Half Moon Sliced)

**C**

Colby Midget Horn

Hot Pepper Jack (Chunk)

Italian Blend (Fancy Shreddred)

Mexican Blend (Fancy Shredded, Shredded)

Monterey Jack (Chunk)

Mozzarella (Fancy Shredded, Shredded, Sliced Shingle)

Mozzarella Low Moisture Part Skim (Bar, Chunk, Shredded, Sliced Chunk, Square, String Cheese)

Muenster (Sliced Shingle)

Parmesan (1/3 Less Fat, Grated)

Parmesan & Romano (Grated)

Pepperjack (Bar, Sliced Stack Pack)

Pizza Blend Shredded

Provolone (Stacked Slice)

Ricotta (Part Skim, Whole Milk)

String Cheese

Swiss (Chunk, Sliced Shingle, Sliced Sandwich Cut)

Taco/Nacho (Fancy Shredded)

**Midwest Country Fare** - American Sandwich Slices, Shredded Cheese (Cheddar, Mozzarella)

**Mini Babybel** - All Varieties

**O Organics** - Shredded (Mild White, Mild White Cheddar & Monterey Jack, Monterey)

**Organic Valley** -

Baby Swiss

Cheddar

Mild (Regular, Shredded)

Raw (Mild, Sharp)

Reduced Fat & Sodium

Sharp

Vermont (Extra Sharp, Medium, Sharp)

Colby

Feta

Mexican Blend Shredded

Monterey Jack (Reduced Fat, Regular)

Mozzarella

Muenster

Pepper Jack

Provolone

Ricotta

Stringles

    Cheddar

    Colby Jack

    Mozzarella

Wisconsin Raw Milk Jack Style

**Primo Taglio -**

    Cheddar (American, Imported Aged White, Medium, Mild)

    Danish Havarti (Regular, w/Dill)

    Jack Hot Pepper

    Lacy Swiss

    Mozzarella (Hot Salami Roll, Prosciutto Roll)

    Muenster

    Provolone

    Smoked Fontina

    Swiss

**Publix -**

    Natural

        Cheddar (Extra Sharp (White, Yellow), Medium, Mild, Sharp)

        Colby

        Colby Jack

        Italian 6 Cheese Blend (Shredded)

        Mexican 4 Cheese Blend (Shredded)

**C**

Monterey Jack (& Cheddar Shredded, Regular, w/Jalapeno Peppers)

Mozzarella

Muenster

Provolone

Ricotta (Skim, Whole)

Swiss

Processed

American (Deluxe Slices)

American Cheese Food Pasteurized Processed Singles (Regular, Thick Slice)

Cheese Spread

Mozzarella (Imitation Shredded)

Swiss Cheese Food (Pasteurized Processed Singles)

Specialty

Asiago Wedge

Blue (Crumbled (Reduced Fat, Regular))

Creative Classic Queso (Blanco, De Freir)

Feta (Chunk, Crumbled, Crumbled Reduced Fat, Reduced Fat Chunk)

Garden Jack (Stick)

Garlic & Herb Cheese Spread

Goat (Crumbled)

Gorgonzola Crumbled (Reduced Fat, Regular)

Horseradish Jack (Stick)

Hot Pepper Cheese Spread

Parmesan (& Romano, Grated, Shredded, Wedge)

Pepper Jack (Reduced Fat)

Salsa Jack (Stick)

**Rice Shreds (Galaxy Nutritional Foods)** - All Varieties (Rice, Rice Vegan, Vegan, Veggie, Veggy, Wholesome Valley Organic)

**C**

**Road's End Organics** - Organic (GF Alfredo Chreese Mix, GF Cheddar Chreese Mix)

**Safeway Brand** - Grated Parmesan

**Safeway Select** - Parmesan (Shredded)

**Sara Lee** - Custom Slices (Baby Swiss, Colby & Monterey Jack, Low Moisture Part Skim Mozzarella, Mild Cheddar, Monterey Jack & Jalapenos, Muenster)

**Sargento -**

 Artisan Blends (Double Cheddar, Mozzarella & Provolone, Parmesan, Parmesan Romano, Swiss, Whole Milk Mozzarella)

 Bistro Blends (Chipotle Cheddar, Mozzarella & Asiago w/Roasted Garlic, Mozzarella w/Sun-Dried Tomatoes & Basil, Nacho & Taco, Taco, Sharp Wisconsin & Vermont Cheddar w/Real Bacon)

 Classic Blends (4 Cheese Mexican, 6 Cheese Italian, Pizza Double)

 Classic Chef Style (Mild Cheddar, Mozzarella, Sharp Cheddar)

 Classic Fancy (Cheddar Jack, Colby Jack, Mild Cheddar, Monterey Jack, Mozzarella, Sharp Cheddar)

 Deli Style (Aged Swiss, American Burger, Baby Swiss, Chipotle Cheddar, Colby (Jack, Jarlsberg), Duo Pack (Medium Cheddar & Colby Jack, Provolone & Mild Cheddar, Swiss & Baby Swiss), Medium Cheddar, Monterey Jack, Mozzarella, Muenster, Pepper Jack, Provolone, Sharp Cheddar, Swiss)

  Limited Editon (Aged Provolone, Pasture Grazed Cheddar)

  Reduced Fat Deli Style (Provolone, Swiss)

 Fine Cheese (Grated Parmesan, Grated Parmesan Romano)

 Limited Edition (Italian Blend Aged Provolone, Pasture Grazed Cheddar)

 Natural (Chipotle Cheddar Sticks, Colby Jack (Cubes, Regular), Light String Cheese, Mild Cheddar (Cheese Cubes, Regular), Scooby Doo Mini String Cheese, Stars & Moons, String, SunBursts, Twirls)

**C**

Reduced Fat (4 Cheese Italian, 4 Cheese Mexican, Mild Cheddar, Mozzarella)

Shredded Cheese

Sliced Cheese

Snacks

  Limited Editon (Aged Provolone, Pasture Grazed Cheddar)

**Smart Balance** - All Varieties

**Spartan Brand** -

American 2% Milk Singles (Fat Free, Regular)

Cheddar Chunk Cheese (Medium, Milk, Sharp, X sharp)

Colby Cheese (Chunks, Shredded, Sliced)

Colby Jack Cheese (Chunks, Shredded, Sliced)

Fancy Shredded Cheese (Colby Jack, Italian Blend, Mexican Blend, Mild Cheddar, Mozzarella, Parmesan, Sharp Cheddar, Taco)

Mild Cheddar Cheese (Shredded, Sliced)

Monterey Jack Cheese (Chunks, Shredded)

Mozzarella Cheese (Chunks, Round, Shredded, Sliced)

NY Sharp Cheddar Cheese (Chunks)

Parmesan Italian Shredded

Parmesan Shredded (Regular, Romano)

Pizza Blend (Shredded)

Processed American (Sliced, Deluxe Sliced)

Sharp Cheddar (Shredded)

String Cheese

Swiss Cheese (Chunks, Sliced)

Taco Spice (Shredded)

**Tasty Bite** - Paneer Makhani

**The Vegetarian Express** - Parma Zaan Sprinkles

**Tillamook** - All Varieties

**Trader Joe's** -

All Blocks, Shredded, Wedges *(Except Blue Cheese)*

Parmesan & Romano Cheese Blend

Soy Cheese Slices

**Vegan (Galaxy Nutritional Foods) -** All Vegan (Blocks, Shreds, Slices, Super Stix, Topping)

**Wegmans Brand -**

American Cheese White Slices

Cheese Spread (Artichoke Asiago, Bacon Chive, Buffalo Wing Cheddar, Garlic & Herb, Horseradish Scallion, Whipped)

Colby Jack (Shredded, Thin Sliced, Block, 2%)

Extra Sharp Cheddar (White, Yellow)

Fancy Shredded (Mexican, Mild Cheddar, Taco, Pizza)

Fat Free American Slices (Regular, Reduced Fat)

Longhorn Style Colby

Mild Cheddar (Shredded, White, White Shredded, Yellow)

Monterey Jack

Mozzarella Cheese Shredded (Low Moisture Part Skim, Low Moisture Part Skim Thin Sliced, Whole Milk, 2%)

Muenster (Thin Sliced, Block)

Parmesan Cheese (Finely Shredded, Grated, Grated w/Romano)

Pepper Jack

Provolone (Thin Sliced)

Romano (Grated, Wedge)

Sharp Cheddar (Fat Free Slices, Reduced Fat Slices, Shredded, Thin Sliced, Vermont White, White, Yellow)

Swiss (Chunk, Thin Sliced, Block)

**Winn Dixie -**

American Pasteurized Process Cheese (American, Deluxe, Reduced Fat)

Blue Cheese

Cheddar (Extra Sharp, Jack, Medium, Mild, NY Extra Sharp, NY Sharp)

Colby (Jack, Regular)

**C**

Feta

Gorgonzola

Italian Blend Shredded

Mexican Blend

Monterey Jack (Regular, w/Jalapeno Peppers)

Mozzarella

Muenster

Parmesan (Grated, & Romano)

Pasteurized Process Swiss Cheese Product

Pimento Cheese (Chunky, Regular, w/Jalapenos)

Provolone

Ricotta (All Types)

String Cheese

Swiss

White Cheddar

**Cheese Puffs... see Snacks**

**Cheese Spread... see Cheese and/or Spread**

**Cheesecake... see Cake/Cake Mix**

**Cherries...** *All **Fresh** Fruits & Vegetables Are **Gluten-Free***

**Cascadian Farm** - Organic Frozen Sweet Cherries

**Cella's** - Chocolate Covered Cherries (Dark, Milk)

**Food Club Brand** - Frozen Dark Sweet Cherries, Maraschino, Red Tart

**Great Value Brand (Wal-Mart)** - Maraschino

**Haribo's** - Cherries (Sour, Twin)

**Hy-Vee** - Frozen Cherry Berry Blend, Red Maraschino Cherries (Regular, w/Stems)

**Lowes Foods Brand** - Maraschino (Red, Red w/Stems)

**Lucky Leaf** - Red Tart Pitted Cherries

**Meijer Brand** - Frozen (Dark Sweet, Tart), Maraschino Cherry (Red, Red w/Stems)

**Midwest Country Fare** - Maraschino Cherries

**Musselman's** - Red Tart Pitted Cherries

**Publix** - Frozen (Cherries, Dark Sweet), Maraschino

**S&W** - All Canned/Jarred Fruits

**Safeway Brand** - Frozen Dark Sweet, Maraschino Cherries

**Spartan Brand** - Frozen Dark Sweet Cherries, Maraschino Cherries (Green, Red, Red w/Stems, Salad)

**Stop & Shop Brand** - Dark Sweet Cherries

**Thrifty Maid** - Maraschino Cherries

**Trader Joe's** - Dark Chocolate Covered Cherries

**Travers Bay Fruit Co.** - Premium Dried Cherries

**Wegmans Brand** - Maraschino (Jumbo w/out Stems, w/Stems, w/out Stems), Sweet, Triple Cherry Fruit Mix In Light Syrup

**Winn Dixie** - Dark Sweet Cherries, Maraschino Cherries

**Woodstock Farms** - Organic Frozen Dark Sweet Cherries

Cherries Jubilee

Lucky Leaf

Musselman's

Chewing Gum

5

B Fresh

Big Red

**Bubblicious** - All Varieties

**Charms** - All Blow Pops (Junior, Regular, Super)

**Dentyne Ice** - All Varieties

Doublemint

Dubble Bubble

Eclipse

Extra

Freedent

**Glee Gum** - All Varieties

**Hubba Bubba** - All Varieties

Juicy Fruit

**Lowes Foods Brand** - Double Bubble Gum

**C**

**Meijer** - Nicotine Gum (Mint, Regular)

**Nicorette**

**Orbit**

**Orbit White**

**Stride** - All Varieties

**Trident** - All Varieties

**Winterfresh**

**Wrigley's** - Spearmint

Chick Peas... see Beans

Chicken... *All Fresh Chicken Is Gluten-Free (Non-Marinated, Unseasoned)*

**Applegate Farms** - Gluten Free Chicken Nuggets, Organic (Roasted Chicken Breast, Smoked Chicken Breast)

**Bakers & Chefs** - Canned All Natural Chicken Breasts

**Bell & Evans** - Gluten Free Breaded Boneless Skinless Chicken Breasts (Garlic Parmesan, Regular), Gluten Free Chicken Nuggets, Gluten Free Chicken Patties

**Boar's Head** - All Varieties

**Butcher's Cut** - Boneless Skinless Chicken Breast, Chicken Jumbo Franks, Young Chicken Thighs

**Butterball** - Thin Sliced Oven Roasted Chicken Breast

**Carl Buddig** - All Meat Products

**Chi-Chi's** - Fiesta Plates (Creamy Chipotle, Salsa, Savory Garlic)

**Dietz & Watson** - BBQ, Buffalo, Gourmet Breast

**Dinty Moore** - Microwave Meal (Rice w/Chicken)

**Empire Kosher** - Chicken Bologna (Slices), Fresh Chill Pack, Fresh Rotisserie, Frozen, Fully Cooked Barbecue Chicken (Fresh, Frozen), Individually Quick Frozen Chicken Parts, Rendered Chicken Fat

**Farmer John** - California Natural Chicken Sausage (Apple Chicken Smoked, Asiago Chicken Smoked, Cajun Style Smoked, Chicken Brat Smoked, Lemon Cracked Pepper Chicken Smoked, Mango & Habanero Smoked)

**Food Club Brand** - Chunk White Chicken

**Garrett County Farms** - Chicken Franks, Dino Shaped Chicken Bites, Frozen Chicken Apple Breakfast Links

**GF Naturals** - 1oz. Boneless Wing●, 2oz. Tender●, 4oz. All Natural Filet●, 4oz. Whole Muscle Filet●

**Gillian's Foods▲** - Chicken Cordon Bleu, Chicken Cutlets

**Great Value Brand (Wal-Mart)** - Chunk Chicken Breast (Canned), Frozen (Boneless Skinless Breast, Drumsticks, Thighs)

**Hannaford Brand** - Chicken Breast Chunk In Water

**Hillshire Farms** - Deli Select Thin Sliced Oven Roasted Chicken Breast

**Homestyle Meals** - Chicken In BBQ Sauce

**Honeysuckle White** - Chicken Breast Deli Meat (BBQ, Buffalo Style, Oil Browned)

**Hormel** - Chunk Meats (Breast of Chicken, Chicken), Natural Choice (Grilled Chicken Strips, Oven Roasted Chicken Strips)

**Hy-Vee** - Thin Sliced Chicken

**Ian's** - Wheat Free Gluten Free Recipe (Chicken Finger Kids Meal, Chicken Nuggets, Chicken Patties)

**Jennie-O** - Deli Chicken Breast (Buffalo Style, Mesquite Smoked, Oven Roasted)

**John Soules Foods** - Fully Cooked Chicken Breast Fillets (Italian Style, Rotisserie), Fully Cooked Chicken Breast Strips (Grilled, Italian Style, Rotisserie), Fully Cooked Chicken Fajitas, Ready To Cook (Chicken Breast For Fajitas, Chicken Thigh For Fajitas)

**Kroger Brand** - Canned, Fresh & Frozen Plain (Breast, Thighs, Wings), Pouch

**Laura Lynn** - Boneless Skinless Chicken Breast

**Lloyd's -** Shredded Chicken In Original BBQ Sauce

**Manor House** - All Varieties In 4lb. Resealable Bags

**Meijer Brand** - Canned Chicken Chunk White, Sliced Chipped Meat

**Member's Mark -** Canned Premium Chunk Chicken Breast, Chicken Sausage (Parmigiano, Spinach Asiago)

**O Organics** - Fresh Chicken Breast (Regular, Tenders), Spinach & Feta Sausage

### C  Organic Prairie

Fresh Organic

Chicken Hot Dogs 12 oz.

Sliced Roast Chicken Breast 6 oz.

Frozen Organic

Boneless Skinless Chicken Breasts

Chicken Hot Dogs 10.5 oz.

Chicken Italian Sausage 12 oz.

Ground Chicken 12 oz.

Whole Young Chicken

### Oscar Mayer -

Chicken Breast Strips (Honey Roasted, Oven Roasted)

Deli Fresh Oven Roasted Chicken Breast

Shaved Deli Fresh (Cajun Seasoned Chicken Breast, Rotisserie Style Chicken Breast)

Thin Sliced Deli Fresh Oven Roasted Chicken Breast

### Perdue -

Buffalo Chicken Wings (Hot 'N Spicy)

Ground Chicken (Breast of Chicken, Burgers)

Individually Frozen Chicken (Breasts, Tenderloins, Wings)

Oven Roasted Carving Chicken Breast

Perfect Portions Boneless Skinless Chicken Breast (Italian Style, Regular, Tomato Basil)

Rotisserie Chicken (Barbeque, Italian, Lemon Pepper, Oven Roasted, Toasted Garlic, Tuscany Herb Roasted)

Rotisserie Oven Stuffer Roaster (Breast, Regular)

Short Cuts Carved Chicken Breast (Grilled Italian, Grilled Lemon Pepper, Grilled Southwestern, Honey Roasted, Original Roasted)

Sliced Chicken Breast Oil Fried

### Primo Taglio - Canned Chunk White Chicken Breast, Chicken Breast Oven Roasted Browned In Hot Cottonseed Oil

**Publix -**
   All Natural Fresh
   Deli Rotisserie Chicken
      Apple Wood Smoked
      Barbecue Flavored w/Barbecue Seasoning (& Sauce, Regular)
      Lemon Pepper Flavored w/Lemon & Herb Seasoning
      Original Roasted
   Frozen
      Boneless Skinless Chicken (Breasts, Cutlets)
      Chicken Breast Tenderloins
      Chicken Wingettes

**Publix GreenWise Market -** Boneless Breast, Boneless Thighs, Cutlet, Drummettes, Drumsticks, Fillet, Ground Chicken, Sausage (Herb & Tomato, Hot Italian, Mild Italian), Skinless Drumstick, Skinless Thighs, Split Breast, Tenderloin, Thighs, Wings, Whole

**Saz's -** Barbecue Chicken Meat Tub

**S'Better Farms▲ -** Chicken (Ballontine, Fingers, Party Wings, Siciliano, Szechwan)

**Sharwood's -** Battered Chicken (Cantonese, Sweet & Sour)

**Shelton's -** Capon, Free Range (Breasts, Thighs, Whole), Organic (Boneless/Skinless Breast, Breast, Cut Up, Whole Chicken, Whole Legs

**Smart Chicken -** All Varieties

**Smart Ones -** Frozen Entrees (Chicken Santa Fe, Creamy Tuscan Chicken, Fiesta Chicken, Grilled Chicken in Garlic Herb Sauce, Home Style Chicken, Lemon Herb Chicken Piccata)

**Spartan Brand -** Chicken Breast Chunk, Frozen Boneless Skinless (Breasts, Tenders)

**Stop & Shop Brand -**
   Premium Chunk Chicken Breast In Water
   Simply Enjoy (Butter Chicken, Pad Thai w/Chicken)

**Sweet Sue -** Premium Chicken Breast (Pouch)

**Thumann's -** All Varieties●

**C**  Trader Joe's -
　　Artichoke Patties
　　BBQ Shredded Chicken
　　Frozen Chicken (Chile Verde, Enchiladas In Salsa Verde,
　　　　Gorgonzola, Pomodoro, Tandoori Rice Bowl, Taquitos, Wings)
　　Fully Cooked & Seasoned Roasted Chicken
　　Grilled Chicken Breast (Balsamic & Rosemary, Lemon Pepper, Plain)
　　Grilled Chicken Salad w/Orange Vinaigrette
　　Grilled Chicken Strips
　　Just Chicken (Plain)
　　Salad
　　Tamales
　　**Tyson Simply Perfect -**
　　100% All Natural Fresh Chicken
　　　　Boneless
　　　　　　Chicken Breast Tenders
　　　　　　Skinless (Chicken Breasts, Split Chicken Breasts)
　　　　　　Thin & Fancy Chicken Breasts
　　**Ukrop's -**
　　　　Chicken Breast (w/Broccoli & Cheddar Cheese, w/Spinach &
　　　　　　Feta Cheese)
　　　　Chicken Kabobs (Marinated, Regular)
　　**Valley Fresh -** All Varieties
　　**Wellshire Farms -** Chicken Franks, Sliced Oven Roasted Chicken Breast
　　**Wellshire Kids -** Dino Shaped Chicken Bites Refrigerated
　　**Wellshire Organic -** Organic Chicken Franks
Chicken Broth... see Broth
Chicken Noodle Soup... see Soup
Chicken Nuggets...see Chicken
Chicken Wings... see Wings
Chiles
　　**Chi-Chi's -** Green Chiles

**Food Club Brand** - Diced Green

**Great Value Brand (Wal-Mart) -** Fire Roasted Green Peeled & Diced

**La Victoria -** Green Chiles (Diced, Whole)

**Meijer Brand -** Diced Mild Mexican Style

**Old El Paso -** Green Chiles (Chopped, Whole)

**Ortega**

**Safeway Brand -** Diced Green

**Spartan Brand -** Green Chiles

Chili

Amy's - Organic Chili (Black Bean, Light In Sodium, Medium, Medium w/Vegetables, Spicy), Southwestern Black Bean

**Food Club Brand** - Chili w/Beans

**Health Valley -**

Organic Chunky Chili -

Mild Vegetarian (Black Bean, Three Bean)

No Salt Added (Mild Vegetarian, Spicy Vegetarian)

Spicy Vegetarian (Black Bean, Regular)

**Healthy Advantage -** Vegetarian

**Hormel -** Chili Master (Chipotle Chicken No Bean, Chipotle Chicken w/Beans, White Chicken Chili w/Beans), Chili w/Beans (Chunky, Hot, Regular)

**Hy-Vee -** Hot Chili w/Beans, Mild w/Beans

**Meijer Brand -** Chili (No Beans Regular, w/Beans Regular), Hot Dog Chili Sauce

**Mimi's Gourmet -** Black Bean & Corn, Chipotle Black Bean Chili w/Rice, Spicy White Bean & Jalapeno, Three Bean w/Rice

**Shelton's -** Mild Chicken, Mild Turkey, Spicy Chicken, Spicy Turkey

**Spartan Brand -** 16 Bean Chili Soup Mix, w/Beans

**Stagg -**

Chunkero

Classic

Dynamite Hot

**C**

    Ranch House Chicken
    Silverado Beef
    Steak House
    Turkey Ranchero
    Vegetable Garden
    White Chicken
  **Texas Pete** - Chili, No Beans
  **Trader Joe's** -
    Beef Chili w/Beans
    Chicken Chili w/Beans
    Organic Vegetarian
    Vegetarian 3 Bean Chili
  **Wegmans Brand** - Spicy Red Lentil Chili

**Chili Paste**
  **Thai Kitchen** - Roasted Red

**Chili Powder**
  **Chugwater Chili**
  **Durkee**
  **Home Harvest Brand**
  **Hy-Vee**
  **Marcum Spices**
  **McCormick**
  **Meijer Brand**
  **Midwest Country Fare**
  **Spartan Brand**
  **Spice Islands**
  **Tone's**

**Chili Sauce**
  **A Taste Of Thai** - Garlic Chili Pepper Sauce, Sweet Red Chili Sauce
  **Food Club Brand**
  **Frank's RedHot** - Chile 'N Lime

Gilligan's
Hannaford Brand
Heinz
La Victoria - Red
Las Palmas - Red Chile
Laura Lynn
Lee Kum Kee - Sriracha Chili
Meijer Brand - Hot Dog Chili
Safeway Brand
Spartan Brand
Thai Kitchen - Spicy Thai, Sweet Red
Trader Joe's - Chili Pepper, Sweet
Wegmans Brand
Winn Dixie - Sweet

Chips
  Anita's Mexican Foods - Everything Tortilla Chips●, Green Mountain●, Three Pepper Tortilla Chips●, Vegetable Tortilla Chips●
  Arico - Casava Chips (Barbeque Bliss, Ginger On Fire, Original, Sea Salt Mist)
  Baked! Lay's - Cheddar & Sour Cream Flavored, Original, Sour Cream & Onion Artificially Flavored, Southwestern Ranch Flavored
  Baked! Ruffles - Cheddar & Sour Cream Flavored, Original
  Baked! Tostitos - Scoops! Tortilla Chips
  Boulder Canyon Natural Foods -
    Canyon Cut Potato Chips
      Salt & Cracked Pepper
      Sour Cream & Chives
      Totally Natural
    Kettle Cooked Potato Chips
      50% Reduced Salt
      Balsamic Vinegar & Rosemary
      Chipotle Ranch

**C**

Hickory Barbeque
Jalapeno Cheddar
Limon
Parmesan & Garlic
Sea Salt & Cracked Pepper
Spinach & Artichoke
Tomato & Basil
Totally Natural
Rice & Adzuki Bean Snack Chips
  Chipotle Cheese
  Natural Salt
**Brothers All Natural ▲** - Potato Crisps (Black Pepper & Sea Salt, Fresh Onion & Garlic, Original w/Sea Salt, Szechuan Pepper & Fresh Chives)
**Cape Cod -**
Potato
  40% Reduced Fat
  Buttermilk Ranch
  Cheddar Jack & Sour Cream
  Classic
  Jalapeno & Aged Cheddar
  Parmesan & Roasted Garlic
  Robust Russet
  Sea Salt & (Cracked Pepper, Vinegar)
  Sweet Mesquite Barbeque
**Chi-Chi's** - All Varieties
**Deep River Snacks** - All Varieties
**Doritos -**
Blazin' Buffalo & Ranch
Collisions Hot Wings & Blue Cheese
Collisions Pizza Cravers & Ranch

Collisions Zesty Taco & Chipotle Ranch

Cool Ranch (Reduced Fat, Regular)

Diablo

Fiery Habanero

Last Call Jalapeno Popper

Salsa Verde

Spicy Nacho

Taco

Tacos At Midnight

Toasted Corn

Toro Habanero

**Dorothy Lane Market** - Kettle Cooked Potato Chips, Organic Tortilla Chips (Blue Corn Sesame, Multigrain)

**Eat Smart** - Soy Crisps (Parmesan Garlic & Olive Oil, Tomato Romano & Olive Oil), Veggie Crisps (Creamy Cucumber & Dill, Regular, Sun Dried Tomato & Pesto)

**Eden** - Brown Rice

**Food Club Brand**

Potato (BBQ, Classic, Jalapeno, Kettle Cooked, Original)

Ripple (Cheddar, Classic, Sour Cream)

Wavy Original

**Food Should Taste Good** - Tortilla Chips (Buffalo●, Chocolate●, Cinnamon●, Jalapeno●, Lime●, Multigrain●, Olive●, Potato & Chive●, Sweet Potato●, The Works!●, Yellow Corn●)

**Fritos** -

Corn Chips (Original, Scoops, Spicy Jalapeno)

Honey BBQ Flavor Twists

**Frontera** - Tortilla Chips (Blue Corn, Lime w/Sea Salt, Restaurant Style, Yellow Corn)

**Full Circle** - All Natural (BBQ, Natural Potato, Ripple), Organic Tortilla Chips (Blue Corn, White Restaurant Style, Yellow Restaurant Style)

**C** **Glenny's -** Spud Delites Natural Potato Crisps (Sea Salt, Sour Cream & Onion, Texas BBQ)

**Goraw** - Super Chips (Pumpkin●, Spirulina●)

**Great Value Brand (Wal-Mart) -** Corn, Corn Diggers

**Health Market Organic** - Tortilla Corn (Blue, White, Yellow)

**Herr's** -

    Potato Chips

        Cheddar & Sour Cream

        Crisp 'N Tasty

        Honey BBQ

        Jalapeno Kettle

        Ketchup

        Lightly Salted

        Mesquite BBQ Kettle

        No Salt

        Old (Bay, Fashioned)

        Original Kettle

        Red Hot

        Ripple

        Russet Kettle

        Salt & (Pepper, Vinegar)

    Tortilla/Corn Chips (All Varieties)

**Home Harvest Brand -** Corn Chips, Tortilla Chips (Ranch, White Round, Yellow Round)

**Hy-Vee -** Baked Chips (Barbecue, Cheddars, Original, Sour Cream), Potato Chips (No Salt, Original, Sour Cream & (Cheddar, Onion))

**J. Higgs** - Regular Potato

**Kettle Brand** -

    Baked Potato Chips

        Aged White Cheddar

        Hickory Honey Barbeque

        Lightly Salted

Salt & Fresh Ground Pepper
Sea Salt & Vinegar
Krinkle Cut Potato Chips
Classic Barbeque
Lightly Salted
Salt & Fresh Ground Pepper
Organic Potato Chips
Chipotle Chili Barbeque
Lightly Salted
Sea Salt & Black Pepper
Potato Chips
Backyard Barbeque
Buffalo Bleu
Death Valley Chipotle
Honey Dijon
Jalapeno
Lightly Salted
New York Cheddar w/Herbs
Salt & Fresh Ground Pepper
Sea Salt & Vinegar
Sour Cream Onion & Chive
Spicy Thai
Sweet Onion
Tuscan Three Cheese
Unsalted
Yogurt Green Onion
**Kroger Brand** - Plain (Potato, Tortilla)
**Laura Lynn** -
Corn Chips
Mini Corn Tortilla
Nacho Tortilla

**C**

Potato Chips
Ranch Tortilla
Ripple Potato
Sour Cream & Onion Potato
Wavy Potato
White Corn Tortilla

**Lay's** -

Potato Chips

Cheddar & Sour Cream Artificially Flavored

Chile Limon

Classic

Deli Style Original

Dill Pickle

Hot & Spicy Barbecue

Kettle Cooked (Jalapeno Flavored Extra Crunchy, Mequite BBQ Extra Crunchy, Original, Reduced Fat Original, Sweet Chili & Sour Cream)

Light Original

Lightly Salted

Limon Tangy Lime

Natural (Country BBQ Thick Cut, Sea Salt Thick Cut)

Salt & Vinegar Artificially Flavored

Sour Cream & Onion Artificially Flavored

Wavy Potato Chips

Au Gratin

Hickory BBQ

Ranch

Regular

**Lay's Stax** -

Potato Crisps

Cheddar

Hot 'N Spicy BBQ

Jalapeno Cheddar

Mesquite Barbecue

Original

Ranch Flavored

Salt & Vinegar Flavored

Sour Cream & Onion Flavored

**Lowes Foods Brand** - Corn Chips, Potato Chips (BBQ, Original, Ripple, Sour Cream & Onion), Tortilla Chips (Authentic White Corn, White Round)

**Lundberg▲** -

Rice Chips

Fiesta Lime

Honey Dijon

Nacho Cheese

Pico de Gallo

Santa Fe Barbecue

Sea Salt

Sesame & Seaweed

Wasabi

**Manischewitz** - Potato Chips (All Varieties)

**Maui Style** - Potato Chips (Regular, Salt & Vinegar Flavored)

**Michael Season's** -

Baked Multigrain Chips (Cheddar, Honey Chipotle, Original)

Baked Thin Potato Crisps (Cheddar & Sour Cream, Original, Sweet Barbecue)

Thin & Crispy (Honey Barbecue, Lightly Salted, Ripple, Salt & Pepper, Unsalted, Yogurt & Green Onion)

**Midwest Country Fare** - Potato Chips (Regular, Rippled, Wavy)

**Miguel's** -

Organic Tortilla Dippers (Everything●, Three Pepper●, Vegetable & Seed●)

Tortilla Chips (Blue Corn●, White Corn●)

**C**

**Miss Vickie's -**

Kettle Cooked Potato Chips

Country Onion w/Three Cheeses

Creamy Buttermilk Ranch

Hand Picked Jalapeno

Salty Sweet

Sea Salt & Vinegar

Simply Sea Salt

Smokehouse BBQ

**Moore's** - Corn Chips (BBQ, Regular), Potato Chips (Barbecue Flavored, Flat Cut, Rippled, Sour Cream & Onion Flavored Rippled)

**Mr. Krispers -**

Baked Nut Chips (Toasted Almond●)

Baked Rice Krisps (Babecue●, Nacho●, Sea Salt & Pepper●, Sour Cream & Onion●, Sun Dried Tomato & Basil●, White Cheddar & Herbs●)

Multi Seed Chips (Original●)

Tasty Snack Crackers (Original Sesame●)

**Munchos** - Regular Potato Crisps

**Nature's Basket -** Corn Chips (Blue, Yellow)

**New Hampshire Wildcats** - White & Blue Corn Tortilla Chips●

**O Organics** - Tortilla Chips (Blue w/Flax Seed, Blue w/Sesame, White, Yellow)

**Old Dutch -**

Arriba Tortilla Chips (All Flavors)

Corn Chips (BBQ, Regular)

Potato Chips (All Dressed, Dill Pickle, Ketchup, Onion & Garlic, Regular, RipL, Roasted Garlic & Cheddar, Salt & Vinegar, Sour Cream & Onion)

Restaurant Tortilla Chips (All Flavors)

**Pan De Oro** - Tortilla Chips (Blue●, Red White & Blue●, Regular●)

## chips

**Pinnacle Gold -** Natural Baked Potato Chips Original, Natural Baked Veggie Chips

**C**

**Pringles** - Fat Free (Original, Sour Cream & Onion)

**Publix** -

Potato Chips (Dip Style, Original Thins, Salt & Vinegar, Sour Cream & Onion, Wavy Style)

Tortilla Chips (White Corn, White Corn Restaurant Style, Yellow Corn Round Style)

**Publix GreenWise Market -** Tortilla Chips (Blue, Yellow)

**RiceWorks -** Rice Crisps (Baked Cinnamon, Parmesan, Salsa Fresca, Sea Salt, Sweet Chili, Wasabi)

**Ruffles** -

Potato Chips

Authentic Barbecue

Cheddar & Sour Cream (Light, Regular)

Natural Reduced Fat Sea Salted

Original (Light, Reduced Fat, Regular)

Sour Cream & Onion

Thick Cut Cheddar Baked Potato

**Sabritas -** Chile Piquin Flavored, Habanero Limon

**Santitas** - Tortilla Chips (White Corn Restaurant Style, Yellow Corn)

**Snyder's Of Hanover** -

Corn Tortilla Chips (Restaurant Style, White, Yellow)

Potato Chips (Barbeque, Hot Buffalo Wing, Jalapeno, Kosher Dill, Original, Ripple Potato, Salt & Vinegar, Sour Cream & Onion)

**Solea** -

Apple Chips

Avocado Chips

Bistro Chips

Au Gratin

Blue Cheese

**C**

    Crème Fraishe
    Sea Salt
  Olive Oil Chips
    Cracked Pepper
    Garlic
    Rosemary
    Sea Salt
  Polenta Chips
    Barbeque
    Guacamole
    Mediterranean Lime
    Sea Salt
  Veggie Chips

**Spartan Brand -**
  Corn
  Potato (Regular, Ripple)
  Sour Cream & Onion

**Stop & Shop Brand -**
  Potato (Kettle Cooked, Plain, Rippled, Salt & Vinegar, Sour Cream & Onion, Wavy Cut)
  Tortilla (Nacho, White Restaurant, White Round, Yellow Round)

**Tostitos -**
  Tortilla Chips
    100% White Corn Restaurant Style
    Bite Size (Gold, Rounds)
    Crispy Rounds
    Light Restaurant Style
    Natural Corn Restaurant Style (Blue, Yellow)
    Restaurant Style w/Hint of Lime Flavor
    Scoops (Hint Of Jalapeno, Regular)

## Trader Joe's -

Regular Chips
  Baked Potato Slims Lightly Salted
  BBQ Potato
  Blue (Corn Tortilla, Potato)
  Corn Tortilla Strips (White, Yellow)
  Hemp Tortilla w/Black Sesame Seeds
  Red Bliss Potato
  Regular Potato
  Round Popped Potato (Barbecue, Salted)
  Salsa Tortilla
  Sea Salt & Pepper Rice Crisps
  Sour Cream & Onion Rice Crisps
  Soy & Flaxseed Tortilla (Regular, Spicy)
  Soy Crisps BBQ
  Sweet Potato
  Vegetable Root
  Veggie (& Flaxseed Tortilla, Regular)
Organic Chips
  Baked Tortilla (Blue Corn, Nacho)
  Corn Dippers
  Corn Tortilla (White, Yellow)
  Restaurant Style White Corn Tortilla
  Tortilla Longboard

## UTZ -

All Natural Kettle Cooked
  Dark Russet
  Gourmet Medley
  Lightly Salted
  Sea Salt & Vinegar
Corn Chips (Barbeque, Plain)

**C**

Grandma
Home Style Kettle Cooked Plain
Kettle Classics
  Dark Russet
  Jalapeno
  Plain
  Smokin' Sweet BBQ
  Sour Cream & Chive
  Sweet Potato
Kettle Cooked (Barbeque, Plain)
Mystic Kettle Cooked Chips
  Dark Russet
  Plain
  Sea Salt & Vinegar
Regular Chips
  Barbeque
  Carolina BBQ
  Cheddar & Sour Cream
  Crab
  Honey BBQ
  No Salt (BBQ, Regular)
  Plain (Flat, Ripple, Wavy Cut)
  Red Hot
  Reduced Fat
  Salt & (Pepper, Vinegar)
  Sour Cream & Onion
Tortilla Chips
  Baked
  Cheesier Nacho
  Restaurant Style
  White Corn

**C**

**Wegmans Brand** -
- Chips (BBQ, Corn)
- Kettle (Memphis Style BBQ Flavor, Original, Salt & Pepper)
- Regular
- Salt & Vinegar
- Sour Cream & Onion
- Tortilla 100% White Corn (Authentic, Blue Corn, Bite Size, Round, Yellow Corn)
- Wavy

**Wise** -
- Cheddar & Sour Cream Flavored Ridgies
- Corn Chips (BBQ Flavored Dipsy Doodles, Dipsy Doodles Rippled, Nacho Twisters)
- New York Deli (Jalapeno Flavored, Kettle Cooked)
- Onion & Garlic
- Potato Chips (Flat Cut, Lightly Salted, Unsalted, Wise Wavy)
- Ridgies
- Salt & Vinegar
- Sour Cream & Onion Flavored Ridgies
- Tortilla Chips Bravos! (Nacho Cheese, Restaurant Style, White Round)

**Woodstock Farms** - Veggie Chips

## Chocolate

**Andes** - Crème de Menthe, Thins (Cherry Jubilee, Crème de Menthe, Mint Parfait, Sugar Free, Toffee Crunch)

**Baker's** - Bittersweet, German's Sweet, Select (Bittersweet, Semi Sweet), Semi Sweet, Unsweetened, White

**Carb Safe** - Sugar Free Chocolate Bars (Dark, Milk)

**Cella's** - Chocolate Covered Cherries (Dark, Milk)

**Cote d'or** - Lait (Intense, Petits), Noir (70% Cacao, 86% Cacao, de Noir Petits, Orange)

**Dagoba** - All Chocolate

**C**

**Dove Chocolate** - All Varieties

**Earth Source Organics** - Organic Raw Chocolate Bar (Acai●, Caramel●, Goji●, Maca●)

**Endangered Species** - Bat Bar●, Black Panther Bar●, Black Rhino Bar●, Bug Bites Treats (Dark●, Milk●), Butterfly Bar●, Cheetah Bar●, Chimp Mints Treats●, Chimpanzee Bar●, Crane Bar●, Dolphin Bar●, Giraffe Bar●, Grizzly Bar●, Halloween Treats (Dark●, Milk●), Hoppy Treats (Dark●, Milk●), Koala Bar●, Lion Bar●, Love Treats (Dark●, Milk●), Otter Bar●, Panther●, Rainforest Bar●, Sea Turtle Bar●, Spider Monkey Bar●, Tiger Bar●, Toucan Bar●, Tree Frog Bar●, Winter Holiday Treats (Dark●, Milk●), Wolf Bar●, Zebra Bar●

**Glutino▲** - Candy Bars (Chocolate Peanut Butter, Dark Chocolate, Milk Chocolate)

**Great Value Brand (Wal-Mart)**-

Creamy Caramel Milk Chocolate Cups

Peanut Butter Milk Chocolate Cups

**Hershey's** -

Heath Bar

Kisses (Milk Chocolate, Milk Chocolate Meltaways, Milk Chocolate w/Almonds, Milk Chocolate w/Caramel, Milk Chocolate w/Cherry Cordial Crème, Special Dark Chocolate)

Milk Chocolate Bar (Original, w/Almonds)

Mr. Goodbar

PayDay

Reese's Peanut Butter Cups (Original)

Skor

York Peppermint Patty

**Manischewitz** - Chocolate Frolic Bears, Chocolate Morsels, Hazelnut Truffles, Mallo Cups, Patties (Peppermint, Tender Coconut), Swiss Chocolate Mints

**Mars** -

Dove Chocolates - All Varieties

M & M's - All Varieties

**C**

Milky Way Products - All Varieties *(Except The Milky Way Bar)*

Munch Bar

Snickers

Snickers Dark Bar

**Necco -**

Banana Split & Mint Julep Chews

Canada Mint & Wintergreen Lozenges

Candy Eggs (Easter)

Clark Bar

Haviland Peppermint & Wintergreen Patties

Haviland Thin Mints & Candy Stix

Mary Janes (Peanut Butter Kisses, Regular)

Skybar

Squirel Nut (Caramels, Zippers)

Sweethearts Conversation Hearts *(Valentines Only)*

Talking Pumpkins (Halloween)

Ultramints

**Nestle -**

Baby Ruth

Bit O Honey

Butterfinger *(Except Crisp & Stixx)*

Goobers

Milk Chocolate

Nips (Regular, Sugar Free)

Oh Henry!

Raisinets

Sno Caps

Spree

**Newman's Own Organics -** All Chocolate Bars *(Except Crisp Rice)*, All Chocolate Cups

**Safeway Select -** Creamy Milk Chocolate, Extra Dark, Milk Chocolate w/Hazelnuts

**C** **Sjaak's ▲** - Organic Chocolate (All Varieties)
**Stop & Shop Brand** -
  Simply Enjoy Dark Chocolate
    Amaretto Coated Cranberries
    Cappuccino Crunch Bits
    Caramel Squares
    Covered (Cherries, Coffee Beans, Cranberries, Kona Almond
      Coffee Beans, Strawberries)
    Raspberry Sticks
  Simply Enjoy Milk Chocolate
    Butter Toffee Squares
    Coated Cashews
    Cocoa Almonds
    Covered (Cashews, Cherries, Peanuts, Raisins)
    Pecan Caramel Patties
  White Chocolate Coated Coffee Nuggets
  Whole Chocolate Covered Raspberries
**thinkThin** - Brownie Crunch, Chocolate (Fudge, Mudslide), Dark
  Chocolate, Peanut Butter (Chunky, Creamy), White Chocolate Chip
**thinkThin bites**- Chocolate Toffee Nut, Cookies and Cream, White
  Chocolate Raspberry
**Toblerone** - Bittersweet, Milk Chocolate, Minis Milk Chocolate,
  Minis White Chocolate, White
**Trader Joe's** -
  70% Belgian Dark Chocolate Sea Shells
  Chocolate
    Almond Clusters
    Covered Blueberries
    Espresso Beans
    Orange & Raspberry Sticks
    Sunflower Seed Drops

Chocolate Bars

    Fair Trade Swiss Chocolate Bars (Dark, Milk)

    Organic Chocolate Bars

    Ounce Plus 3pk Bars

    Pound Plus Bars

Confection Perfection Dark Chocolate Cubes

Dark Chocolate (Mint Creams, Mint UFO's)

Dark Chocolate Almonds Sea Salt & Sugar

Dark Chocolate Covered (Almonds, Caramels, Cherries, Espresso Beans, Ginger, Raisins, Salted Nuts, Toffee)

Milk & Dark Chocolate Covered Almonds

Milk Chocolate

    Clouds

    Covered Raisins

    Peanut Butter Chips

    Peanut Butter Cups (Mini, Regular)

Sipping Chocolate

Unsweetened Belgian Baking Chocolate

**Tropical Source** - All Chocolate Bars

**Woodstock Farms -** Chocolate (Almonds, Ginger, Raisins) w/Evaporated Cane Juice, Organic Chocolate (Dark, Milk) Almonds w/Evaporated Cane Juice, Organic Dark Chocolate Chips w/Evaporated Cane Juice

**Chocolate Bars... see Candy/Candy Bars and/or Chocolate**

**Chocolate Chips... see Baking Chips**

**Chocolate Dip**

    **Lighthouse Foods** - Chocolate Dip

    **T. Marzetti** - Chocolate Fruit Dip

    **Walden Farms** - Chocolate Fruit Dip

**Chocolate Milk... see Milk**

**Chocolate Sauce**

    **Wegmans Brand** - Chocolate (Milk, Triple Chocolate)

**C** Chocolate Syrup... see Syrup

Chole

    **Tamarind Tree** - Alu Chole

Chutney

    **Baxters** -

        Albert's Victorian

        Cranberry & Caramelized Red Onion

        Crushed Pineapple & Sweet Pepper

        Spanish Tomato & Black Olive

        Spiced Fruit

        Spicy Mango

        Sweet Caramelized Onion Carrot & Orange

        Tomato

    **Native Forest -** Chutney (All Varieties)

    **Patak's** - Chutney (Hot Mango, Major Grey, Sweet Mango)

    **Sharwood's -** Green Label (Mango, Mango Chili, Smooth)

    **Trader Joe's** - Apple Cranberry, Mango Ginger

    **Wild Thymes** - Apricot Cranberry Walnut, Caribbean Peach Lime, Mango Papaya, Plum Currant Ginger

Cider/Cider Mix

    **Cider Jack**

    **Crispin -** Natural Hard Apple Cider (Brut, Light, Original)

    **Doc's Draft** - Apple, Pear, Raspberry (Alcoholic)

    **Kroger Brand** - Instant Spiced

    **Lucky Leaf** - Apple Cider, Sparkling Apple Cider

    **Magners** - Cider (Alcoholic)

    **Musselman's -** Cider, Fresh Pressed, Sparkling Cider

    **Safeway Brand** - Apple Cider

    **Sonoma Sparkler** - Natural (Peach, Pear, Raspberry), Organic (Apple, Lemonade)

    **Strongbow -** (Alcoholic)

    **Woodchuck▲** - Draft Ciders (All Varieties) (Alcoholic)

**C**

**Woodpecker** - Cider (Alcoholic)

**Wyder's** - All Styles (Alcoholic)

Cinnamon

**Albertsons**

**Durkee**

**McCormick**

**Spice Islands**

**Tone's**

**Watkins**

Cinnamon Rolls

**Andrea's Fine Foods**▲

**Chebe**▲ - Cinnamon Roll Mix

**Celiac Specialties**▲

**Everybody Eats**▲ - Cinnamon Sticky Buns

**Gluten-Free Creations**▲ - Cinnamon Rolls●,

Clams... *All Fresh Seafood Is Gluten-Free (Non-Marinated, Unseasoned)*

**Bumble Bee** - Chopped, Fancy Smoked, Fancy Whole Baby, Minced

**Chicken Of The Sea** - Chopped, Minced, Premium Whole Baby Clams, Whole Baby Clams

**Crown Prince** -

Natural (Boiled Baby Clams, Clam Juice, Smoked Baby Clams In Olive Oil)

Regular (Baby Clams Smoked In Oil, Baby Boiled, Chopped, Clam Juice, Minced)

**Ocean Prince** - Chopped

Club Soda... see Soda Pop/Carbonated Beverages

Coating

**A Taste Of Thai** - Peanut Bake

**Aleia's**▲ - Italian●, Plain●

**Andrea's Fine Foods**▲ - Seasoned Bread Crumbs, Stuffing Croutons

**Dakota Lakes** - Gourmet Coating●

**El Peto**▲- Bread Crumbs

**C**

**Ener-G▲** - Breadcrumbs

**Gillian's Foods▲** - Breadcrumbs (Cajun Style, Italian Style, Plain)

**Gluten-Free Essentials▲** - Breading & Batter Mix (Seasoned●, Unseasoned●)

**Gluten-Free Pantry▲** - Crisp & Crumble Topping

**Hol Grain** - Crispy Chicken Coating Mix, Brown Rice Bread Crumbs

**Katz Gluten Free▲** - Bread Crumbs

**Kinnikinnick▲** - Bread Crumbs, Chocolate Cookie Crumbs, Coating Mix (Crispy Chicken, General), Graham Style Wafer Crumbs

**Laurel's Sweet Treats▲** - All Purpose Batter Mix

**Miller's Gluten Free Bread Co.▲** - Seasoned Bread Crumbs

**Nu-World Foods** - Amaranth Bread Crumbs●

**Orgran▲** - All Purpose Rice Crumbs, Corn Crispy Crumbs

**Schar▲** - Bread Crumbs

**Southern Homestyle** - Corn Flake Crumbs, Tortilla Crumbs

Cocktail Mix

**Holland House** - All Varieties

**Margaritaville** - Margarita Mix

**Mr. & Mrs. T's** -

Mai Tai

Margarita

Pina Colada

Sea Breeze

Strawberry Daiquiri/Margarita

Sweet & Sour

Whiskey Sour

**On The Border** - Buckets (Cran-Appletini, Mango Passion, Margarita, Mojito, Pina Colada, Pomegranate, Sangria, Strawberry Mango), Straight-Ups (Cosmopolitan, Cran-Appletini, Mango Passion, Margarita, Margarita Lite, Mojito, Pina Colada, Pomegranate, Sangria, Strawberry Mango, Strawberry Margarita)

**Rose's** - Grenadine, Infusions (Blue Raspberry, Cranberry Twist,

Sour Apple), Mojito (Mango, Original, Passion Fruit), Sweetened Lime Juice, Sweet 'N Sour, Triple Sec

**Stop & Shop Brand** - Simply Enjoy Mixer (Cosmopolitan, Lemon Drop Martini, Margarita Cocktail, Mojito Cocktail, Watermelon Martini)

## Cocktail Sauce... see also Seafood Sauce

**Captain's Choice**

**Food Club Brand**

**Frontera** - Cocktail & Ceviche Sauce (Cilantro Lime, Tomato Chipotle)

**Great Value Brand (Wal-Mart)**

**Hannaford Brand**

**Heinz** - Cocktail Sauce

**Hy-Vee** - Cocktail Sauce For Seafood

**Ken's** - Blue Label, Green Label

**Laura Lynn**

**Lee Kum Kee** - Shrimp Sauce

**Lou's Famous** - Cocktail Sauce

**McCormick** - Extra Hot, Gold Dipt (Regular), Original, Seafood Sauce (Cajun Style, Lemon Butter Dill (Fat Free, Regular), Lemon Herb, Mediterranean, Santa Fe Style, Scampi)

**Old Bay**

**Publix** - Seafood Cocktail Sauce

**Safeway Brand**

**Spartan Brand**

**Stop & Shop Brand** - Seafood Cocktail Sauce

**Trader Joe's** - Seafood Cocktail Sauce

**Ukrop's** - Cocktail Sauce

## Cocoa Mix/Powder

**Coburn Farms** - Cocoa Mix

**Dagoba** - Authentic Hot Chocolate, Chocolate Syrup, Organic Cacao Powder, Unsweetened Hot Chocolate, Xocolatl Hot Chocolate

C

**Food Club Brand** - Hot Cocoa (Milk Chocolate, Mini Marshmallows)

**Full Circle** - Organic Milk Chocolate Hot Cocoa

**Ghirardelli** -

Double Chocolate

Hazelnut

Mocha

Premium Unsweetened Cocoa

Sweet Ground Chocolate & Cocoa

White Mocha

**Ginger Evans** - Cocoa

**Gloria Jean's** - All Hot Chocolate Varieties

**Hershey's** - Chocolate Syrup (Lite, Regular, Special Dark), Cocoa (Special Dark, Unsweetened Regular)

**Home Harvest Brand** - Hot Cocoa Mix (Regular, w/Marshmallows)

**Hy-Vee** - Instant Chocolate Flavored Drink Mix, Instant Hot Cocoa (No Sugar Added, Regular)

**Kroger Brand** - Instant Cocoa

**Laura Lynn** - Cocoa

**Lowes Foods Brand** - Hot Cocoa Mix (Regular, w/Marshmallows)

**Meijer Brand** -

Instant Marshmallow

No Sugar Added

Organic Regular

Regular

Sugar Free

w/Marshmallows

**Midwest Country Fare** - Hot Cocoa Mix, Instant Chocolate Flavored Drink Mix, No Sugar, Regular, w/Marshmallows, Rich Chocolate

**Safeway Brand** - Hot Cocoa Mix (Fat Free, w/Marshmallows), Instant Chocolate Drink Mix

**Safeway Select** - Cocoa Mix, European Café Style (Regular, White Chocolate)

**Shiloh Farms -** Cocoa Powder

**Spartan Brand -** Cocoa Canned, Hot Cocoa Mix (Regular, w/Marshmallows)

**Stop & Shop Brand** - Hot Cocoa (Fat Free No Sugar Added, Light, Mini Marshmallows, Regular)

**Swiss Miss -** Hot Cocoa Mix (Diet w/Calcium, Fat Free w/Calcium, Marshmallow Lovers, Milk Chocolate, Milk Chocolate w/Marshmallows, Rich Chocolate)

**Trader Joe's** - Conacado Organic Cocoa, Organic Cocoa Powder, Sipping Chocolate

**Watkins -** Baking Cocoa

Coconut

**Baker's** - Coconut (Bags, Cans)

**Food Club** - Sweetened Coconut

**Great Value Brand (Wal-Mart)** - Sweetened Flaked Coconut

**Hannaford Brand -** Fancy Sweetened

**Hy-Vee** - Coconut, Flake Coconut

**Kroger Brand -** Regular, Sweetened

**Laura Lynn**

**Let's Do...Organic -** Creamed, Flakes, Shredded (Reduced Fat, Regular, Unsweetened)

**Lowes Foods Brand** - Flakes

**Publix** - Coconut Flakes

**Safeway Brand** - Coconut (Sweetened)

**Spartan Brand** - Coconut Flakes

**Wegmans Brand** - Sweetened Flakes

**Woodstock Farms -** Coconut Medium Shred

Coconut Milk

**A Taste Of Thai** - Coconut Milk (Lite, Regular)

**Native Forest** - Organic Coconut Milk (Light, Regular)

**So Delicious** - Original●, Unsweetened●, Vanilla●

**Thai Kitchen** - Thailand (Lite, Lite Organic, Premium, Premium Organic)

**C** Trader Joe's - Light

Cod... see Fish

*All *Fresh* Fish Is *Gluten-Free (Non-Marinated, Unseasoned)**

Coffee

**Brown Gold -** All Varieties

**Caribou -** All Iced Coffee

**Folger's** - All Instant & Roasts

**Food Club Brand** - Instant Coffee (Decaf, Regular), Ground Coffee (Classic Roast, Columbian, Decaf, French Roast, Lite Classic Roast)

**Full Circle -** Organic (Espresso Blend Ground, French Roast, Ground, Guatamalan Reserve Ground, Morning Blend Ground, Morning Blend Whole Bean, Signature Blend Ground)

**General Foods International Coffee -**

Café Francais

Café Vienna (Regular, Sugar Free)

Chai Latte

Crème Caramel

Dark Mayan Chocolate

French Vanilla (Decaf, Decaf Sugar Free, Regular, Sugar Free)

French Vanilla Nut

Hazelnut Belgian Café

Italian Cappucino

Orange Cappuccino

Peppermint Mocha

Pumpkin Spice

Swiss Mocha (Decaf Sugar Free, Regular, Sugar Free)

Swiss White Chocolate

Viennese Chocolate

**Gloria Jean's -** All Brewed Coffee

**Great Value Brand (Wal-Mart) -**

100% Arabica Premium (Ground Coffee, Instant Coffee)

100% Colombian Premium Ground Coffee (Naturally Decaf, Regular)

French Roast - 100% Arabica Premium Ground Coffee

Naturally Decaf Premium Instant Coffee

**Green Mountain** - All Varieties *(Except French Vanilla Café Au Lait Café Escapes)*

**Higgins & Burke** - All Varieties

**Home Harvest Brand** - Instant

**Hy-Vee** -

    100% Colombian

    Breakfast Blend

    Classic Blend

    Classic Decaf

    Coffee (Instant, Regular)

    Decaf (Instant, Regular)

    French Roast

**Kroger Brand** - Unflavored (Ground, Instant, Whole)

**Laura Lynn** - All Varieties

**Lowes Foods Brand** -

    Bag (100% Colombian (Decaf, Regular), French Roast, Signature Blend)

    Brick (100% Colombian, Decaf, French Roast, Lite, Regular)

    Can (Regular)

    Instant (Decaf, Regular)

    Singles (Microwaveable)

**Maxwell House** -

    Coffee Bags (Decaf, Master Blend, Regular)

    Ground (Breakfast Blend, Dark Roast, Hazelnut, Original, Slow Roast, Vanilla)

    Filter Packs & Singles (Decaf, Original)

    Instant (Decaf, Reduced Caffeine/Lite, Original)

**C**

**Meijer Brand** - Decaf, French Roast, Ground (Colombian, French Roast, Lite 50% Decaf), Regular

**Member's Mark** - Cappuccino French Vanilla

**Midwest Country Fare** - Classic Blend

**Millstone** - All Flavors

**Mountain Blend** - Instant

**Nescafe** - Classic Instant, Taster's Choice Instant (Flavored, Non Flavored)

**O Organics** - All Coffee Beans

**Prestige** - 100% Colombian Whole Bean

**Publix** - All Varieties

**Safeway Brand** - Decaf Classic Roast, Espresso Coffee Beans

**Safeway Select** -
   Coffee Sticks (French Vanilla, Mocha)
   European Coffee Creamy Hazelnut Coffee Beverage
   Whole Bean (Flavored)

**Sanka** - Decaf Coffee

**Shamrock Farms** - Café Mocha

**Spartan Brand** -
   Coffee (French Roast, Instant, Instant Decaf, Regular)
   Coffee Ground (Colombian, Decaf, Light, Regular)

**Starbucks** -
   All Coffee Beans
   All Ground Coffee
   Double Shot (Cinnamon Dulce, Coffee Drink, Energy Coffee, Energy Mocha, Energy Vanilla, Light Coffee Drink)
   Frappuccino (Caramel, Coffee, Dark Chocolate Mocha, Mocha, Mocha Lite, Vanilla)
   Iced Coffee (Light, Regular)

**Taster's Choice** - All Varieties

**Trader Joe's** - All Coffee

**Wegmans Brand** -
   Ground (100% Colombian, 100% Colombian Medium Roast,

## cookie mix

**C**

Breakfast Blend Light Roast, Breakfast Blend Light Roast Decaf, Caffeine Lite, Decaf, Espresso Dark Roast, French Roast, Traditional)

Instant

Pure Origin Coffee (Day Break Roast, Ground Jamaican Mid Day, Kona Evening, Smooth Morning, Sumatra Night)

The Ultimate Coffee Adventure (All Varieties)

Traditional Coffee Singles

Whole Bean Coffee (100% Colombian Medium Roast, Breakfast Blend Light Roast, Espresso Dark Roast, Espresso Dark Roast Decaf)

**Yuban** -

Instant (Decaf, Reduced Caffeine/Lite, Regular)

Roast & Ground (Decaf, Reduced Caffeine/Lite, Regular)

**Coffee Creamer... see Creamer**

**Coffee Syrup -**

**Nescafe** - Ice Java Coffee Syrup (All Flavors)

**Cold Cuts... see Deli Meat**

**Cole Slaw Dressing... see Salad Dressing**

**Collards... see Greens**

**Communion Wafers**

**Ener-G** ▲ Communion Wafers

**Concentrate... see Drinks/Juice**

**Cones**

**Barkat -** Ice Cream Cones, Waffle Cones

**Cerrone Cone -** Waffle Cones

**Goldbaum's -** Gluten Free Ice Cream Cones (Regular, Sugar)

**Let's Do...Organic -** Gluten Free Ice Cream Cones

**Cookie Mix... see also Cookies/Cookie Dough**

**1-2-3 Gluten Free**▲ **-** Chewy Chipless Scrumdelicious Cookies●, Lindsay's Lipsmackin' Roll Out & Cut Sugar Cookies●, Sweet Goodness Pan Bars●

**3 Fellers Bakery**▲ **-** Cookie Dough (Chocolate & White Chip

**C**

w/Pecans●, Chocolate Chip●, Chocolate Chip w/Pecans●, Oatmeal Raisin●, Sugar●)

**365 Everyday Value** - Gluten Free Chocolate Chip Cookie Mix

**Arrowhead Mills** - Gluten Free Chocolate Chip Mix

**Betty Crocker▲** - Gluten Free Chocolate Chip Cookie Mix

**Bob's Red Mill▲** - Chocolate Chip

**Cause You're Special▲** - Chocolate Chip, Classic Sugar

**Cherrybrook Kitchen** - Gluten Free Chocolate Chip Cookie Mix, Gluten Free Sugar Cookie Mix *(Box Must Say Gluten-Free)*

**Earthly Treats ▲** - Sugar Cookie Mix ●

**Food-Tek Fast & Fresh** - Cookie Mix (Chocolate Chip, Double Chocolate Chip, Sugar)

**Gluten Free Sensations** - Chocolate Chip Cookie Mix

**Gluten-Free Essentials▲** - Chocolate Chip Cookie Mix●, Cocoa Mudslide●, Speedy Bake Mix (Chocolate Chip●, Make Mine Chocolate●)

**Gluten-Free Life▲** - The Ultimate Gluten Free Cookie Mix

**Gluten-Free Pantry▲** - Cookie & Cake Mix (Chocolate Chip, Old Fashioned)

**Hol Grain** - Chocolate Chip

**InclusiLife▲** - Cookie Dough (Chocolate Chip, Fudge Brownie, Sugar)

**Jules Gluten Free▲** - Graham Cracker/Gingersnap Mix●

**Katy Sweet▲** -

Chewy Pralines (Coconut Pecan●, Maple Walnut●, Peanut Pie, Pecan●)

Cookie Cutters (Bayou Bites●, Enchantments●, Fleur-De-Lis●, Lone Stars●, Longhorns●, Razorbacks●, Sooners●)

Creamy Pralines (Fudge Pecan●, Maple Walnut●, Original Pecan●, Original Walnut●)

No Sugar Added Chewy Pralines (Almond●, Mixed●, Pecan●, Walnut●)

Organic Chewy Pralines (Maple Walnut●, Original Pecan●)

Organic Creamy Pralines (Fudge Pecan●, Maple Walnut●, Original Pecan●, Original Walnut●)

**Kinnikinnick**▲ - Cookie Mix

**Laurel's Sweet Treats** ▲ - Chocolate Chip, Gourmet Chocolate Cookie w/White Milk Chocolate Chips, Roll 'Em Out Sugar

**Maggie's Gluten Free Goodies** ▲ - Super Duper Sugar Cookie Mix

**Namaste Foods**▲ - Blondies, Cookie

**Only Oats** - Grandma's Oatmeal Cookie Mix●

**Pure Living** - Cookie Mix (European Chocolate Truffle w/Tart Cherry Slivers●, Julienne Cranberries Zante Currants & Essence Of Raspberry-Orange Blossom●, Saigon Cinnamon Oat Zante Currants & Essence Of Chai Tea●)

**Really Great Food Company**▲ - Butter, Chocolate Crinkle, Coconut Macaroon, Biscotti (Anise, Lemon Poppy), Versatile

**Ruby Range** - Old Fashioned Cookies Gluten Free Baking Mix●

**Simply Organic**▲ - Honeypot Ginger Cookie Mix●

**Tastefully Gluten Free**▲ - Chocolate Chip, Cookie Dough, Sugar

**The Cravings Place**▲ - Chocolate Chunk (Double, Regular), Peanut Butter, Raisin Spice

**WOW Baking Company**▲ - Cookie Dough (Chocolate Chip●, Ginger Molasses●, Peanut Butter●, Sugar●)

## Cookies/Cookie Dough

**Aleia's**▲ - Almond Horn●, Chocolate Chip●, Chocolate Coconut Macaroon●, Coconut Macaroon●, Ginger Snap●, Peanut Butter●, Pignoli Nut●, Snickerdoodle●

**Andrea's Fine Foods**▲ - Chocolate Chip, Oatmeal, Pecan Shortbread, Sugar

**Apple's Bakery**▲ - Gluten Free Cookies (Butterscotch Walnut, Chocolate Cherry Ranch Fudge, Chocolate Chip No Nut, Coconut Meltaway, Dried Cranberry White Chocolate, Dusty Miller Molasses, Lemon Drop, Spice Gem, White Chocolate Macadamia Nut)

**Aunt Gussie's**▲ - Cookies (Chocolate Chip, Chocolate Spritz, Sugar Free Chocolate Chip, Sugar Free Vanilla Spritz)

**Choices Rice Bakery**▲ -

Almond Stars & Moons

Bird's Nest

**C**

Brownie White Chocolate Chip

Chocolate Chip

Cranberry Almond Biscotti

Fruit & Nut Power Cookie

Ginger

Mediterranean Macaroons

Raisin Sunflower

**Cookie Momsters** ▲ - Chocolate Chip, Dark Chocolate Chip, Sugar

**Crave Bakery** ▲ - Monster Cookie

**Cupoladua Oven** - Cupola Cookies (Chai Pistachio●, Chocolate Cashew●, Espresso Walnut●)

**Cybros Inc.** - Lemon Almond, Peanut Butter, Sugar

**Deerfields Bakery** ▲ - Cherry Dreams, Chips 'N Wally, Chocolate Dreams, Day Dreams, Lemon Buttons, Lotsa Chips, Oats 'N Chips, Oats 'N Raisins, Sugar Buttons, Triple Chips

**Di Manufacturing** - Gluten Free Cookies (Chocolate Chip●, Chocolate Chunk●, English Toffee●, M & M●, Macadamia Nut●, Oatmeal Raisin●, Peanut Butter●, Snickerdoodle●, Sugar●)

**El Peto** ▲ - Almond Shortbread, Carob Chip, Chocolate (Chip, Coconut Macaroons, Hazelnut), Cinnamon/Hazelnut, Coconut Macaroons, Gingersnaps, Hazelnut/Raspberry, Old Fashion Sugar

**Ener-G** ▲

Chocolate (Chip Biscotti, Chip Potato, Regular)

Cinnamon

Ginger

Sunflower Cookies

Vanilla

White Chocolate Chip

**Enjoy Life** ▲ - Chewy Chocolate Chip●, Double Chocolate Brownie●, Gingerbread Spice●, Happy Apple●, Lively Lemon●, No Oats "Oatmeal"●, Snickerdoodle●

**Everybody Eats** ▲ - Chocolate Chip, Sugar

**Foods By George** ▲ - Pecan Tarts

## cookies/cookie dough

**C**

**French Meadow Bakery -** Gluten Free (Chocolate Chip Cookie Dough●, Chocolate Chip Cookies●, Coconutty Macaroons●)

**Gillian's Foods▲** - Chocolate Chip, Cookie Dough, M&M, Sugar

**Glow Gluten Free▲** - Chocolate Chip, Double Chocolate Chip, Gingersnap, Snickerdoodle

**Glutafin** - Chocolate Chip

**Gluten Free & Fabulous▲** - Bites (Brownie●, Butterscotch●, Chocolate Chip Cookies●, Savory●, Shortbread●)

**Gluten Free Life▲** - Deluxe (Chocolate Chip, Flax Shortbread, Snicker Doodle, Sugar)

**Gluten-Free Creations▲** - Chocolate Chip●, Frozen Cookie Dough●, Nutty Trail Mix●, Oatmeal Raisin●, Pecan Wedding●, Snickerdoodle●

**Gluten-Free Essentials▲** - Vanilla Sugar Cookies●

**GlutenFreeda▲** - Real Cookies (Chip Chip Hooray, Chocolate Minty Python, Peanut Envy, Snicker Poodles, Sugar Kookies)

**Glutano▲** - Cookies (Butterkeks, Choco Chip, Chocolate O's, Cocoa Wafers, Custard Creams, Hoops, Lemon Wafers, Luxury Digestive, Rissini)

**Glutino▲** -

Chocolate Chip Cookies

Chocolate Vanilla Cream

Shortcake Dreams Cookies

Wafers (Chocolate w/Chocolate Coating, Lemon, Strawberry, Vanilla w/Chocolate Coating)

Vanilla Cream Cookies

**Good Juju Bakery▲** - Chocolate Cranberry, Oatmeal Cranberry, Walnut Cookies

**Gopal's -** Nature's Gift Cookies (Almond Raisin, Goldenberry Brazil, Hazelnut Cherry, Macadamia Goji, Pineapple Flax

**Goraw** - Super Cookies (Chocolate●, Original●)

**Ian's -** Wheat Free Gluten Free Cookie Buttons (Chocolate Chip, Crunchy Cinnamon)

**C**

**Jennies** - Zero Carb Macaroons (Carob, Chocolate, Coconut)

**Jo-Sef** - Chocolate Chip (Pecan, Regular), Cinnamon, Crème Filled (Chocolate, Cinnamon, Coffee, Double Chocolate), Egg Free Chocolate Chip, Fancy Sandwich w/Chocolate, Lemon, Linzer, Orange, Sugar, Vanilla

**Kinnikinnick▲** -

Almond (Biscotti, Regular)

Chocolate (Cookie Crumbs, Covered Almond Biscotti)

Double Chocolate Almond

Ginger Snap

KinniBetik Chunky Chocolate

KinniKritters Animal Cookies

KinniToos Sandwich (Chocolate Vanilla, Vanilla Crème)

Lemon Cranberry

Montana's Chocolate Chip

**Kookie Karma** - All Varieties●

**Manischewitz** -

Caramel Cashew Patties

Chocolate Frolic Bears

Macaroons (Banana Split, Cappuccino Chip, Chocolate, Chocolate Chip, Chocolate Chunk Cherry, Coconut, Fudgey Nut Brownie, Honey Nut, Rocky Road, Toffee Crunch, Ultimate Triple Chocolate)

Max's Magic Lollycones

Tender Coconut Patties

**Mi-Del** - Arrowroot Animal, Chocolate Chip, Cinnamon Snaps, Ginger Snaps, Pecan, Sandwich (Chocolate, Royal Vanilla)*(Package Must Say Gluten Free)*

**Montana Monster Munchies** - Legacy Valley Original Cookie●

**Namaste Foods▲** - Blondies Mix, Cookie Mix

**Nana's** - Cookie Bars (Berry Vanilla, Chocolate Munch, Nana Banana), No Gluten Cookie (Chocolate, Chocolate Crunch, Ginger, Lemon), Cookie Bites (Ginger, Fudge, Lemon Dreams, Spice)

## cookies/cookie dough

**C**

**Nature's Path Organic** - Animal Cookies (Vanilla)

**Orgran▲** -

Amaretti Biscotti

Classic Chocolate Biscotti

Classic Chocolate Cookie

Itsy Bitsy Bears

Mini Outback Animals (Chocolate, Vanilla)

Outback Animals (Chocolate, Vanilla)

Wild Raspberry Fruit Flavored Biscuits

**Pamela's Products▲** -

Butter Shortbread

Chocolate Chip (Mini, Walnut)

Chunky Chocolate Chip

Extreme Chocolate Mini Cookies

Ginger (Mini Snapz, w/Sliced Almonds)

Lemon Shortbread

Organic (Chocolate Chunk Pecan Shortbread, Dark Chocolate/Chocolate Chunk, Espresso Chocolate Chunk, Old Fashion Raisin Walnut, Peanut Butter Chocolate Chip, Spicy Ginger w/Crystallized Ginger)

Peanut Butter

Pecan Shortbread

Shortbread Swirl

**Rose's Bakery▲** - All Varieties●

**Schar ▲**- Chocolate Dipped Cookies, Chocolate Hazelnut Bars, Cocoa Wafers, Hazelnut Wafers, Ladyfingers, Shortbread Cookies, Vanilla Wafers

**Skye Foods** - Chocolate Chip●, White Chocolate Macadamia Nut●

**Trader Joe's** - Flourless Chocolate Walnut Cookies, Gluten Free Ginger Snaps, Meringues (All Varieties)

**Whole Foods Market Gluten Free Bakehouse ▲**- Almond Scones, Chocolate Chip, Cranberry Orange Scone, Molasses Ginger, Nutmeal Raisin, Peanut Butter

**C**  **WOW Baking Company** - Cookie (Chocolate● Ginger Molasses●, Oregon Oatmeal●, Peanut Butter●, Snickerdoodle●, Sugar●)

**Cooking Spray**

**Albertsons -** Buttery, Canola Oil, Vegetable

**Crisco** - Butter, Olive Oil, Original

**Emeril's** - Buttery, Canola Oil

**Food Club Brand** - Canola Oil, Olive Oil

**Full Circle -** Cooking Spray (Olive Oil, Vegetable)

**Great Value Brand (Wal-Mart)** - Butter, Canola, Olive, Regular

**Hannaford Brand -** Butter Flavored, Canola, Olive Oil

**Hy-Vee -** Butter, Canola, Olive Oil, Vegetable Oil

**Lowes Foods Brand** - Butter, Regular

**Manischewitz** - All Varieties

**Mazola -** All Cooking Sprays

**Meijer Brand** - Butter, Olive Oil Extra Virgin, Vegetable Oil

**Midwest Country Fare -** Vegetable Oil

**O Organics -** Canola, Olive

**Pam** - Butter Flavor, Olive Oil, Original

**Publix** - Butter Flavored, Grill, Olive Oil, Original Canola

**Safeway Brand** - Butter Flavored, Canola, Grill, Olive Oil, Vegetable

**Smart Balance** - All Varieties

**Spartan Brand** - Butter Flavored, Regular

**Stop & Shop Brand** - Butter Flavored, Canola, Garlic Flavored, Grill Spray, Olive Oil, Vegetable

**Trader Joe's** - Canola Oil Spray (All)

**Wegmans Brand** - Canola Oil, Corn Oil, Natural Butter Flavor Canola Oil, Olive Oil

**Cooking Wine**

**Eden** - Rice Mirin

**Holland House -** All Varieties

**Publix**

**Regina** - All Varieties

**C**

**Corn...** *All Fresh Fruits & Vegetables Are Gluten-Free*

**365 Every Day Value** -

Canned Whole Kernel Corn (No Salt Added)

Frozen Cut Corn

**365 Organic Every Day Value** -

Canned Whole Kernel Corn

Frozen Super Sweet Corn (Regular, White)

**Albertsons** - Canned (Creamed Style, Regular), Frozen

**Birds Eye** - All Plain Frozen Vegetables *(Except With Sauce)*

**C & W** - All Plain Frozen Vegetables

**Cascadian Farm** - Organic Frozen (Super Sweet Corn, Sweet Corn)

**Del Monte** - All Canned Vegetables

**Food Club Brand** - Canned (Cream Style, Golden, White, w/Peppers), Frozen (Golden, White)

**Freshlike** - Frozen Plain Vegetables *(Except Pasta Combos & Seasoned Blends)*

**Full Circle -** Organic Frozen Whole Kernel Corn, Organic Gold Corn

**Grand Selections** - Frozen (Super Sweet Cut, White Shoepeg)

**Great Value Brand (Wal-Mart)** -

Canned (Cream Style Corn, Golden Sweet Whole Kernel Corn, No Salt Added Golden Sweet Whole Kernel Corn)

Frozen (Corn On The Cob, Whole Kernel Corn)

Microwaveable (Golden Whole Kernel Corn (Plastic Cups))

**Green Giant** -

Canned

Cream Style Sweet Corn

Mexicorn

Niblets (Extra Sweet, No Salt Added, Whole Kernel Extra Sweet Corn, Whole Kernel Sweet Corn)

Southwestern Style

Super Sweet Yellow & White Corn

White Shoepeg Corn

**C**

Frozen

Cream Style Corn

Nibblers (12 Count, 24 Count)

Shoepeg White Corn & Butter Sauce

Steamers Niblets Corn

**Haggen** - Whole Kernel Corn

**Hannaford Brand -** Cream Style, Crisp & Sweet, Mexican Style, Whole Kernel

**Health Market** - Organic Whole Kernel

**Home Harvest Brand** - Canned, Frozen Whole Kernel Gold

**Hy-Vee** - Corn On The Cob, Cream Style (Golden Corn), Frozen Cut Golden Corn, Steam In A Bag Frozen Corn, Whole Kernel (Corn, Gold Corn, White Sweet Corn)

**Kroger Brand -** All Plain Vegetables (Canned, Frozen)

**Laura Lynn** - Corn (Cream Style, Gold 'N White, No Salt Whole Kernel, Vacuum Packed, Whole Kernel)

**Lowes Foods Brand -**

Frozen (Corn Cob Full Ear, Corn Cob Mini Ear, Cut)

Canned (White)

**Meijer Brand -**

Canned (Cream Style, Golden Sweet Organic, Whole Kernel (Crisp & Sweet, Golden, Golden No Salt, White)

Frozen (Corn Cob Mini Ear, Corn On Cob, Whole Kernel, Whole Kernel Golden)

**Midwest Country Fare** - Cream Style, Frozen Cut, Whole Kernel

**Native Forest -** Organic Cut Baby Corn

**Nature's Promise** - Organic Corn (Cut, On The Cob)

**O Organics -** Canned Whole Kernel, Frozen Golden Cut

**Pictsweet** - All Plain Vegetables (Frozen)

**Publix -**

Canned (Cream Style Golden, Golden Sweet, Whole Kernel Crispy, Whole Kernel Crispy 50% Less Salt)

Frozen (Corn On Cob, Cut)

**C**

**Publix GreenWise Market** - Organic Canned Whole Kernel

**S&W** - All Canned Vegetables

**Safeway Brand** - Cream Style, Frozen Corn On The Cob, No Salt Whole Kernel, Steam In Bag (Petite, White)

**Spartan Brand -**

Canned Corn

Frozen (Baby Corn Blend, Corn On The Cob, Mini Ear Corn On The Cob, Plain, White Super Sweet)

**Stop & Shop Brand** - Corn (& Butter, & Peas, Cut, Mexican Style, On The Cob, Super Sweet Corn On The Cob), Whole Kernel Corn

**Trader Joe's** - All Frozen Plain Vegetables

**Wegmans Brand -**

Canned (Bread & Butter, Cream Style Golden Sweet, Crisp 'n Sweet Whole Kernel, Whole Kernel, Whole Kernel No Salt)

Frozen (Baby Corn Cleaned And Cut, Bread & Butter Sweet Whole Kernel, Super Sweet Steamable, Whole Kernel In Butter Sauce)

**Winn Dixie -**

Canned (Creamed Style, Mexican Style, White Whole Kernel, Yellow Whole Kernel, Yellow Whole Kernel No Salt)

Frozen Corn (Organic Yellow Cut, Steamable Yellow Cut, White Cut, Yellow Cut)

Frozen Corn On The Cob (Mini, Regular)

**Woodstock Farms** - Organic Frozen Cut Corn (Regular, Supersweet (Regular, White)), Toasted Corn

## Corn Dog

**Garrett County Farms** - Uncured Corn Dogs (Beef, Chicken)

**Ian's** - Wheat Free Gluten Free Recipe Popcorn Turkey Corn Dogs

**S'Better Farms▲** - Beef Corn Dogs

**Wellshire Kids** - Uncured Corn Dogs (Beef, Chicken)

## Corn Oil... see Oil

## Corn Starch... see Starch

## Corn Syrup... see Syrup

**C** Cornbread/Cornbread Mix

    **365 Everyday Value** - Gluten Free Cornbread & Muffin Mix

    **Andrea's Fine Foods▲** - Corn Muffins

    **Celiac Specialties▲** - Corn Bread Mix

    **Chi-Chi's** - Fiesta Sweet Corn Cake Mix

    **Bob's Red Mill▲** - Gluten Free Cornbread Mix

    **El Torito** - Sweet Corn Cake Mix

    **Food-Tek Fast & Fresh** - Dairy Free Minute Cornbread Mix

    **Gluten-Free Pantry▲** - Yankee Cornbread

    **Glutino▲** - Premium Cornbread

    **Kinnikinnick▲** - Cornbread & Muffin Mix

    **Laurel's Sweet Treats ▲** - Good Ol' Corn Bread

    **Mixes From The Heartland▲** - Corn Bread Mix●

    **Orgran▲** - Cornbread & Muffin Mix

    **Whole Foods Market Gluten Free Bakehouse ▲** - Cornbread

Corned Beef... see also Beef

    **Armour** - Corned Beef, Corned Beef Hash

    **Carl Buddig**

    **Dietz & Watson -** Corned Beef Brisket, Corned Beef Flat (Extra Lean)

    **Food Club Brand** - Hash

    **Great Value Brand (Wal-Mart)**

    **Hargis House** - Hash

    **Hormel** - Corned Beef, Corned Beef Hash, Deli Sliced Cooked Corned Beef

    **Meijer Brand** - Hash, Sliced Chipped Corned Beef Meat

    **Safeway Brand -** Hash

    **Spartan Brand -** Hash

    **Wellshire Farms -** Corned Beef Brisket (Regular, Whole), Round Corned Beef, Sliced Round Corned Beef

Cornish Hens

    **Shelton's** - Game Hens

**C**

**Cornflake Crumbs... see Coating**

**Cornmeal**

**Arrowhead Mills** - Organic Blue, Organic Yellow

**Hodgson Mill** - Organic Yellow, Plain White, Plain Yellow

**Kinnikinnick**▲

**Publix** - Plain Yellow

**Safeway Brand** - Yellow Corn Meal

**Shiloh Farms** - Corn Meal

**Cottage Cheese**

**Albertsons** - 4%, Lowfat 1%

**Breakstone** - Large Curd (2% Milkfat, 4% Milkfat), Small Curd (2 % Milkfat, 4% Milkfat, Fat Free)

**Cabot** - All Varieties

**Food Club** - Low Fat, Regular

**Friendship** - All Varieties

**Hood** - All Varieties

**Horizon Organic** - All Varieties

**Hy-Vee** - 1% Low Fat Small Curd, 4% Large Curd, 4% Small Curd

**Kemps** - All Varieties

**Kroger Brand** - All Varieties

**Lactaid** - All Varieties

**Laura Lynn**

**Lowes Foods Brand** - 1%, Nonfat, Small Curd

**Lucerne** - Cottage Cheese *(Except Fruit Added)*

**Michigan Brand** - All Varieties

**Midwest Country Fare** - 1% Small Curd, 4% Small Curd

**Nancy's** - All Cultured Dairy & Soy Products

**Prairie Farms** - Fat Free, Large Curd, Lowfat, Small Curd

**Publix** - Fat Free, Large Curd (4% Milk Fat), Low Fat, Low Fat w/Pineapple, Small Curd (4% Milk Fat)

**C**

**Shamrock Farms -** Dry, Cottage Cheese w/ (Apple Cinnamon, Mixed Berries, Peaches, Pineapple, Stawberries, Strawberry Banana), Fat Free, Low Fat, Traditional

**Spartan Brand** - Large Curd 4% Milk Fat, Low Fat 1%, Small Curd (Nonfat, Regular)

**Stop & Shop Brand** - Cottage Cheese (Calcium Added, Low Fat, Nonfat w/Pineapple)

**Wegmans Brand** - 1% Large Curd, Nonfat, Pineapple (Fat Free), Small Curd (1%, 4%)

**Winn Dixie -** 4% Large Curd, 4% Small Curd, Fat Free, Low Fat

**Crabmeat...** *All Fresh Seafood Is **Gluten-Free (Non-Marinated, Unseasoned)***

**Chicken Of The Sea** - All Crab Products *(Except Crabtastic! Imitation Crab)*

**Crown Prince** - Natural (Fancy White Lump), Regular (Fancy Pink, Fancy White, Lump White)

**Great Value Brand (Wal-Mart)** - Crab Meat

**Ocean Prince** - Pink

**Trader Joe's** - Crabmeat

**Crackers**

**Andre's** -

Crackerbread

Cheddar Cheese

Country Onion

Old World Rye

Original

Roasted Garlic

Sweet Cinnamon

Tangy Parmesan

Toasted Sesame

Zesty Italian

**Blue Diamond Natural** - Nut Thins (Almond, Cheddar Cheese, Country Ranch, Hazelnut, Pecan, Smokehouse)

**C**

**Crunchmaster** - Multi Grain●, Multi Seed (Original●, Roasted Garlic●, Rosemary & Olive Oil●, Sweet Onion●), Rice Crackers (Artisan Four Cheese●, Toasted Sesame●)

**Eden** - Brown Rice, Nori Maki Rice

**Edward & Sons** - Brown Rice Snaps (Black Sesame, Cheddar, Onion Garlic, Salsa, Tamari (Seaweed, Sesame), Exotic Rice Toast (Brown Jasmine Rice & Spring Onion, Purple Rice & Black Sesame, Thai Red Rice & Flaxseeds), Toasted Onion, Unsalted Plain, Unsalted Sesame, Vegetable)

**Ener-G** ▲ Cinnamon, Gourmet, Gourmet Onion, Seattle

**Foods Alive** - Flax Crackers (BBQ, Hemp, Italian Zest, Maple & Cinnamon, Mexican Harvest, Mustard, Onion Garlic, Original)

**Glutano**▲ - Crackers

**Glutino**▲ - Gluten Free Crackers (Cheddar, Multigrain, Original, Vegetable)

**Healthy Valley** - Rice Bran Crackers

**Hol Grain** - Brown Rice (Lightly Salted, Onion & Garlic, No Salt, Organic, w/Sesame Seeds Lightly Salted

**Jo-Sef** - Graham Crackers (Chocolate, Cinnamon, Coffee, Vanilla)

**Ka-Me** - Rice Crackers (Black Sesame & Soy Sauce, Cheese, Plain, Seaweed, Sesame, Wasabi)*(Package Must Say Gluten Free)*

**Kinnikinnick**▲ - Graham Style Cracker Crumbs

**Kookie Karma** - All Varieties●

**Mary's Gone Crackers**▲ - Black Pepper, Caraway, Herb, Onion, Original

**Mr. Krispers** - Tasty Snack Crackers (Original Sesame●)

**Orgran**▲ - Crispbreads (Corn, Rice, Rice & Cracked Pepper, Rice & Garden Herb, Salsa Corn), Crispibites (Balsamic Herb, Corn, Onion & Chive), Crackers (Premium Deli)

**Real Foods** - Corn Thins (Cracked Pepper & Lemon, Feta & Sundried Tomato, Multigrain, Original, Sesame, Sour Cream & Chives, Soy & Linseed, Tasty Cheese), Rice Thins (WholeGrain)

**Roland** - Rice Crackers (Nori Seaweed, Original, Wasabi)

**C**

Sakata -

360 Degrees Global Infusion (Greek Feta & Herb, Italian Roast Tomato & Balsamic, Mexican Salsa & Cheese, Moroccan Spice)

Apero (Honey & Dijon Mustard, Sweet Chili & Coriander, Tomato Basil & Cream Cheese)

Mini's Multipacks (BBQ/Chicken, Cheese/Plain)

Original Rice (Barbecue, Cheddar Cheese, Chicken, Classic BBQ, Plain, Tomato Salsa, Sour Cream & Chives)

Snakata Pops (Barbecue, Cheese Supreme, Chicken, Multi Pack (Barbecue/Sea Salt & Red Vinegar, Cheese/Nachos), Nachos Cheese, Sea Salt & Red Vinegar, Sour Cream & Chives)

Wholegrain (Authentically Original, Basil Pesto, Chili)

**San-J** - Rice Crackers (Black Sesame, Sesame, Tamari)

**Schar ▲** - Table Crackers

**Sharwood's** - Thai Chilli

**The Kitchen Table Bakers** - Gourmet Wafer Crisps (Aged Parmesan, Everything, Flax Seed, Garlic, Italian Herb, Jalapeno, Rosemary, Sesame)

**Trader Joe's** - Savory Thins (Edamame, Minis, Multiseed w/Soy Sauce, Original)

Cranberries... *All *Fresh* Fruits & Vegetables Are **Gluten-Free***

**Publix** - Frozen Cranberries

**Stop & Shop Brand** - Yogurt Coated Cranberries

**Woodstock Farms** - Dried Yogurt Covered

Cranberry Sauce

**Baxters**

**Food Club Brand**

**Great Value Brand (Wal-Mart)** - Jellied, Whole Berry

**Hy-Vee** - Jellied, Whole Berry

**Lowes Foods Brand**

**Ocean Spray** - Jellied, Whole Berry

**S&W** - All Canned/Jarred Fruits

**Safeway Brand** - Jellied, Whole

**Spartan Brand** - Jellied, Whole

**Wegmans Brand** - Jellied, Whole Berry

**Wild Thymes** - Cranberry Apple Walnut, Cranberry Fig, Cranberry Raspberry, Original

**Winn Dixie** - Jellied

Cream... see Milk and/or Creamer

Cream Cheese

**Albertsons** - Neufchatel, Regular, Spread Light, Whipped

**Food Club** - Plain (Neufchatel Soft Style (Lite, Regular), Box Style Regular)

**Great Value Brand (Wal-Mart)** - 1/3 Less Fat, Chive & Onion, Fat Free, Light, Regular, Strawberry, Whipped

**Home Harvest Brand** - Cream Cheese Bar

**Horizon Organic** - All Varieties

**Hy-Vee** - 1/3 Less Fat, Blueberry, Fat Free (Regular, Soft, Strawberry), Garden Vegetable, Onion & Chives, Regular, Soft (Light, Regular), Strawberry, Whipped

**Kroger Brand** - All Varieties

**Laura Lynn** - Cream Cheese Bar (Fat Free, Regular), Neufchatel Bar, Onion & Chive, Soft, Strawberry, Whipped

**Lowes Foods Brand** - Bar, Neufchatel Bar Less Fat, Soft (Light, Regular)

**Lucerne** - Soft Bars (Fat Free, Garden Vegetable, Light, Neufchatel, Onion & Chive, Strawberry, Whipped Spread)

**Nancy's** - All Cultured Dairy & Soy Products

**Nature's Promise** - Organic Cream Cheese

**Organic Valley** - Neufchatel, Regular

**Philadelphia Cream Cheese** -

    Block

        Fat Free

        Light

        Neufchatel 1/3 Less Fat

        Regular

**C**

Cream Swirls
  Peaches 'N Cream
Tubs
  1/3 Less Fat
  Blueberry
  Cheesecake
  Chive & Onion (1/3 Less Fat, Regular)
  Fat Free
  Garden Vegetable (1/3 Less Fat, Regular)
  Honey Nut
  Light
  Neufchatel 1/3 Less Fat
  Pineapple
  Raspberry
  Regular
  Roasted Garlic Light
  Salmon
  Strawberry (1/3 Less Fat, Fat Free, Regular)
Whipped
  Cinnamon 'N Brown Sugar
  Garlic 'N Herb
  Mixed Berry
  Ranch
  Regular
  w/Chives
**Publix** - Fat Free, Neufchatel, Regular, Soft (All Flavors, Fat Free, Light, Neufchatel, Regular, Whipped)
**Spartan Brand** - Cream Cheese (Bar, Soft Tub), Lite Tub, Neufchatel, Soft (Garden Vegetable, Strawberry)
**Stop & Shop Brand** - Fat Free, Lite (Chive & Onion, Garden Vegetable, Honey Walnut, Plain, Strawberry), Neufchatel Cheese
**Tofutti** - Better Than Cream Cheese

**Trader Joe's** - All Varieties

**Wegmans Brand** - Chive & Onion, Fat Free, Honey Nut, Light, Neufchatel 1/3 Less Fat, Original, Pineapple, Strawberry, Whipped

**Winn Dixie** - Lite, Regular, Soft

## Creamer

**Albertsons** - Coffee Creamers (All Flavors Liquid & Powder), Non Dairy Creamer

**Coffee-Mate** - All Varieties (Liquid, Powder)

**Cremora** - Non Dairy Creamer (Lite & Creamy, Original)

**Food Club Brand** -
  Coffee Creamer (Refrigerated French Vanilla)
  Non Dairy Coffee Creamer (Fat Free, French Vanilla, Hazelnut, Original)

**Garelick** - Fresh Extra Heavy Whipping Cream

**Great Value Brand (Wal-Mart)** - Refrigerated Liquid Coffee Creamer Ultra Pasteurized (French Vanilla, Original), Powdered (Non Dairy, Regular)

**Home Harvest Brand** - Non Dairy Coffee Creamer Powder

**Hood** - All Creams, Country Creamer (Fat Free, Regular)

**Horizon Organic** - All Varieties

**Hy-Vee** -
  Coffee Creamer (Creamy Chocolate, Fat Free, French Vanilla, Hazelnut, Original, Vanilla Caramel)
  Refrigerated (French Vanilla, Hazelnut)
  Refrigerated Fat Free (French Vanilla, Hazelnut)

**International Delight** - All Varieties

**Laura Lynn** - Half & Half, Refrigerated Non Dairy Creamer

**Lowes Foods Brand** - Non Dairy (Fat Free French Vanilla, French Vanilla, Hazelnut, Lite, Original)

**Lucerne** - Coffee Creamer (French Vanilla, Original, Powdered), Half & Half, Light Non Dairy Creamer, Liquid Creamer (French Vanilla, Hazelnut, Irish Cream)

**Meijer Brand** - Ultra Pasteurized Non Dairy Creamer

**C**

**MimicCreme** - Sugar Free Sweetened, Sweetened, Unsweetened

**Nestle** - Coffee Mate All Varieties (Liquid, Powder)

**Prairie Farms** - Half & Half (Fat Free, Heavy Whipping, Regular, Ultra Pasteurized, Ultra Pasteurized Heavy Whipping Cream, Whipped Cream Aerosol)

**Publix** -

Liquid (Coffee Creamer, Fat Free Non Dairy Creamer, Half & Half (Fat Free, Regular))

Powder Non Dairy Creamer (Hazelnut, French Vanilla, Lite, Regular)

**Shamrock Farms** - Fat Free Half & Half (French Vanilla, Hazelnut, Regular), Fresh Whipping, Gourmet Heavy Cream

**Silk Soymilk** - French Vanilla, Hazelnut, Original

**Simply Smart** - Half & Half Fat Free

**Spartan Brand** - Coffee Creamer Powdered Non Dairy (French Vanilla, Hazelnut, Lite, Regular, Vanilla & Hazelnut)

**Stop & Shop Brand** - Fat Free Non Dairy Creamer, Instant Nonfat Dry Milk

**Winn Dixie** - Half & Half (Fat Free, Regular), Non Dairy Coffee Creamer (Fat Free, Original), Whipping (Regular, Heavy)

## Crispbread

**Orgran▲** - Crispbread (Corn, Rice & Cracked Pepper, Rice & Garden Herb, Salsa Corn)

## Crisps

**Baked Lay's** - Potato Crisps (Cheddar & Sour Cream, Original, Sour Cream & Onion, Southwestern Ranch)

**Baked Ruffles** - Potato Crisps (Cheddar & Sour Cream, Original)

**Brothers All Natural▲** -

Fruit Crisps (Asian Pear, Banana, Fuji Apple, Pineapple, Strawberry, Strawberry Banana, White & Yellow Peach)

Potato Crips (Black Pepper & Sea Salt, Fresh Onion & Garlic, Original w/Sea Salt, Szechuan Pepper & Fresh Chives)

**Eat Smart** - Soy Crisps (Parmesan Garlic & Olive Oil, Tomato Romano & Olive Oil), Veggie Crisps (Creamy Cucumber & Dill, Regular, Sun Dried Tomato & Pesto)

**Glenny's** -
Soy Crisps
Apple Cinnamon
Barbeque (Organic, Regular)
Cheddar
Cool Ranch
Lightly Salted
No Salt Added
Onion & Garlic
Salt & Pepper
White Cheddar

**Grace Island Specialty Foods** - All Varieties

**Herr's** - Veggie Crisps

**Hy-Vee** - Rice Crisps (Caramel Corn, Cheddar Cheese, Ranch)

**Lay's Stax** -
Potato Crisps
Cheddar
Hot 'N Spicy BBQ
Jalapeno Cheddar
Mesquite Barbecue
Original
Ranch
Salt & Vinegar
Sour Cream & Onion

**Michael Season's** - Baked Thin Potato Crisps (Cheddar & Sour Cream, Original, Sweet Barbecue)

**Mr. Krispers** -
Baked Nut Chips (Toasted Almond●)
Baked Rice Krisps (Barbecue●, Nacho●, Sea Salt & Pepper●, Sour Cream & Onion●, Sun Dried Tomato & Basil●, White Cheddar & Herbs●)

**C**

    Multi Seed Chips (Original●)

    Tasty Snack Crackers (Original Sesame●)

**Nature's Promise** - Soy Crisps (BBQ, Ranch)

**Orgran▲** - Crispibites (Balsamic Herb, Onion & Chive, Original Corn)

**The Kitchen Table Bakers** - All Parmesan Gourmet Wafer Crisps

**Trader Joe's** - Sea Salt & Pepper Rice Crisps, Sour Cream & Onion Rice Crisps, Soy Crisps BBQ

Croutons

    **Aleia's▲** - Classic●, Parmesan●

    **Andrea's Fine Foods▲** - Stuffing Croutons

    **Ener-G ▲** - Plain Croutons

    **Gillian's Foods▲** - Garlic Croutons

    **Gluten-Free Pantry▲** - Olive Oil & Garlic Croutons

Cucumbers... *All Fresh Fruits & Vegetables Are **Gluten-Free***

Cupcakes... see also Cake/Cake Mix

    **Crave Bakery▲** - Chocolate

    **Miller's Gluten Free Bread Co.▲** - Chocolate, Vanilla

    **Simply Organic▲** - Cocoa Cayenne Cupcake Mix●

Curry Paste

    **A Taste Of Thai** - Curry Paste (Green, Panang, Red, Yellow)

    **Patak's** - Curry Paste (Biryani, Butter Chicken, Mild Douce, Hot Tres Epicee, Madras, Tandoori, Tikka, Vindaloo)

    **Sharwood's** - Green, Red

    **Thai Kitchen** - Curry Paste (Green, Red, Roasted Red Chili)

Curry Powder

    **Durkee**

    **McCormick**

    **Spice Island**

    **Tones**

Curry Sauce

    **Patak's** - Balti Coriander & Cumin

**Sharwood's** - Thai (Green, Red)

**Custard**

   **Orgran▲** - Custard Mix

# D

## Deli Meat

### Applegate Farms -

Organic (Genoa Salami, Herb Turkey Breast, Roast Beef, Roasted Chicken, Smoked Chicken, Smoked Turkey Breast, Uncured Ham)

Natural (Black Forest Ham, Coppa, Genoa Salami, Herb Turkey, Honey & Maple Turkey Breast, Honey Ham, Hot Genoa Salami, Hot Soppressata, Pancetta, Pepperoni, Roast Beef, Roasted Turkey, Slow Cooked Ham, Smoked Turkey Breast, Soppressata, Turkey Bologna, Turkey Salami)

### Boar's Head - All Varieties

### Busseto - Premium Genoa Salami

### Butterball

Extra Thin Turkey Breast (Honey Roasted, Oven Roasted, Smoked)

Extra Thin Sliced Deep Fried Turkey Breast (Buttery Herb, Cajun Style, Original, Thanksgiving Style)

Lean Family Size (Honey Roasted Turkey Breast, Oven Roasted Turkey Breast, Smoked Turkey Breast, Turkey Bologna, Turkey Ham)

Thick Sliced Deep Fried Turkey Breast (Cajun Style, Original, Thanksgiving Style)

Thin Sliced Oven Roasted Chicken Breast

Thin Sliced Turkey Breast (Honey Roasted, Oven Roasted, Smoked)

### Carl Buddig - All Meat Products

### Castle Wood Reserve - Herb Roasted Turkey, Sliced Angus Beef, Thinly Sliced (Black Forest Ham, Oven Roasted Turkey)

### Celebrity - Healthy Ham

**D**

**Colombus** - Deli Meats (All)

**Dietz & Watson** - All Lunch Meat *(Except Bockwurst, Rotisserie Style Chicken, Scrapple)*

**Farmer John** - Lunch Meats (Black Forest Ham, Bologna, Brown Sugar & Honey Ham, Chopped Ham, Cotto Salami, Ham Roll, Headcheese, Mission Loaf, Original Premium Liverwurst, Premium Braunschweiger, Premium Liverwurst w/Bacon, Premium Oven Roasted Turkey Breast, Sliced Cooked Ham)

**Great Value Brand (Wal-Mart)** -

97% Fat Free (Baked Ham Water Added, Cooked Ham, Honey Ham Water Added)

Fat Free (Smoked Turkey Breast, Turkey Breast)

Thinly Sliced (Roast Beef, Smoked Ham, Smoked Honey Ham, Smoked Turkey Breast)

**Hebrew National** -

From The Deli Counter (Beef Bologna, Beef Salami, Corned Beef, Pastrami)

Sliced Lunch Meats (Beef Salami)

**Hillshire Farms** -

Deli Select

Baked Ham

Honey (Ham, Roasted Turkey Breast)

Deli Select Premium Hearty Slices

Honey (Ham, Roasted Turkey)

Oven Roasted Turkey Breast

Virginia Brand Baked Ham

Deli Select Thin Sliced

Brown Sugar Baked Ham

Corned Beef

Honey Roasted Turkey Breast

Mesquite Smoked Turkey Breast

Oven Roasted (Chicken Breast, Turkey Breast)

Roast Beef

Smoked (Chicken Breast, Ham, Turkey Breast)

Deli Select Ultra Thin

Brown Sugar Baked Ham

Hard Salami

Honey (Ham, Roasted Turkey Breast)

Mesquite Smoked Turkey

Oven Roasted Turkey Breast

Pastrami

Roast Beef

Smoked Ham

**Honeysuckle White** -

Chicken Breast (BBQ, Buffalo Style, Oil Browned)

Deli Sliced (Turkey Breast Hickory Smoked, Turkey Breast Oven Roasted, Turkey Pastrami)

Hickory Smoked Cooked Turkey Salami

Hickory Smoked Turkey Ham

Hickory Smoked Turkey Pastrami

Lunch Meats Deli Sliced

Hickory Smoked Turkey Breast (Honey, Regular)

Oven Roasted Turkey Breast

Turkey Pastrami

Original Rotisserie Turkey Ham

Turkey Bologna

Turkey Breast Deli Meats

Cajun Style Hickory Smoked

Golden Roasted

Hickory (Smoked, Smoked Peppered)

Honey Mesquite Smoked

Oil Browned

Original Rotisserie

Oven Prepared

**D**

Turkey Breast Estate Recipe
- Buffalo Style
- Canadian Brand Maple
- Dry Roasted
- Hickory Smoked (Honey Pepper, Original, Sun Dried Tomato)
- Honey Smoked
- Mesquite Smoked

**Hormel** -
- Deli Sliced
  - Black Forest
  - Cooked (Corned Beef, Ham, Pastrami)
  - Double Smoked Ham
  - Honey Ham
  - Oven Roasted Turkey Breast
  - Prosciutto Ham
  - Seasoned Roast Beef
  - Smoked Turkey Breast
- Diced Ham
- Homeland Hard Salami
- Julienne (Ham, Turkey)
- Natural Choice
  - Cooked Deli Ham
  - Hard Salami
  - Honey Deli (Ham, Turkey)
  - Oven Roasted Deli Turkey
  - Pepperoni
  - Roast Beef
  - Smoked Deli (Ham, Turkey)

**Hy-Vee** - Ham & Cheese, Loaf (Old Fashioned, Pickle, Spiced Luncheon), Luncheon Meat

**D**

**Jennie-O** -

Grand Champion Turkey Breast

Hickory Smoked

Homestyle Pan Roasted

Honey Cured

Mesquite Smoked

Oven Roasted

Tender Browned

Natural Choice Turkey Breast

Oven Roasted

Peppered

Tender Browned

Turkey Breast

Apple Cinnamon

Garlic Peppered

Honey (Maple, Mesquite)

Hot Red Peppered

Italian Style

Maple Spiced

Mesquite Smoked

Oven Roasted

Peppered

Smoked (Peppered, Regular)

Tender Browned

Tomato Basil

Turkey Store

Deli Chicken Breast (Buffalo Style, Mesquite Smoked, Oven Roasted)

Hickory Smoked Turkey Breast (Cracked Pepper, Garlic Pesto, Honey Cured, Sun Dried Tomato)

**D**

Oven Roasted Turkey Breast

Smoked Turkey Breast (Hickory, Honey Cured, Mesquite)

**Kayem** - Deli Sliced Honey Cured Ham, Honey Smoked Turkey Breast, Roast Beef, Turkey Breast

**Nature's Promise** - All Varieties

**Norwestern Deli Turkey** - Hickory Smoked, Oven Roasted, Turkey Pastrami

**Oscar Mayer** -

Deli Fresh Meats

Cooked Ham (96% Fat Free, Regular)

Honey Ham

Oven Roasted (98% Fat Free Turkey, Chicken Breast, Turkey Breast)

Smoked (Ham, Turkey Breast)

Shaved Deli Fresh Meats (Black Forest Ham, Brown Sugar Ham, Cajun Seasoned Chicken Breast, Cracked Black Peppered Turkey Breast, French Dip Roast Beef, Honey Ham, Honey Smoked Turkey Breast, Mesquite Turkey Breast, Oven Roasted Turkey Breast, Rotisserie Style Chicken Breast, Slow Roasted Roast Beef, Smoked Ham, Smoked Turkey Breast, Virginia Brand Ham)

Thin Sliced Deli Fresh (97% Fat Free Smoked Ham, Brown Sugar Ham, Honey Smoked Turkey Breast, Mesquite Turkey Breast, Oven Roasted Chicken Breast, Oven Roasted Turkey Breast, Smoked Turkey Breast)

**Perdue** -

Deli Dark Turkey Pastrami Hickory Smoked

Deli Pick Ups Sliced Turkey (Golden Browned, Honey Smoked, Mesquite Smoked, Oven Roasted, Smoked)

Deli Pick Ups Sliced Turkey Ham Honey Smoked

Deli Turkey (Bologna, Breast Oil Browned, Ham Hickory Smoked, Salami)

Sliced Chicken Breast Oil Fried

**Primo Naturale** - Sliced (Dried Pepperoni, Original Salami, Premium

Genoa Salami, Salami w/Herbs, Salami w/Black Pepper, Sopressata)

## Primo Taglio

Black Forest Ham w/Natural Juices (Coated w/Caramel Color)

Cervelat Salami

Chicken Breast Oven Roasted Browned In Hot Cottonseed Oil

Cooked Corned Beef

Genoa Salami

Maple Ham Old Fashioned w/Natural Juices

Mortadella (Black Pepper Added)

Pancetta

Pastrami Coated w/Spices (Caramel Color Added)

Prosciutto Dry Cured Ham

Roast Beef Coated w/Seasonings (Caramel Color Added)

Salami Coated w/Gelatin & Black Pepper

Sopressata

Turkey Breastw/Natural Smoke Flavoring

## Publix -

Deli Pre-Pack Sliced Lunch Meat

Beef (Bologna, Bottom Round Roast)

Cooked Ham

Corned Beef

Extra Thin Sliced (Honey Ham, Oven Roasted Turkey Breast, Smoked Turkey Breast)

German Bologna

Hard Salami Reduced Fat

Low Salt Ham

Pickle & Pimento Loaf

Smoked Turkey

Spanish Style Pork

Sweet Ham

**D**

     Tavern Ham

     Turkey Breast

     Virginia Brand Ham

**Smithfield** - Ham (Black Forest, Brown Sugar, Chopped, Cooked, Turkey, Virginia Brand), Turkey Breast (Mesquite, Oven Roasted, Smoked)

**Thumann's** - All Varieties●

**Trader Joe's** - Mesquite Smoked Turkey Breast Sliced, Prosciutto Di Italia

**Wegmans** - Chicken Breast Cutlets (Honey Mustard, Italian, Rosemary Balsamic Tangy), Corned Beef w/ Juices, Pork Tenderloin Honey Mustard, Roast Beef Organic, Turkey Breast No Salt, Turkey Oven Browned

**Dill Pickles... see Pickles**

**Dinner Meals... see Meals**

**Dip/Dip Mix**

   **Cabot** - Horseradish, Nacho, Ranch, Salsa Grande, Veggie

   **Cedarlane** - 5 Layer Mexican Dip

   **Eat Smart -** Salsa Con Queso, Tres Bean Dip

   **Fantastic World Foods -** Original Hummus

   **Food Club Brand** - French Onion Dip

   **Fritos** -

     Bean

     Chili Cheese

     Hot Bean

     Jalapeno & Cheddar Flavored Cheese

     Mild Cheddar Flavored Cheese

   **Hannaford Brand -** Ranch Dip Mix

   **Herr's** - Bean, Jalapeno Cheddar, Mild Cheddar, Salsa & Cheese

   **Hy-Vee** -

     Bacon & Cheddar

     Dill Vegetable

**D**

French Onion
Fruit Dip
Ranch & Dill
Salsa
Toasted Onion
Vegetable Party

**Great Value Brand (Wal-Mart)** - French Onion, Ranch Chip, Salsa Con Queso, White Salsa Con Queso

**Laura Lynn** - All Refrigerated Dips, Ranch Dip Mix

**Lay's** -
Creamy Ranch
Flavored Dry Mix (French Onion, Green Onion, Ranch)
French Onion

**Lipton** - Recipe Secrets Onion Soup & Dip Mix

**Litehouse** -
Avocado
Chocolate (Caramel, Regular, Yogurt Fruit)
Dilly Dip (Lite, Regular)
Garden Ranch
Litehouse 100 Calorie Chocolate Dip
Low Fat Caramel
Onion
Organic Ranch
Original Caramel
Ranch
Ranch Veggie Dippers
Southwest Ranch
Spinach Parmesan
Strawberry Yogurt Fruit
Toffee Caramel
Vanilla Yogurt Fruit

**D**

**Lowes Foods Brand** - French Onion, Ranch

**Prairie Farms** - French Onion, Ranch

**Publix** - French Onion, Green Onion, Guacamole, Onion Soup/Dip Mix

**Road's End Organics -** Non Dairy Nacho Chreese Dip (Mild, Spicy)

**Safeway Select** - Balsamic Garlic Dipping Sauce

**Salpica** - Dip (Chipotle Black Bean, Mexican Red Bean, Salsa Con Queso)

**Scarpetta** - Spreads (Artichoke & Olive, Asparagus, Olive & Almond, Red Pepper & Eggplant, Spicy Red Pepper)

**Sharwood's -** Bengal Spiced Tomato & Red Pepper, Green Label Mango Chutney & Chilli

**Spartan Brand -** Dip (French Onion, Ranch), Onion Soup & Dip Mix

**Stop & Shop Brand** - Refrigerated (Artichoke & Cheese, French Onion, Ranch, Spinach, Veggie)

**T. Marzetti** -

Blue Cheese

Caramel Apple (Fat Free, Light, Old Fashioned, Peanut Butter)

Chocolate Fruit

Cream Cheese Fruit (Regular, Strawberry)

Dill (Fat Free, Light, Regular)

French Onion (Light, Regular)

French Vanilla Yogurt Fruit (Light)

Guacamole

Horseradish

Ranch (Fat Free, Light, Organic, Regular)

Spinach

**Taco Bell -** Black Bean Con Queso, Chili Con Queso w/Beef, Salsa Con Queso (Medium, Mild)

**Tostitos** -

Creamy (Southwestern Ranch Dip, Spinach Dip)

Monterey Jack Queso

Salsa Con Queso

Spicy Nacho Cheese Dip

Spicy Queso Supreme

Zesty Bean & Cheese Dip

**Trader Joe's -**

Blue Cheese w/Roasted Pecan

Cilantro & Chive Yogurt

Fat Free Spicy Black Bean

Guacamole (All Varieties)

Spinach

**Ukrop's -** Buffalo Chicken, Fruit, Garlic Herb, Seven Layered, Spinach Artichoke

**UTZ -** Cheddar & Jalapeno, Mild Cheddar Cheese, Mt. Misery Mike's Salsa Dip, Sweet Salsa Dip

**Walden Farms -** Fruit Dip (Caramel, Chocolate, Marshmallow), Veggie & Chip Dip (Bacon, Blue Cheese, French Onion, Ranch)

**Wegmans Brand -** French Onion, Salsa Con Queso (Cheddar Cheese Dip), Veggies & Dip

**Wise -** Green Onion Mix, Nacho Cheese Canned Dip

## Donuts/Doughnuts

### Celiac Specialties▲ -

Gluten Free

Chocolate Donuts

Cinnamon Sugar (Donut Holes, Donuts, Mini Donuts)

Coconut Donuts

Glazed (Donut Holes, Donuts)

Plain (Donut Holes, Donuts, Mini Donuts)

Powder Sugar (Donut Holes, Donuts, Mini Donuts)

Gluten Free/Casein Free

Cinnamon Sugar Donut Holes

Glazed Donut Holes

Plain Donut Holes

Powder Sugar Donut Holes

**D** Ener-G ▲ - Chocolate Iced Doughnuts, Plain Doughnut (Holes, Regular)

Gluten-Free Creations▲ - Chocolate●, Chocolate Marble●, Cinnamon & Sugar●, Insane Chocolate●, Plain Jane●, Superb Sprinkles●

Kinnikinnick▲ - Chocolate Dipped, Cinnamon Sugar, Glazed Chocolate, Maple Dipped, Vanilla Dipped

**Dressing... see Salad Dressing**

**Dried Fruit**

Bare Fruit - Bananas, Bananas & Cherries, Cherries, Cinnamon Apple, Granny Smith Apple, Fuji Apple, Mangos, Pears, Pineapple & Mangos, Pineapples

Baxters - Chilli & Lime Marinated Beetroot, Garlic & Rosemary Marinated Beetroot

Brothers All Natural▲ - Fruit Crisps (Asian Pear, Banana, Fuji Apple, Pineapple, Strawberry, Strawberry Banana, White & Yellow Peach)

Crunchies - Blueberries, Mango, Mixed Fruit, Strawberries, Tropical Fruit

Dole - All Dried Fruit *(Except Real Fruit Bites)*

Eden - Cranberries, Montmorency Dried Tart Cherries, Wild Blueberries

Great Value Brand (Wal-Mart) - Apples, Apricots, Banana Chips, California Sun Dried Raisins (100% Natural), Cherries, Cranberries, Mixed Berries, Pitted Prunes

Home Harvest Brand - Prunes Medium Whole, Raisins Seedless

Hy-Vee - Apples, Apricots, Banana Chips, Blueberries, Cherries, Cranberries, Mixed (Berries, Fruit), Pineapple

Member's Mark - 7 Fruit Blend, Mediterranean Dried Apricots

Mrs. May's Naturals - All Varieties●

Nonuttin' Foods▲ - Fruit Snacks

Publix - Dried Plums, Fruit Snacks (Curious George, Dinosaurs, Sharks, Snoopy, Veggie Tales)

Safeway Brand - Berries & Cherries, Cranberries, Island Inspirations, Phillipine Mango, Prunes, Raisins, Tropical Treasures

Sensible Foods - Apple Harvest, Cherry Berry, Orchard Blend, Tropical Blend

**Spartan Brand** - Cranberries, Pitted Prunes, Raisins

**Sun-Maid** - Raisins (Baking, Golden, Natural California, Regular), Zante Currants

**Trader Joe's** - All Dried Fruit *(Except Black Currants)*, Roasted Plantain Chips

**Traverse Bay Fruit Co.** - Premium Dried Cherries

**Wegmans Brand** - Dried (Apricots, Cherries, Cranberries, Philippine Mango, Pitted Prunes, Plums, Tropical Pineapple, Wild Blueberries), Seedless Raisins

**Woodstock Farms**

Apple Rings (Regular, Unsulphured)

Apricots Turkish

Banana Chips (Regular, Sweetened)

Black Mission Figs

Blueberries

Calmyrna Figs

Cherries Unsulphured

Cranberries (Sweetened, Yogurt Covered)

Dates Deglet w/Pit

Flame Raisins

Ginger (Crystallized, Slices Unsulphured)

Goji Berries

Kiwi Slices

Mango (Diced, Slices (Regular, Unsulphured))

Medjool Dates w/Pit

Papaya Spears Lo Sugar Unsulphered

Pineapple Slices Unsulphered

Prunes Pitted

Thompson Raisins

## Drink Mix

**Country Time** - All Flavors

**D** Crystal Light -
Decaf Iced Tea (Lemon, Regular)
Fruit Punch
Green Tea Raspberry
Iced Tea (Peach, Raspberry, Regular)
Immunity Natural Cherry Pomegranate
Lemonade
Pineapple Orange
Raspberry (Lemonade, Peach)
Strawberry Kiwi
Sunrise (Berry Tangerine Morning, Classic Orange, Orange Wake
Up, Ruby Red Grapefruit, Tangerine Strawberry, Tropical Morning)
White Grape

**Flavor Aid -** Powdered Soft Drinks

**Food Club Brand -** Chocolate Drink Mix, Drink Mixes (Cherry,
Grape, Orange, Tropical Punch)

**Great Value Brand (Wal-Mart) -** All Powedered Drink Mixes (Regular,
Sugar Free)

**Hannaford Brand -**
Regular (Cherry, Fruit Punch, Lemonade, Orange, Strawberry)
Sugar Free (Fruit Punch, Iced Tea, Lemon Lime, Lemonade,
Raspberry Lemonade)

**Hawaiian Punch -** All Varieties

**Hy-Vee -**
Splash Drink Mix (Cherry, Grape, Lemonade, Orange, Strawberry,
Tropical, Tropical Fruit Punch)
Sugar Free Splash Drink Mix (Fruit Punch, Iced Tea, Lemonade,
Pink Lemonade, Raspberry)

**Kool-Aid -** Soft Drink Mix Sugar Sweetened (Cherry, Grape,
Lemonade, Strawberry), Soft Drink Mix Unsweetened (Cherry,
Grape, Lemonade, Strawberry, Tropical Punch)

**Langers Juices -** All Juices

**Meijer Brand -**
  Breakfast Orange
  Cherry
  Chocolate Flavor
  Grape
  Ice Tea
  Lemon Sugar Free
  Lemonade
  Lemonade Stix
  Orange (Free & Lite, Regular)
  Pink Lemonade (Regular, Sugar Free)
  Punch
  Raspberry Stix
  Raspberry Sugar Free
  Strawberry (Flavor, Regular)
  Strawberry/Orange/Banana

**Nestea -** Iced Tea Mix Unsweetened (Decaf, Regular)

**Safeway Brand -** Cherry (Light, Regular), Instant Chocolate, Peach (Light, Regular), Pink (Light, Regular), Spiced Apple Cider, Strawberry (Light, Regular), Strawberry Star Fruit, Sugar Free Raspberry & Lemonade

**Snapple -** All Diet Drink Mixes

**Spartan Brand -** Cherry, Grape, Lemonade Flavor, Pink Lemonade, Raspberry, Tropical Punch

**Tang -** Grape, Orange, Orange Kiwi, Tropical Passionfruit, Wild Berry

**Wegmans Brand -** Powdered Drink Mix (Lemonade Flavor, Pink Lemonade)

**Winn Dixie -**
  Regular (Cherry, Fruit Punch, Grape, Lemonade, Orange, Pink Lemonade, Raspberry, Strawberry Kiwi)
  Sugar Free (Fruit Punch, Lemon Iced Tea, Lemonade, Peach Iced Tea, Pink Lemonade)

**Wyler's -** Powdered Soft Drinks (Light, Sugar Free, Regular)

**D** Drinks/Juice (Non-Carbonated)... (Carbonated Drinks... see Soda Pop/Carbonated Beverages)

**Apple & Eve** - All Products

**Campbell's** - Tomato Juice (Healthy Request, Low Sodium, Organic, Original)

**Capri Sun** - All Flavors

**Cascadian Farm** - Organic Frozen Juice Concentrate (Apple, Cranberry, Grape, Lemonade, Orange, Raspberry)

**Ceres** - All Varieties

**Cott** - All Varieties

**Country Time** - Lemonade

**Dei Fratelli** - Juice (Tomato (Regular, Tasty Tom Spicy), Vegetable)

**Dole** - All Fruit Juice

**Eden Organic** - Apple Juice, Cherry Concentrate, Montmorency Tart Cherry Juice

**Enviga** - Sparkling Green Tea (Berry, Regular)

**Food Club Brand** -

Cranberry (Apple, Grape, Light Grape, Light Raspberry, Raspberry, White Cranberry Strawberry)

Frozen (Apple, Lemonade, OJ Original, OJ Pulp Free, Pink Lemonade)

Juices (Apple, Cranberry, Grapefruit & Tangerine, Lemon, Lime, Pineapple, Pomegranate, Pomegranate Blueberry, Prune, Ruby Red Grapefruit, Tomato, Vegetable, White Grape, White Grapefruit)

Refrigerated (OJ (w/Calcium, w/Omega 3), OJ Groves Best, OJ Premium )

Thirst Splashers (Fruit Punch, Iced Tea, Lemonade, Raspberry Ice, Raspberry Lemonade)

**Fruit2O** - All Varieties

**Full Circle** - Organic (Apple Natural, Blueberry 100% Juice, Cranberry Cocktail, Cranberry Raspberry, Grape 100% Juice, Orange Carafe, Tomato Juice, Vegetable Juice)

**Fuze** - All Varieties

**D**

**Gardner Groves** - 100% Grapefruit Juice

**Gatorade** - All Varieties (Be Tough X-Factor, Bring It Fierce, Elite Series Endurance Formula, Elite Series Gatorade Performance Series, Focus Gatorade Tiger, G2, Gatorade, No Excuses Rain, Powder, Shine On Gatorade AM)

**Gold Peak** - Iced Tea (Diet, Green Sweetened, Lemon, Sweetened, Unsweetened)

**Great Value Brand (Wal-Mart)** -

Juice

100% Juice Apple Juice (Juice Boxes)

100% Juice Fruit Punch (Juice Boxes)

Prune Juice

From Concentrate

100% Juice Apple Juice Punch Blend

100% Juice Unsweetened Apple Juice

Fruit Punch

Kiwi Strawberry Punch

Lemon Berry Punch

Light Apple Juice Cocktail

Natural Strength Lemon Juice

Tomato Juice

Unsweetened White Grapefruit Juice

Vegetable Juice

Frozen Juice Concentrate

Country Style Orange Juice Pure Unsweetened

Florida Grapefruit Juice Pure Unsweetened

Fruit Punch

Grape Juice Drink

Limeade

Orange Juice with Calcium

Pink Lemonade

**D**

Refrigerated Drinks
Country Style Orange Juice
Fruit Punch
Grape Drink
Orange Juice (Regular, w/Calcium)

**Hansen's** - All Varieties

**Hawaiian Punch** - All Varieties

**Home Harvest Brand** - Apple Juice, Cranberry Juice Cocktail, Original Orange Juice, Tomato Juice, Vegetable Juice Cocktail

**Honest Ade** - Cranberry Lemonade, Limeade, Orange Mango w/Mangosteen, Pomegranate, Super Fruit Punch

**Honest Kids** - Berry Berry Good Lemonade, Goodness Greatness, Tropical Tangopunch

**Honest Mate** - Agave Mate, Sublime Mate, Tropical Mate

**Hood** - All Juices

**Hy-Vee** -

100% Juice Blend (Cranberry, Cranberry Apple, Cranberry Raspberry)

Chocolate Nutritional Supplement (Plus, Regular)

Concord Grape Juice

Frozen Concentrate (Apple (Light Regular), Fruit Punch, Grape Juice Cocktail, Grapefruit Juice, Lemonade, Limeade, Orange (Regular, w/Calcium), Pineapple, Pink Lemonade)

Juice Cocktail From Concentrate (Cranberry, Cranberry Apple, Cranberry Grape, Cranberry Raspberry, Grapefruit, Lemon, Light Cranberry Raspberry, Ruby Red Grapefruit)

Juice From Concentrate (100% Apple, 100% Unsweetened Prune, 100% White Grape, Apple, Apple Kiwi, Country Style Orange, Lemonade, Light Apple Raspberry, Light Grape Cranberry, Orange Juice, Orange Juice w/Calcium, Pineapple, Pomegranate, Prune Juice, Tomato, Unsweetened Apple Cider, Vegetable)

Strawberry Nutritional Supplement (Plus, Regular)

Vanilla Nutritional Supplement (Plus, Regular)

**D**

**Izze** - All Varieties

**Knudsen** - All Varieties

**Kroger Brand -** Active Lifestyle Drink Sticks, Fruit Juices, In An Instant Drink Powders, Shelf Stable Juices, Vegetable Juice

**Lakewood** - All Organic Juices

**Laura Lynn** - Juices

  Apple

  Cocktail

  Cranberry (Blend, Regular)

  Grape

  Grapefruit

  Lemon

  Light (Cranberry Blends, Fruit Punch)

  Orange Breakfast Drink

  Organic

  Peach

  Prune

  Sports Drink

  Vegetable

  White (Cranberry, Cranberry Blend, Grape)

**Lincoln -** Apple Juice

**Lowes Foods Brand -**

  Juice

    Apple (Natural, Regular)

    Concord Grape

    Cranberry Apple

    Cranberry Cocktail (Light, Regular)

    Cranberry Grape (Light, Regular)

    Cranberry Raspberry

    Grape Cocktail Light

    Lemon (Regular, Squeeze)

**D**

Orange (Regular, Unsweetened)
Pink Grapefruit
Premium Cranberry Cocktail 100% Juice
Prune
Ruby Red Grapefruit Tangerine
Tomato
Vegetable Cocktail
White (Grape, Grapefruit)

**Lucky Leaf** - Apple (Cider, Juice, Premium Juice, Sparkling Cider)
**Manischewitz** - Grape Juice
**Marsh Brand** - Orange Juice Refrigerated
**Meijer Brand** -

100% Juice (Berry, Cherry, Cranberry/Raspberry, Grape, Punch)

Cranberry Juice Drink (Grape, Raspberry, Strawberry, White)

Drink Thirst Quencher (Fruit Punch, Lemon Lime, Orange)

Frozen Concentrate Juice (Apple, Fruit Punch, Grape, Grapefruit, Lemonade, Limeade, Orange, Pink Lemonade, White Grape)

Frozen Concentrate Orange Juice (High Pulp, Pulp Free, w/Calcium)

Fruit Punch (Genuine, Light, Regular)

Juice (Apple, Apple Natural, Cherry, Grape, Grapefruit, Fruit Mix, Lemon, Lime, Pineapple, Pink Grapefruit, Prune, Ruby Red Grapefruit, Tangerine & Ruby Red, White Grape, White Grapefruit)

Juice Blend (Acai & Blueberry, Acai & Grape, Pomegranate & Blueberry, Pomegranate & Cranberry, White Cranberry, White Grape & Raspberry, White Grape & Peach)

Juice Cocktail (Cranapple, Cranberry (Light, Regular), Cranberry Grape (Light, Regular), Cranberry Raspberry (Light, Regular), Cranberry Strawberry, Cranberry White Peach, Light Grape Splenda, Ruby Red Grapefruit (Light, Light 22%, Regular), White Cranberry, White Cranberry Peach, White Cranberry Strawberry, White Grape, White Grapefruit)

Juice Refrigerated Orange (Original, Reconstituted)

Juice Refrigerated Orange Premium (Calcium Carafe, Carafe, Hi Pulp Carafe, Original, Pulp, w/Calcium)

Lemon Juice Squeeze Bottle

Organic Juice (Apple, Concord Grape, Cranberry, Lemonade)

Orange Reconstituted (Original, Pulp, w/Calcium)

Splash (Berry Blend, Strawberry/Kiwi, Tropical Blend)

**Midwest Country Fare** -100 % Unsweetened From Concentrate (Apple Cider, Apple Juice)

**Minute Maid -**

Punch (Berry, Citrus, Fruit, Grape, Tropical)

Lemonade (Light, Original, Pink)

Limonada/Limeade

Orange Juice (Country Style, Heart Wise, Home Squeezed Style, Kids +, Low Acid, Multi Vitamin, Original, Original + Calcium, Pulp Free)

Orange Tangerine

Pomegranate Blueberry

**Mondo -** All Fruit Squeezers

**Mott's -** All Varieties

**Musselman's -** Apple (Cider, Fresh Pressed Apple Cider, Juice, Premium Juice, Sparkling Cider)

**Nantucket Nectars -** All Varieties

**Nestea -** Citrus Green Tea (Diet, Regular), Lemon (Diet, Sweetened), Red Tea, White Tea Berry Honey (Diet, Regular)

**Nestle -** Juicy Juice (All Flavors), Juicy Juice Harvest Surprise (All Flavors)

**Newman's Own -**

Grape Juice

Green Tea w/Honey

Lemonade (Lightly Sweetened, Organic, Pink, Reduced Sugar Pink, Regular)

Lemonade Iced Tea

**D**

Limeade

Orange Mango

Raspberry Kiwi Juice Cocktail

**O Organics** - Bottle Juices (Apple, Berry Blend, Blueberry Blend, Cranberry Cocktail, Grape, Lemonade, Unfiltered Apple), Orange Juice (Refrigerated)

**Ocean Spray** - All Varieties

**Odwalla** - All Juices *(Except Super Protein Vanilla Al Mondo & Superfood)*

**Organic Valley** - Orange Juice (Pulp Added, Pulp Free, w/Calcium)

**Powerade** - Grape, Ion 4, Mountain Blast

**Prairie Farms** -

Flavored Drinks (Blue Raspberry, Fruit Punch, Grape, Lemon, Lemon Lime, Lemonade, Orange, Pink Lemonade)

Orange Juice (Light Pulp Premium, No Pulp, Plus Calcium, Regular)

**Publix** -

From Concentrate

Orange Juice (Regular, w/Calcium)

Ruby Red Grapefruit Juice

Refrigerated

Premium Orange Juice (Calcium Plus, Grove Pure, Old Fashioned, Original)

Premium Ruby Red Grapefruit Juice

Shelf Stable

Apple

Cranberry (Apple Juice Cocktail, Juice Cocktail, Reduced Calorie Cocktail, w/Calcium)

Grape

Grape Cranberry Juice Cocktail

Lemonade (Deli Old Fashion)

Pineapple

Raspberry Cranberry Juice Cocktail

**D**

Ruby Red Grapefruit (Regular, w/Tangerine)

Tomato

White Grape

**Publix GreenWise Market** - Organic (Apple, Cranberry, Grape, Lemonade, Tomato)

**ReaLemon** - 100% Lemon Juice

**ReaLime** - 100% Lime Juice

**Safeway Brand** -

Frozen (Apple, Berry Punch, Cranberry, Grape, Lemonade, Limeade, Orange, Orange Country Style, Orange w/Calcium, Pink Lemonade, Raspberry Lemonade)

Juice

Apple (Cider, Regular)

Cranberry (Apple, Cocktail, Light Cocktail, Light Raspberry, Raspberry)

Grape (Light, Regular)

Grapefruit (Cocktail, Pink, Regular, Ruby Red Cocktail, White)

Lemon

Orange

Prune

Tomato

Vegetable

White Grape

**Shelby's Grove** - Apple Juice 100% Juice

**Simply Apple**

**Simply Grapefruit**

**Simply Lemonade** - Original, w/Raspberry

**Simply Limeade**

**Simply Orange** - Calcium Pulp Free, Country Stand Medium Pulp w/Calcium, Grove Made High Pulp, Original Pulp Free, w/Pineapple Pulp Free, w/Mango Pulp Free

**Snapple** - All Varieties

**D** SoBe -

    Adrenaline Rush (Original, Sugar Free)

    Black & Blue Berry Brew

    Elixir (Cranberry Grapefruit, Orange Carrot)

    Energy

    Green Tea

    Lean Diet (Blackberry Currant, Cranberry Grapefruit, Energy, Green Tea, Mango Melon, Peach Tea)

    Liz Blizz

    Lizard (Fuel, Lava)

    Nirvana

    Power

    Tsunami

    Yummy Pomegranate

**Sonoma Sparkler** - Natural (Peach, Pear, Raspberry), Organic (Apple, Lemonade)

**Spartan Brand** -

    Apple Juice (Natural, Regular)

    Cranberry Juice Cocktail (Low Calorie, Regular)

    Cranberry Juice Drink (Apple, Grape, Raspberry, Strawberry)

    Frozen Concentrate (Apple Juice, Grape Juice Cocktail, Fruit Punch, Grapefruit Juice, Lemonade, Orange Juice (Country Style, Pulp Free, Regular, w/Calcium), Pink Lemonade)

    Grape Juice (Regular, White)

    Grapefruit Juice

    Lemon Juice

    Premium Orange Juice (Country Style Pulp, Regular, w/Calcium)

    Premium Ruby Red Grapefruit

    Prune Juice

    Reconstituted Orange Juice (Country Style Pulp, Regular, w/Calcium)

**D**

Ruby Red Grapefruit Juice

Tomato Juice

Vegetable Juice Cocktail

**Sunny D** - All Varieties

**Thrifty Maid -**

Coolers (Blue Raspberry, Cherry, Fruit Punch, Grape, Lemon Lime, Orange)

Drinks (Fruit Punch, Lemon, Orange, Strawberry)

**Tipton Grove -** Apple Juice 100% Juice

**Trader Joe's -**

All Juices *(Except Green Juice Blend (Fresh) and Green Plant Shelf-Stable)*

Concentrate (Lemon, Orange)

Organic Mango Lemonade

**Tropicana -** All 100% Juices

**V8 -**

Diet Splash (Berry Blend, Tropical Blend)

Splash (Berry Blend, Fruit Medley, Mango Peach, Strawberry Kiwi Blend, Tropical Blend)

Splash Smoothies (Strawberry Banana, Tropical Colada)

V-Fusion (Acai Berry, Goji Raspberry, Passionfruit Tangerine, Peach Mango, Pomegrante Blueberry, Strawberry Banana, Tropical Orange)

V-Fusion Light (Peach Mango, Pomegranate Blueberry, Strawberry Banana)

Vegetable Juice (ACE Vitamin Rich, Calcium Enriched, Fiber, Low Sodium, Organic, Original, Spicy Hot)

**Vitaminwater (Glaceau)** - All Varieties

**Vruit -** Apple Carrot, Berry Veggie, Orange Veggie, Tropical

**Wegmans Brand -**

100% Juice

Cranberry (Blend, Raspberry)

Ruby Red Grapefruit Blend

**D**

Frozen Juice Concentrate
- Apple
- Fruit Punch
- Lemonade
- Limeade
- Pink Lemonade

Juice
- Apple (Natural, Regular)
- Cranberry (Peach, Raspberry, Regular)
- Grape (Juice Cocktail, Regular, White)
- Grapefruit
- Juice Blends (Berry, Cherry, Concord Grape Cranberry, Cranberry Apple, Orange Peach Mango, Ruby Red Grapefruit, Sparkling Cranberry, White Grape Cranberry, White Grape Peach)
- Lemon Juice Reconstituted
- Orange (Regular, Unsweetened)
- Prune
- White Grape (Peach Blend, Raspberry Blend, Regular)

Juice From Concentrate
- 100% Juice (Orange, Tomato, Vegetable (No Salt Added, Regular))
- Blueberry Flavor Juice Blend
- Lemon
- Lemonade
- Limeade
- Orange Juice (Regular, w/Calcium)
- Pomegranate Flavor Juice Blend
- Prune

Organic Juice From Concentrate
- Apple
- Apricot Nectar

**D**

Cranberry

Mango Nectar

Orange

Punch (Berry, Fruit, Pineapple Orange)

Premium 100% Juice

Orange (Extra Pulp, No Pulp, Some Pulp, w/Calcium, w/Calcium & Vitamins)

Ruby Red Grapefruit

Premium Orange Juice (No Pulp, Some Pulp)

Sparkling Beverage

Calorie Free (Lemon, Mandarin Orange, Mixed Berry, Tangerine Lime, Raspberry Lime)

Diet (Black Cherry, Cranberry Raspberry, Key Lime, Kiwi Strawberry, Mixed Berry, Peach, Peach Grapefruit, Tangerine Lime, White Grape)

Lemonade

Sparkling Grape Juice Alcohol Free (Pink, Red, White)

**Welch's -** All Varieties

**Winn & Lovett -** Juice (Black Cherry, Cranberry, Pomegranate)

**Winn Dixie -**

Orange Juice (From Concentrate, From Concentrate w/Calcium, Premium Not From Concentrate)

Juice (Cranberry, Cranberry Apple, Cranberry Raspberry, Light Cranberry, Light Cranberry Grape, Light Grape, Pomegranate Blend, Pomegranate Blueberry Blend, Pomegranate Cranberry Blend, Premium Apple, Reconstituted Lemon, Ruby Red Grapefruit, Ruby Red Grapefruit Cocktail, Vegetable)

Juice From Concentrate (Apple, Apple Cider, Grape, Grapefruit, Prune, Prune w/Pulp, White Grape)

Nectar Drinks (Guava, Mango, Mango Pineapple Guava, Peach, Pear)

Organic Juice (Apple, Cranberry, Grape, Lemonade, Mango Acai Berry Blend, Orange Mango Blend, Tomato)

**D**
**Woodstock Farms** - Non Organic Juices (All Varieties), Organic Juices (All Varieties)
**Yoo Hoo** - All Varieties
**E**
**Zola** - Original, w/Blueberry, w/Pineapple

Duck... *All Fresh Meat Is Gluten-Free (Non-Marinated, Unseasoned)*
**Shelton's** - Duckling
**Wellshire Farms** - Smoked Duck Breast

Duck Sauce
**Lee Kum Kee** - Duck Sauce

Dumplings

**Mixes From The Heartland▲** - Country Dumpling Mix●

# E

Edamame
**365 Every Day Value** - Pods, Shelled Beans (Blanched)
**365 Organic Every Day Value** - Pods, Shelled
**Cascadian Farm** - Organic Frozen (Edamame, Shelled Edamame)
**Imperial** - All Natural Edamame
**Meijer Brand** - Edamame (Soybeans)
**Melissa's** - In Shell
**O Organics** - Frozen
**Safeway Brand** - Edamame
**Stop & Shop Brand** - In Pod
**Sunrich Naturals** - Fiesta Blend, In The Shell, Organic, Shelled
**Trader Joe's** - Dry Roasted
**Woodstock Farms** - Organic Frozen Edamame (Shelled, Whole Pods)
Egg Replacer/Substitute
**Albertsons** - Egg Substitute (Amazing Eggs, Amazing Egg Whites)
**All Whites** - All Varieties

## eggplant

**E**

**Better'n Eggs** - All Varieties

**Eggbeaters** - Garden Vegetable, Original, Southwestern Style

**Eggsactly**

**Ener-G ▲** - Egg Replacer

**Food Club Brand** - Great Egg Spectations

**Harry Ramsdens** - Pickled Eggs

**Horizon Organic** - All Varieties

**Hy-Vee** - Refrigerated Egg Substitute

**Kroger Brand** - Liquid, Powdered

**Laura Lynn** - Egg Starts

**Lucerne** - Best Of The Egg

**Meijer Brand** - Refrigerated Egg Substitute

**NuLaid** - Egg Substitute

**Orgran▲** - No Egg Egg Replacer

**Publix** - Egg Stirs

**Spartan Brand** - Eggmates

**Wegmans Brand** - Egg Busters, Liquid Egg Whites

**Eggnog**

**Hood** - Cinnamon, Gingerbread, Golden, Light, Pumpkin, Sugar Cookie, Vanilla

**Horizon Organic**

**Kroger Brand** - Liquid, Powdered

**Lactaid**

**Prairie Farms** - Regular

**Publix** - Low Fat, Original

**Shamrock Farms** - Light, Regular

**Stop & Shop Brand** - Light, Regular

**Trader Joe's**

**Vitasoy** - Holly Nog

**Eggplant...** *All **Fresh** Fruits & Vegetables Are **Gluten-Free***

**Tasty Bite** - Punjab Eggplant

**E**

**Trader Joe's** - Caponata Appetizer, Garlic Spread, Eggplant Parmesan *(Grilled Not Fried)*

**Eggs...** *All Fresh Eggs Are Gluten-Free*

**Enchilada Sauce**

  **Frontera** - Chipotle Garlic, Classic Red Chile

  **La Victoria** - Green Mild, Red (Hot, Mild)

  **Las Palmas** - Red

  **McCormick** - Enchilada Seasoning Packet

  ~~Old El Paso - Hot, Medium, Mild (NOT Green Chile Mild)~~

  **Safeway Select** - Mild

**Enchiladas**

  **Amy's** -

    Black Bean Vegetable (Light In Sodium, Regular, Whole Meal)

    Cheese (Regular, Whole Meal)

    Santa Fe Enchilada Bowl

  **Cedarlane** - Three Layer Enchilada Pie

  **El Monterey** - Cheese, Spicy Beef

  **Trader Joe's** - Chicken In Salsa Verde, Organic Black Bean & Corn

**Energy Bars... see Bars**

**Energy Drinks**

  **AMP** - Elevate, Lightning, Overdrive, ReLaunch, Sugar Free, Traction, w/Black Tea, w/Green Tea

  **Hansen's** - All Varieties

  **Inko's** - White Tea Energy

  **Monster** - Assault, Hitman (Lobo, Original, Sniper), Import, Java (Chai Hai, Irish Blend, Lo Ball, Loco Moca, Mean Bean, Originale, Russian), Khaos, Lo Carb, M 80, MIXXD, Regular (Green)

  **NOS** - All Varieties

  **No Fear** - Bloodshot, Motherload, Super Energy

  **Red Bull** - Regular, Sugar Free

  **Red Rain** - Diet, Regular

  **Rehab**

**extract**

**E**

**SoBe -** Adrenaline Rush (Original, Sugar Free), Energy, Lean Diet Energy, Lizard Fuel, Power

**Vio -** Vibrancy Drinks

**Vitaminenergy (Glaceau) -** All Varieties

## English Muffins

**Ener-G▲** - Brown Rice English Muffins w/(Flax, Tofu), English Muffins

**Foods By George▲ -**

English Muffins (Cinnamon Currant, No-Rye Rye, Original)

Muffins (Blueberry, Corn)

**Gluten-Free Creations▲** - English Muffins●

**Glutino▲** - Premium English Muffins

**Kinnikinnick▲** - Blueberry, Carrot, Chocolate Chip, Tapioca Rice

## Espresso... see Coffee

## Extract

**365 Organic Every Day Value -** Vanilla Extract

**Albertsons -** Imitation Vanilla, Pure Vanilla

**Durkee -** Vanilla (Imitation, Pure)

**Flavorganics -** Almond, Anise, Caramel, Chocolate, Coconut, Hazelnut, Lemon, Orange, Peppermint, Rum, Vanilla

**Great Value Brand (Wal-Mart) -** Vanilla (Imitation, Pure)

**Hannaford Brand -** Imitation (Almond, Vanilla), Pure (Lemon, Vanilla)

**Hy-Vee -** Imitation Vanilla, Pure

**Kroger Brand -** All Extracts

**Marcin -** Imitation Vanilla, Pure

**Marcum -** Imitation Vanilla, Pure

**McCormick -** Pure Vanilla

**Meijer Brand -** Imitation Vanilla, Vanilla

**Midwest Country Fare -** Imitation Vanilla Flavor

**Nielsen-Massey -** Orange Blossom Water●, Pure (Almond●, Chocolate●, Coffee●, Lemon●, Madagascar Bourbon Vanilla●, Mexican Vanilla●, Orange●, Organic Vanilla●, Peppermint●, Tahitian Vanilla●, Vanilla Extract Blend●), Rose Water●

**E**
**F**

Publix - Almond, Lemon, Vanilla
Spartan Brand - Imitation Vanilla, Vanilla
Spice Island - Vanilla (Imitation, Pure)
Tones - Vanilla (Imitation, Pure)
Trader Joe's - Vanilla (All)
Wegmans Brand - Vanilla Extract

# F

Fajita Seasoning Mix... see also Seasonings
  McCormick - Seasoning Packet
  Old El Paso - Seasoning Mix
  Safeway Brand
Falafel Mix
  Authentic Foods▲
  Orgran▲
Feta Cheese... see Cheese
Fettuccini... see Pasta
Fiber
  Kinnikinnick▲ - Easy White Fiber Mix, Pea Hull Fibre
Fish... *All Fresh Fish Is Gluten-Free (Non-Marinated, Unseasoned)*
  Appa - Smoked Salmon Roulade
  Captain's Choice - Cod Fillets
  Chicken Of The Sea - All Products *(Except Ahi Tuna Steak In Grilled Herb Marinade, Ahi Tuna Steak In Teriyaki Sauce, Crab tastic!, Salmon Steak In Mandarin Orange Glaze, Mandarin Orange Salmon Cups, Teriyaki Tuna Cups, Tuna Salad Kits w/Crackers)*
  Crown Prince - All Varieties
  Dr. Praeger's - All Natural Potato Crusted (Fish Fillets, Fish Sticks, Fishies)
  Full Circle - All Natural (Alaskan Cod Fillets, Alaskan Halibut Steaks,

**F**

Alaskan Sockeye Salmon Fillets, Skinless Mahi Mahi Fillets, Swordfish Steaks, Yellowfin Tuna Steaks)

**Hy-Vee -** Canned Alaskan Pink Salmon, Frozen (Salmon, Tilapia), Red Salmon

**Ian's -** Wheat Free Gluten Free Recipe (Fish Sticks, Lightly Battered Fish)

**Meijer Brand -** Canned Salmon (Pink, Sock Eye Red)

**Morey's -** Wild Alaskan Salmon

**Publix -** Fillets (Bass, Cod, Flounder, Haddock, Halibut, Mahi Mahi, Orange Roughy, Snapper, Swordfish Fillets, Whiting

**Starfish -** Crispy Battered Wild Caught Fish (Cod●, Haddock●, Halibut●)

**Trader Joe's -**

Marinated Ahi Tuna Steaks

Pink Salmon (Skinless/Boneless)

Premium Salmon Patties

Salmon Burger

Seasoned Mahi Mahi Fillets

Skinless Boneless Sardines in Olive Oil

Smoked Salmon

**Ukrop's -** Tilapia (w/Garlic Lemongrass Butter, w/Mango Salsa)

**Wegmans Brand -**

Alaskan Halibut

Atlantic Salmon Fillets (Farm Raised)

Chilean Sea Bass

Lobster Tail

Orange Roughy

Pacific Cod

Smoked Salmon (Nova, Scottish Style)

Sockeye Salmon

Swordfish

Tilapia Fillets (Farm Raised)

Yellowfin Tuna (Sashimi Grade)

**F**

**Whole Catch** - Frozen Fillet (Cod, Mahi Mahi, Sockeye Salmon, Swordfish)

**Winn Dixie** - Frozen (Grouper, Tilapia)

**Fish Sauce**

   **A Taste Of Thai** - Regular

   **Thai Kitchen** - Regular

**Fish Steaks**

   **Crown Prince** - In Lousiana Hot Sauce, In Mustard, w/Green Chilies

   **Ocean Prince** - In Lousiana Hot Sauce, In Oil, w/Green Chilies

**Fish Sticks**

   **Dr. Praeger's** - All Natural Potato Crusted (Fish Sticks, Fishies)

   **Ian's** - Wheat Free Gluten Free Recipe Fish Sticks

**Flan**

   **Kozy Shack** - All Flan

   **Royal** - All Varieties

**Flax Seed**

   **Arrowhead Mills** - Flax Seed Meal, Flax Seeds (Golden, Regular)

   **Bob's Red Mill▲** - Flaxseed Meal (Golden, Original), Organic Flaxseed (Golden, Original)

   **Hodgson Mill▲** - Brown Milled, Organic Golden Milled, Travel Flax All Natural Milled, Travel Flax Organic Golden Milled, Whole Grain Brown

   **Nature's Path** -

      Organic FlaxPlus Meal

      Organic FlaxPlus Flaxseeds

   **Shiloh Farms** - Golden Flax Seeds, Real Cold Milled Flax Meal

   **Spectrum** - Organic Ground Essential Flax Seed

   **Trader Joe's** - Golden Roasted (Flax Seed w/Blueberries, Whole)

**Flax Seed Oil... see Oil**

**Flour**

   **AgVantage Naturals▲** - Master Blend●, Millet Flour●, Premium Fine Milled Sorghum Flour●, Quinoa Flour●, Rice Flour●

**Amazing Grains** - Montina (All Purpose Flour Blend●, Pure Baking Flour Supplement●)

**Andrea's Fine Foods▲** - Gluten Free Flour Blend, Super Fine Grind Rice (Brown, Sweet)

**Arrowhead Mills** - All Purpose Baking Mix, Brown Rice, Organic (Buckwheat, Millet, Soy, White Rice)

**Authentic Foods▲** -

Almond Meal

Arrowroot

Bette's Flour Blend (Featherlight Rice, Four)

Brown Rice Flour Superfine

Garbanzo

Garfava

Gluten Free Classical Blend

Multi Blend Gluten Free

Potato (Flour, Starch)

Sorghum

Sweet Rice Flour Superfine

Tapioca

White (Corn, Rice Flour Superfine)

**Better Batter** - Gluten Free All Purpose Flour

**Bob's Red Mill▲** -

Almond Meal/Flour

Black Bean

Brown Rice

Fava Bean

Garbanzo & Fava

Garbanzo Bean

Gluten Free (All Purpose Baking, Sweet White Sorghum)

Green Pea

Hazelnut Meal/Flour

Millet

**F**

    Organic (Amaranth, Brown Rice, Coconut, Quinoa, White Rice)

    Potato

    Sweet White Rice

    Tapioca

    Teff

    White (Bean, Rice)

**Celiac Specialties▲** - Flour Blend

**Chateau Cream Hill Estates** - Lara's Whole Grain Oat Flour●

**ConAgra Mills** -

    5 Grain Whole Grain Blend●

    Conventional (Amaranth Seed●, Millet Seed●, Quinoa Seed●, Sorghum Seed●, Teff Seed●, Whole Amaranth Flour●, Whole Millet Flour●, Whole Quinoa Flour●, Whole Sorghum Flour●, Whole Teff Flour●)

    Organic (Amaranth Seed●, Millet Seed●, Quinoa Seed●, Whole Amaranth Flour●, Whole Millet Flour●, Whole Quinoa Flour●)

**Deerfields Bakery▲** - Quick Mix For Sugar Buttons

**Domata** - Gluten Free All Purpose Flour●

**Dowd & Rogers▲** - California Almond, Italian Chestnut

**El Peto▲** - All Purpose Flour Mix, Arrowroot, Bean, Brown Rice, Corn, Flax Seed, Garbanzo Fava Bean, Millet, Organic Amaranth, Potato, Quinoa, Sorghum, Soya, Sweet Rice, Tapioca Starch, White Rice

**Ener-G ▲**

    Brown Rice

    Gluten Free Gourmet Blend

    Potato (Flour, Starch)

    Sweet Rice

    Tapioca

    White Rice

**Expandex▲** - Modified Tapioca Starch●

**Flour Nut** - Almond Flour

**F**

**Gillian's Foods▲ -**

Brown Rice

Chick Pea

Imported Tapioca

Potato (Regular, Starch)

Rice

**Glutano▲ -** Flour Mix It!

**Gluten Free Mama▲ -** Almond Blend●, Coconut Blend●

**Gluten-Free Creations -** Baking Flours (Basic, Enriched, Sweet)

**Gluten-Free Pantry▲ -** Beth's All Purpose Gluten Free Baking Flour

**Hodgson Mill -** Soy Flour (Brown Rice, Buckwheat, Organic, Regular)

**Jules Gluten Free▲ -** All Purpose Flour●

**Kinnikinnick▲ -**

All Purpose Celiac

Brown Rice

Corn

Soya

Sweet Rice

White Rice

**Laurel's Sweet Treats ▲-** Baking Flour Mix

**Lotus Foods -** Bhutanese Red Rice Flour

**Lundberg▲ -** Brown Rice Flour (California Nutra Farmed, Organic California)

**Meister's Gluten Free Mixtures▲ -** All Purpose Gluten Free Flour●

**Montana Monster Munchies -** Whole Grain Oat Flour●

**Montina -** All Purpose Baking Flour Blend, Pure Baking Supplement

**Namaste Foods▲ -** Perfect Flour Blend

**Nu-World Foods -** Amaranth (Flour●, Pre Gel Powder●, Toasted Bran Flour●)

**Only Oats -** Oat Flour●

**Organ▲ -** All Purpose Pastry Mix, Gluten Substitute, Plain All Purpose, Self Raising

**F**

**Pocono** - Buckwheat

**Ruby Range** - Mesquite, Ruby Range Mix (Basic, Flour, Spice), Teff

**Shiloh Farms** - Almond, Brown Rice, Corn, Mesquite, Potato, Quinoa, Tapioca, Teff

**Sylvan Border Farm** - General Purpose Flour

**Twin Valley Mills ▲** - Sorghum

**Food Coloring**

**Durkee**

**Great Value Brand (Wal-Mart)**

**Hy-Vee** - Assorted

**Kroger Brand** - Food Colors

**McCormick** - All Varieties

**Safeway Brand** - Assorted

**Spice Islands**

**Tones**

**Frankfurters... see Sausage**

**French Fries**

**Alexia Foods** -

    Crispy Potatoes w/Seasoned Salt Waffle Fries

    Julienne Fries (Spicy Sweet Potato, Sweet Potato, w/Sea Salt Yukon Gold)

    Olive Oil & Sea Salt Oven Fries

    Olive Oil Rosemary & Garlic Oven Fries

    Olive Oil Parmesan & Roasted Garlic Oven Reds

    Olive Oil Sun Dried Tomatoes & Pesto Oven Reds

    Organic (Classic Oven Crinkles, Oven Crinkles Onion & Garlic, Oven Crinkles Salt & Pepper, Yukon Gold Julienne Fries w/Sea Salt)

    Yukon Gold Potatoes w/Seasoned Salt Potato Nuggets

**Cascadian Farm** - Organic Frozen (Country Style Potatoes, Crinkle Cut French Fries, Shoe String Fries, Spud Puppies, Straight Cut French Fries, Wedge Cut Oven Fries)

**Chester's** - Flamin' Hot Flavored Fries

**Funster -** Natural Potato Letters

**Home Harvest Brand -** Frozen French Fries

**Ian's -** Alphatots

**Lowes Foods Brand -** Crinkle Cut, Shoestring, Steak Cut

**Meijer Brand -** Crinkle Cut, Original, Shoestring, Steak Cut

**Ore-Ida -**

Frozen

Cottage Fries

Country Style Steak Fries

Crispers

Extra Crispy (Crinkle Cut, Fast Food Fries, Seasoned Crinkle Cut)

Fast Food Fries

Golden (Crinkles, Crinkles 8 lb. (Costco Only, Sam's Club Only), Fries)

Pixie Crinkles

Potato Wedges w/Skins

Seasoned French Fries (8 lb. Sam's Club only)

Shoestrings

Steak Fries

Waffle Fries

Zesties

**Publix -** Frozen (Crinkle Cut Fries, Extra Crispy Fries, Golden Fries (Fast Food Style, Regular), Original Cut Fries, Shoestring Fries, Southern Style Hash Browns, Steak Fries, Tater Bites)

**Spartan Brand -** Frozen Shoestring

**Woodstock Farms -** Organic Frozen (Crinkle Cut Oven Fries, Shredded Hash Browns, Tastee Taters)

**French Toast**

**Ian's -** Wheat Free Gluten Free Recipe French Toast Sticks

**Van's -** Wheat Free French Toast Sticks

**Frosting... see Baking Decorations & Frostings**

**F** Frozen Desserts... see Ice Cream
Frozen Dinners... see Meals
Frozen Vegetables... see Mixed Vegetables
Frozen Yogurt... see Ice Cream
Fruit Bars... see Bars
Fruit Cocktail
   **Albertsons** - (Heavy Syrup, Light)
   **Del Monte** -
      Canned/Jarred Fruit (All Varieties)
      Fruit Snack Cups (Metal, Plastic)
   **Food Club Brand** - In Heavy Syrup, Lite
   **Great Value Brand (Wal-Mart)** - Fruit Cocktail (In Heavy Syrup,
     Sweetened w/Splenda)
   **Hy-Vee** - Lite, Regular
   **Meijer Brand** - Heavy Syrup, In Juice, In Pear Juice Lite
   **Midwest Country Fare**
   **Laura Lynn** - Canned
   **Lowes Foods Brand** - In Heavy Syrup, In Juice
   **Publix** - Canned (In Heavy Syrup, Lite In Pear Syrup)
   **Safeway Brand** - Canned (Lite, Regular)
   **Spartan Brand** - Heavy Syrup, Light Juice
   **Stop & Shop Brand** - Heavy Syrup, Pear Juice, Splenda
   **Wegmans Brand** - In Heavy Syrup, In Pear Juice
   **Winn Dixie** - Fruit Cocktail (Heavy Syrup, Light Syrup)
Fruit Drinks... see Drinks/Juice
Fruit Leather...see also Fruit Snacks
   **Fruit Flip**
   **Stretch Island Fruit Co.** - All Varieties
   **Trader Joe's** - All Varieties
Fruit Salad
   **Meijer Brand** - Tropical

**Native Forest** - Organic Tropical

**Safeway Brand** - Tropical Fruit

**Fruit Snacks... see also Snacks**

**Albertsons** - Fruit Snacks

**Annie's** - Organic Bunny Fruit Snacks (Berry Patch, Tropical Treat)

**Brothers All Natural▲** - Fruit Crisps (Asian Pear, Banana, Fuji Apple, Pineapple, Strawberry, Strawberry Banana, White & Yellow Peach)

**Food Club Brand** - Fruit Snacks (Curious George, Dinosaurs, Sharks, Variety Pack)

**Fruit By The Foot -**

Berry Berry Twist

Berry Tie Dye

Color By The Foot

Flavor Kickers (Berry Blast, Tropical Twist)

Mini Feet (Berry Wave)

Razzle Blue Blitz

Strawberry

Variety Pack (Berry Tie Dye, Color By The Foot, Strawberry)

Watermelon

**Fruit Flavored Snacks -**

Batman

Care Bears

Create A Bug

Create A Dino

Looney Tunes

My Little Pony

Scooby Doo

Shark Bites

Spiderman

Teenage Mutant Ninja Turtles

Tonka

Transformers

**F**

**Fruit Gushers -**
  Passion Berry Punch
  Punch Berry
  Rockin' Blue Raspberry
  Strawberry Splash
  Triple Berry Shock
  Tropical Flavors
  Variety Pack (Strawberry Splash, Tropical Flavors, Watermelon Blast)
  Watermelon Blast
**Fruit Roll-Ups -**
  Berry Berry Cool
  Blastin' Berry Hot Colors
  Crazy Pix (Cool Chix Berry Wave, Wild Ones Blastin' Berry)
  Electric Blue Raspberry
  Flavor Wave
  Strawberry (Kiwi Kick, Regular)
  Stickerz (Berry Cool Punch, Stars Mixed Berry, Twisters Tropical Berry)
  Tropical Tie Dye
  Variety Pack (Cherry Orange Wildfire, Strawberry, Tropical Tie Dye)
**Great Value Brand (Wal-Mart) -** Fruit Smiles
**Kroger Brand**
**Laura Lynn -** Fruit Snacks (Aliens, Animal, Creapy, Dinosaur)
**Nonuttin' Foods▲ -** Fruit Snacks
**Publix -** Fruit Snacks (Curious George, Dinosaurs, Sharks, Snoopy,
  Veggie Tales)
**Safeway Brand -** Assorted, Creatures, Fruity Shapes, Strawberry,
  Yogurty Fruit Snacks
**Spartan Brand -** Curious George, Dinosaurs, Fruit Rolls (Strawberry,
  Wild Berry), Justice League, Rescue Heroes, Sharks
**Welch's -** All Varieties
**Fruit Spread... see Jam/Jelly... see Spread**

**F**
**G**

## Fudge

**Katy Sweet▲** - Fudge (Pecan●, Plain●, Walnut●), Organic Fudge (Pecan●, Plain●, Walnut●)

# G

**Gai Lan...** *All Fresh Fruits & Vegetables Are Gluten-Free*

**Garbanzo Beans... see Beans**

**Garlic...** *All Fresh Garlic Is Gluten-Free*

**Earthbound Farm -** Organic Chopped Garlic

**Lee Kum Kee -** Minced

**Trader Joe's -** Crushed

**Garlic Powder... see Seasonings**

**Garlic Salt... see Seasonings**

**Gelatin**

**Food Club Brand** - All Regular & Sugar Free Flavors

**Great Value Brand (Wal-Mart) -**

Cherry (Regular, Sugar Free)

Lemon (Regular)

Lime (Regular, Sugar Free)

Orange (Regular, Sugar Free)

Peach (Regular, Sugar Free)

Raspberry (Sugar Free)

Strawberry (Regular, Sugar Free)

Strawberry Banana (Sugar Free)

**Hannaford Brand -**

Fat Free (Cherry, Orange, Raspberry)

Sugar Free (Cherry, Lime, Orange, Raspberry)

**Hy-Vee -**

Gelatin (Berry Blue, Cherry, Cranberry, Lemon, Lime, Orange, Raspberry, Strawberry, Strawberry Banana)

**G**

Sugar Free (Cherry, Cranberry, Lime, Orange, Raspberry, Strawberry)

**Jell-O -**

Regular Instant (Apricot, Berry Blue, Black Cherry, Blackberry Fusion, Cherry, Cranberry, Grape, Island Pineapple, Lemon, Lime, Margarita, Melon Fusion, Orange, Peach, Pina Colada, Raspberry, Strawberry (Banana, Daquiri, Kiwi, Regular), Tropical Fusion, Watermelon, Wild Strawberry)

Sugar Free Low Calorie (Black Cherry, Cherry, Cranberry, Lemon, Lime, Mixed Fruit, Orange, Peach, Raspberry, Strawberry (Banana, Kiwi, Regular))

Snack Cups (Strawberry, Strawberry/Orange, Strawberry/Raspberry)

Sugar Free Snack Cups (Cherry/Black Cherry, Lime/Orange, Peach/Watermelon, Raspberry/Orange, Strawberry, Strawberry Kiwi/ Tropical Berry)

**Jelly Belly -** All Varieties

**Kroger Brand -** Flavored, Plain, Snack Cups

**Laura Lynn -** Gelatins RTE Dairy (All Items)

**Meijer Brand -**

Gelatin Dessert (Berry Blue, Cherry, Cranberry, Grape, Lime, Orange, Raspberry, Strawberry, Unflavored, Wild Strawberry)

Sugar Free Gelatin Dessert (Cherry, Cranberry, Lime, Orange, Raspberry, Strawberry)

**Publix -** Sugar Free (Black Cherry/Cherry, Raspberry/Orange, Strawberry)

**Royal -** All Varieties

**Spartan Brand -** Berry Blue, Cherry (Regular, Sugar Free), Lemon, Lime (Regular, Sugar Free), Orange (Regular, Sugar Free), Raspberry (Regular, Sugar Free), Strawberry (Regular, Sugar Free), Unflavored

**Stop & Shop Brand -**

Gelatin (Cherry, Cranberry, Orange, Raspberry)

Refrigerated (Gelatin Fun Pack, Rainbow Fruit Gelatin)

Refrigerated Sugar Free Gelatin Fun Pack

**Wegmans Brand -**
Strawberry
Sugar Free (Cherry & Black Cherry, Lemon Lime & Orange,
Orange & Raspberry, Strawberry)

**Gin...** *All **Distilled** Alcohol Is **Gluten-Free** [2]

**Ginger**
**Lee Kum Kee** - Minced Ginger
**Wel-Pac** - Sushi Ginger

**Ginger Ale... see Soda Pop/Carbonated Beverages**

**Glaze**
**Daddy Sam's** - Salmon Glaze
**Litehouse** - Dessert Glaze (Peach, Strawberry, Sugar Free Strawberry)
**San-J** - Gluten Free Sweet & Tangy Polynesian Glazing & Dipping
Sauce
**Spartan Brand** - All Pie Glazes
**T. Marzetti** - Fruit Glaze (Blueberry, Peach, Strawberry, Sugar Free
Strawberry)

**Graham Crackers**
**Grainless Bakery** - Gluten Free Graham Crackers
**Jo-Sef** - Graham Crackers (Chocolate, Cinnamon, Vanilla)
**Jules Gluten Free▲** - Graham Cracker/Gingersnap Mix●
**Kinnikinnick▲** - Graham Style Cracker Crumbs
**Laurel's Sweet Treats ▲**- Honey Grahamless Crackers

**Grains**
**Arrowhead Mills** - Amaranth, Hulled Millet, Quinoa
**Bob's Red Mill▲** - Organic Amaranth, Quinoa Organic, Teff Whole
**Eden Organic** - Brown Rice Flakes, Buckwheat, Millet, Quinoa, Red
Quinoa, Wild Rice)
**Shiloh Farms** - Millet Grain, Sorghum Grain

**Granola**
**Bakery On Main** - Gluten Free Granola (Apple Raisin Walnut,
Cranberry Orange Cashew, Extreme Fruit & Nut, Nutty Maple
Cranberry, Rainforest)

**G**   Enjoy Life▲ - Granola Crunch (Cinnamon●, Cranapple●, Very Berry●)

Gluten Free Sensations - Apple Crisp, Cherry Vanilla Almond,
   Cranberry Pecan, French Vanilla Almond

Goraw - Granola (Apple Cinnamon●, Live●, Live Chocolate●, Simple●)

Kookie Karma - All Varieties●

Madwoman Foods▲ - Nutty Granola

Nonuttin' Foods▲ - Granola Clusters Vanilla (Caramel, Cinnamon)

Rose's Bakery ▲ - All Varieties●

Trader Joe's - Gluten Free Granola

Whole Foods Market Gluten Free Bakehouse ▲ - Fruit & Nut Granola

Grapefruit... *All **Fresh** Fruits & Vegetables Are **Gluten-Free**

Del Monte -

   Canned/Jarred Fruit (All Varieties)

   Fruit Snack Cups (Metal, Plastic)

Meijer Brand - Sections (In Juice, In Syrup)

Winn Dixie - Canned

Grapes... *All **Fresh** Fruits & Vegetables Are **Gluten-Free**

Gravy/Gravy Mix

Barkat - Vegetable Gravy

Emeril's - Sicilian Gravy Pasta Sauce

Full Flavor Foods▲ - Gravy (Beef●, Chicken●, Pork●, Turkey●)

Glutino▲ - Brown Gravy Base

Lawry's - Turkey Gravy

Massel - Gravy Mix (Chicken Style, Supreme)

Maxwell's Kitchen - Gravy Mix (Brown Beef, Chicken, Pork, Turkey)

Mayacamas - Brown, Chicken, Savory Herb, Turkey

Orgran▲ - Gravy Mix

Road's End Organics - Organic Gravy Mix (Golden, Savory Herb,
   Shitake Mushroom)

Trader Joe's - All Natural Turkey Gravy

Green Beans... see Beans

Green Olives... see Olives

**G**

**Green Peppers...** *All **Fresh** Fruits & Vegetables Are **Gluten-Free***
**Green Tea... see Tea**
**Greens...** *All **Fresh** Fruits & Vegetables Are **Gluten-Free***
   **Albertsons** - Canned & Frozen Turnip Greens
   **Birds Eye** - All Plain Frozen Vegetables *(Except With Sauce)*
   **Bush's Best** - Chopped (Collard, Kale, Mixed, Mustard, Turnip, Turnip w/Diced Turnips)
   **C & W** - All Plain Frozen Vegetables
   **Great Value Brand (Wal-Mart)** - Canned Greens (Collard, Mustard, Turnip)
   **Laura Lynn** - Canned (Chopped Collard Greens, Chopped Mustard Greens, Turnip Greens, Turnip Greens w/Diced Turnips), Mustard Greens
   **Lowes Foods Brand** - Frozen (Chopped Collard, Turnip Greens)
   **Meijer Brand** - Canned Chopped (Kale, Mustard, Turnip), Chopped (Collards, Kale, Mustard, Turnip)
   **Pictsweet** - All Plain Vegetables (Frozen)
   **Publix** - Frozen (Collard Chopped, Turnip Chopped, Turnip w/Diced Turnips)
   **Spartan Brand** - Chopped (Collard, Mustard, Turnip)
   **Stop & Shop Brand** - Collard Greens, Mustard Greens
   **Trader Joe's** - All Plain Vegetables (Frozen)
   **Winn Dixie** -
      Canned (Collard No Salt, Mustard, Turnip)
      Frozen (Collard Greens Chopped, Mustard Greens, Steamable Mixed Vegetables)
**Grits**
   **Bob's Red Mill▲** - Gluten Free Corn Grits/Polenta, Soy Grits
   **Food Club** - Instant Grits
   **Meijer Brand** - Butter Flavored Instant, Quick
**Groats**
   **Arrowhead Mills** - Buckwheat

**G**

Chateau Cream Hill Estates - Lara's Oat Groats●

Montana Monster Munchies - Raw & Sproutable Oat Groats●

**H**

Pocono - Whole Buckwheat

Ground Beef... see Beef

*All Fresh Meat Is Gluten-Free (Non-Marinated, Unseasoned)*

Ground Turkey... see Turkey

*All Fresh Meat Is Gluten-Free (Non-Marinated, Unseasoned)*

Guacamole... see also Dip/Dip Mix

Calavo

Fischer & Wieser - Just Add Avocados Guacamole Starter

Ortega - Guacamole Mix

Publix

Santa Barbara

T. Marzetti

Trader Joe's - All Varieties

Guar Gum

AgVantage Naturals▲

Bob's Red Mill▲

Gluten-Free Essentials▲●

Kinnikinnick▲

Gum... see Chewing Gum

# H

Half & Half... see Milk

Halibut ...see Fish

Ham

Applegate Farms - Natural (Black Forest, Honey, Slow Cooked), Organic Uncured Ham

Bar S -

Classic Chopped

Deli Shaved (Black Forest, Honey, Smoked)

Deli Style (Honey, Low Fat, Smoked)

Deli Thin Cut (Honey, Smoked)

Extra Lean Cooked

Steaks (Honey, Smoked)

Premium Deli (Honey, Smoked)

**Black Label -** Canned Hams

**Boar's Head -** All Varieties

**Butcher's Cut -** 95% Fat Free Cooked Ham, Preglazed Spiral Sliced, Shank Cut Ham, Spiral Sliced *(Glazed Packet Is Not Gluten Free)*

**Carl Buddig -** All Meat Products

**Celebrity -** Healthy Ham

**Cure 81**

**Dietz & Watson -**

Black Forest Smoked w/Natural Juices

Breakfast Ham Slices w/Water Added

Brown Sugar & Molasses w/Natural Juices

Capocolla

Chef Carved Pre Sliced Honey Cured & Glazed

Classic Trimmed & Tied w/Natural Juices

Gourmet Lite (Tavern, Virginia Baked)

Ham Steak w/Natural Juices

Honey (Cured Dinner w/Natural Juices, Cured Tavern w/Natural Juices, Cured w/Natural Juices)

Imported (Prosciuttini Italian Style, w/Water Added)

Prosciutto (Classico Trimmed, Regular)

Rosemary

Semi Boneless Smoked w/Natural Juices

Spiral Sliced

Tavern w/Water Added

Tiffany Boneless w/Natural Juices

Tomato & Basil

Virginia Baked w/Water Added

**H** Farmer John -

Bone In Ham Premium (Butt & Shank Portions, Gold Wrap, Half, Sliced Ham Steaks, Spiral Sliced, Spiral Sliced Half)

Bone In Ham Whole

Boneless Ham (Canless Honey Ham, Flat Tavern Half, Golden Tradition, Golden Tradition Premium Black Forest, Golden Tradition Premium Original Whole & Half, Golden Tradition Premium Brown Sugar & Honey, Pee Wee Half)

Ham Steaks (Clove, Maple, Original, Pineapple & Mango, Smoked)

Lunch Meats Ham (Black Forest, Brown Sugar & Honey, Chopped, Ham Roll, Sliced Cooked)

**Five Star Brand -** Bavarian, Cottage Ham, Golden Hickory, Honey Cured, Lower Sodium Vermont, Spiced Cello

**Garrett County Farms -**

Black Forest Boneless Nugget

Deli (Black Forest, Virginia)

Sliced (Black Forest, Breakfast Virgina Brand (Boneless Ham Steak, Deli Ham), Turkey Ham (Ham Steak, Original))

**Giant Eagle Brand -**

Bavarian

Bone In Ham Steak

Boneless (Half, Quarter, Steak, Whole)

Deli Shaved Extra Lean (Black Forest, Honey, Smoked)

Extra Lean Cooked

Gourmet (Half, Whole)

Half (Semi Boneless, Spiral Bone In)

Honey

Maple

Off The Bone

Premium Hot

Spiral Sliced Half

Virginia

Whole (Semi Boneless, Spiral Bone In)

**Girgenti** - Hot Ham Capicola

**Great Value Brand (Wal-Mart) -**

Deli Meat

97% Fat Free (Baked Ham Water Added, Cooked Ham, Honey Ham Water Added)

Thinly Sliced Smoked (Ham, Honey Ham)

**Healthy Choice** - Honey Maple, Virginia

**Hillshire Farms -**

Deli Select Thin Sliced (Brown Sugar Baked Ham, Smoked Ham)

Deli Select Ultra Thin (Brown Sugar Baked Ham, Honey Ham)

**Hormel -**

Black Label (Canned, Chopped)

Chunk Meats Ham

Deli Sliced (Black Forest, Cooked, Double Smoked, Honey, Prosciutto)

Diced

Ham Patties

Julienne

Natural Choice Ham (Cooked Deli, Honey Deli, Smoked Deli)

**Hy-Vee -**

Deli Thin Slices (Honey, Smoked)

Ham & Cheese Loaf

Thin Sliced (Ham w/Natural Juices, Honey Ham w/Natural Juices)

**Isaly's** - All Deli Meat

**Jennie-O** - Refrigerated Turkey Ham (Honey Cured, Regular)

**Jones Dairy Farm**

Dainty Ham Smoked (Cherrywood●, Hickory Wood●)

Deli Style Ham Slices (Honey & Brown Sugar●, Old Fashioned Cured●)

Family Ham (Half●, Whole●)

Old Fashioned Whole Hickory Smoked Ham●

**H**

Semi Boneless Spiral Carved Whole Ham Hickory Smoked●

Skinless Shankless (Spiral Carved Half Ham Hickory Smoked●, Whole & Half Ham Hickory Smoked●)

Slices●

Steak (Cherrywood Smoked●, Regular●)

Whole Fully Cooked (Hickory Smoked●, Semi-Boneless●)

**Kayem** - Deli Ham (Amber Honey Cured, Black Forest, Carving, Honey Pear Shape Baked, Maple Carving, Olde English Tavern, Peppercrust)

**Krakus** - Imported Polish Ham

**Meijer Brand** -

97% Fat Free (Honey Ham, Sliced Cooked Ham)

Double Smoked

Honey Roasted

Sliced Chipped

**Nature's Basket** - Applewood Smoked

**Oscar Mayer** -

Deli Fresh Meats (Cooked Ham (96% Fat Free, Regular), Honey Ham, Smoked Ham)

Shaved Deli Fresh Meats (Black Forest Ham, Brown Sugar Ham, Honey Ham, Smoked Ham, Virginia Brand Ham)

Thin Sliced Deli Fresh (97% Fat Free Smoked Ham, Brown Sugar Ham)

**Primo Taglio** - Black Forest Ham w/Natural Juices, Maple Ham Old Fashioned, Prosciutto Dry Cured Ham

**Publix** -

Deli Pre Pack Lunch Meat (Cooked Ham, Extra Thin Sliced Honey Ham, Low Salt Ham, Sweet Ham, Tavern Ham, Virginia Brand Ham)

Deli Salad Ham

Hickory Smoked Ham (Semi Boneless, Fully Cooked)

Honey Cured Ham w/Brown Sugar Glaze (Bone In Ham, Boneless Ham)

**Russer** - Reduced Sodium Cooked, Virginia

**Safeway Brand** - Boneless Honey

**Smithfield** - All Spiral & Glazed Hams *(Except HEB Private Label Glaze)*, Boneless Ham, Ham Steak, Quarter Ham

**SPAM** - Classic, Less Sodium, Lite, Oven Roasted Turkey, Smoke Flavored

**Spartan Brand** - Frozen Ham Loaf, Whole Boneless

**Stop & Shop Brand** -
Cooked Ham (97% Fat Free, w/Natural Juices 98% Fat Free)
Danish Brand Ham w/Natural Juices 97% Fat Free

**Trader Joe's** - Spiral w/Glaze Pack

**Ukrop's** - Virginia Style Ham

**Underwood Spreads** - Deviled

**Wegmans Brand** - 97% Fat Free, Boneless Brown Sugar Cured, Ham Slices Boneless, Maple Cured, Old Fashioned Off The Bone (Brown Sugar Cured Ham, Double Smoked Ham), Organic Uncured, Thin Shaved (Ham, Honey Maple Flavored Ham, Smoked Ham, Smoked Honey Ham), Virginia Baked

**Wellshire Farms** -
Black Forest (Boneless Nugget, Deli, Sliced)
Buffet Half
Glazed Boneless (Half, Spiral Sliced Half, Spiral Sliced Whole)
Old Fashioned Boneless (Half, Whole)
Semi Boneless (Half, Whole)
Sliced (Breakfast, Tavern)
Smoked Ham (Hocks, Shanks)
Top Round Ham Boneless
Turkey Half Ham
Virginia Brand (Boneless Steak, Buffet, Deli, Nugget Honey, Quarter, Sliced)

**Hamburger Buns... see Buns**

**Hamburgers... see Burgers...** *All Fresh Meat Is Gluten-Free (Non-Marinated, Unseasoned)*

**H** Hash Browns... see Potatoes

Hearts Of Palm... *All Fresh Fruits & Vegetables Are Gluten-Free*
  Del Monte - All Canned Vegetables
  Native Forest - Organic Hearts Of Palm
  Trader Joe's - All Varieties

Herbal Tea... see Tea

Hoisin Sauce
  Premier Japan - Wheat Free
  Wok Mei

Hollandaise Sauce
  Mayacamas - Gourmet Sauce

Hominy
  Bush's Best - Golden, White
  Great Value Brand (Wal-Mart) - Canned (White, Yellow)
  Hy-Vee - Golden, White
  Lowes Foods Brand - White
  Meijer Brand - White
  Safeway Brand - Golden, White
  Spartan Brand - Gold, White
  Winn Dixie - Golden, White

Honey
  Albertsons - Honey
  Bramley's - Golden
  Full Circle - Organic 100% Pure Honey
  Great Value Brand (Wal-Mart) - Clover Honey
  Hannaford Brand - Pure Clover
  Home Harvest Brand - Pure Clover, Squeeze Bear
  Hy-Vee - Honey, Honey Squeeze Bear
  Lowes Foods Brand - Honey
  Meijer Brand - Honey, Honey Squeeze Bear
  Publix - Clover, Orange Blossom

## hot sauce

**H**

   **Publix GreenWise Market** - Organic Honey
   **Safeway Brand** - Pure
   **Safeway Select**
   **Spartan Brand**
   **Trader Joe's** - Honey (All)
   **Virginia Brand** - 100% All Natural
   **Wegmans Brand** - 100% Pure Clover, Clover, Orange Blossom, Squeezable Bear
Honey Mustard Sauce... see Mustard
Horseradish Sauce
   **Baxters**
   **Di Lusso**
   **Dietz & Watson** - Cranberry, Hot & Chunky, Smokey
   **Heinz** - Horseradish Sauce
   **Hy-Vee** - Prepared Horseradish
   **Lou's Famous** - Horseradish (Creamy, Regular)
   **Manischewitz** - All Varieties
   **Simply Delicious** - Organic Creamed Horseradish
   **T. Marzetti** - Horseradish Veggie Dip
   **Wegmans Brand** - Horseradish Cream, Prepared Horseradish
Hot Chocolate Mix... see Cocoa Mix
Hot Dog Buns... see Buns
Hot Dogs... see Sausage
Hot Sauce
   **Bone Suckin'** - Habanero Sauce
   **Food Club Brand** - Hot Sauce
   **Frank's RedHot** - Chile 'N Lime, Original, Xtra Hot
   **Frontera** - Hot Sauce (Chipotle, Habanero, Jalapeno, Red Pepper)
   **Gifts of Nature▲** - Sriracha Hot Sauce
   **Great Value Brand (Wal-Mart)** - Louisiana Hot Sauce
   **La Victoria** - Jalapeno, Salsa Brava

**H**

**Mr. Spice Organic** - Tangy Bang! Hot

**Santa Barbara** - Pepper Sauce (Original Blend California, Taco Style California)

**Texas Pete** - Garlic, Hotter Hot, Original

**The Wizard's** - Hot Stuff

**Trader Joe's** - Jalapeno Hot

**Trappey** - Hot Sauce

**Winn Dixie** - Louisiana (Extra Hot, Hot)

Hummus

Athenos -

Hummus

Artichoke & Garlic

Black Olive

Cucumber Dill

Greek Style

Original

Pesto

Roasted (Eggplant, Garlic, Red Pepper)

Scallion

Spicy Three Pepper

NeoClassic Hummus

Original

Original w/Sesame Seeds & Parsley

Roasted Garlic w/Garlic & Parsley

Roasted Red Pepper w/Red Peppers & Parsley

**Casbah Natural Foods** - Hummus

**Fantastic World Foods** - Original Hummus

**T. Marzetti** - Original, Roasted Garlic, Roasted Red Pepper

**Trader Joe's** - All Varieties *(Except White Bean and White Bean & Basil)*

**Tribe Mediterranean Foods** - All Natural Hummus (All Varieties)

**Wegmans** - Regular

**Wild Garden** - Black Olive, Fire Roasted Red Pepper, Jalapeno, Red Hot Chili Pepper, Roasted Garlic, Sundried Tomato, Sweet Pepper, Traditional

# I

## Ice Cream... (includes Frozen Desserts, Frozen Yogurt, Sherbet, Sorbet)

**Albertsons** - Sherbet (Lime, Orange, Rainbow)

**Chapman's** -

Blueberry Cheesecake

Butterscotch Ripple

Canadian Vanilla, Eh!

Cherry Vanilla

Chocolate (& Vanilla, Caramel, Ripple)

Dutch Chocolate

French Vanilla

Maple Twist

Mint Chip

Neapolitan

Orange (Pineapple, Sorbet)

Rainbow Sorbet

Raspberry (Ripple, Sorbet)

Rum & Raisin

Strawberry (Banana, Regular)

Swiss Mocca

Tiger Tail

Vanilla

Vanilla Chip

**Cool Fruits** - Fruit Juice Freezers (Grape & Cherry, Sour Apple)

**Double Rainbow Sorbet** - Chocolate, Lemon, Mango Tangerine

**Dove** -
>   Dark Chocolate Ice Cream Bar With (Almonds, Chocolate, Vanilla Ice)
>   Milk Chocolate Ice Cream Bar With Vanilla Ice

**Dreyer's** -
>   Fruit Bars
>>   Creamy Coconut
>>   Grape
>>   Lemonade
>>   Lime
>>   Orange & Cream
>>   Snack Size (Cherry, Grape, Lime & Cream, Orange & Cream, Raspberry, Tropical)
>>   Strawberry
>>   Tangerine
>>   Variety Pack (Lime, Strawberry & Wildberry)
>>   Variety Pack No Sugar Added (Black Cherry, Mixed Berry, Strawberry, Strawberry Kiwi, Tangerine & Raspberry)
>   Fun Flavors
>>   Banana Split
>>   Butter Pecan
>>   Cherry Chocolate Chip
>>   Dulce De Leche
>>   Mocha Almond Fudge
>>   Peanut Butter Cup
>>   Root Beer Float Limited Edition
>>   Spumoni
>   Grand
>>   Chocolate (Chip, Regular)
>>   Coffee
>>   Double Vanilla
>>   French Vanilla
>>   Fudge Swirl

I

    Mint Chocolate Chip
    Neapolitan
    Real Strawberry
    Rocky Road
    Vanilla (Bean, Chocolate, Regular)
Sherbet
    Berry Rainbow
    Orange Cream
    Swiss Orange
    Tropical Rainbow
Slow Churned Rich & Creamy
    Butter Pecan (No Sugar Added, Regular)
    Caramel Delight
    Chocolate (Chip, Fudge Chunk, Regular)
    Coffee (No Sugar Added, Regular)
    French Vanilla (No Sugar Added, Regular)
    Fudge Tracks (No Sugar Added, Regular)
    Mint Chocolate Chip (No Sugar Added, Regular)
    Neapolitan (No Sugar Added, Regular)
    Peanut Butter Cup
    Red White And No More Blues
    Rocky Road
    Strawberry
    Take The Cake
    Triple Chocolate No Sugar Added
    Vanilla (No Sugar Added, Regular)
    Vanilla Bean (No Sugar Added, Regular)
Yogurt Blends
    Black Cherry Vanilla Swirl
    Cappucino Chip
    Caramel Praline Crunch

Chocolate Vanilla Swirl

Strawberry

Tart (Honey, Mango)

Vanilla

**Edy's -**

Fruit Bars

Creamy Coconut

Grape

Lemonade

Lime

Orange & Cream

Snack Size (Cherry, Grape, Lime & Cream, Orange & Cream, Raspberry, Tropical)

Strawberry

Tangerine

Variety Pack (Lime, Strawberry & Wildberry)

Variety Pack No Sugar Added (Black Cherry, Mixed Berry, Strawberry, Strawberry Kiwi, Tangerine & Raspberry)

Fun Flavors

Banana Split

Butter Pecan

Cherry Chocolate Chip

Dulce De Leche

Mocha Almond Fudge

Peanut Butter Cup

Root Beer Float Limited Edition

Spumoni

Grand

Chocolate (Chip, Regular)

Coffee

Double Vanilla

French Vanilla

I

    Fudge Swirl
    Mint Chocolate Chip
    Neapolitan
    Real Strawberry
    Rocky Road
    Vanilla (Bean, Chocolate, Regular)
Sherbet
    Berry Rainbow
    Orange Cream
    Swiss Orange
    Tropical Rainbow
Slow Churned Rich & Creamy
    Butter Pecan (No Sugar Added, Regular)
    Caramel Delight
    Chocolate (Chip, Fudge Chunk, Regular)
    Coffee (No Sugar Added, Regular)
    French Vanilla (No Sugar Added, Regular)
    Fudge Tracks (No Sugar Added, Regular)
    Mint Chocolate Chip (No Sugar Added, Regular)
    Neapolitan (No Sugar Added, Regular)
    Peanut Butter Cup
    Red White And No More Blues
    Rocky Road
    Strawberry
    Take The Cake
    Triple Chocolate No Sugar Added
    Vanilla (No Sugar Added, Regular)
    Vanilla Bean (No Sugar Added, Regular)
Yogurt Blends
    Black Cherry Vanilla Swirl
    Cappucino Chip

Caramel Praline Crunch

Chocolate Vanilla Swirl

Strawberry

Tart (Honey, Mango)

Vanilla

**Fla-Vor-Ice** - Freezer Bars (Light, Plus, Regular)

**Food Club Brand** - Ice Cream (Chocolate Chip, Churned Butter Pecan, Churned Vanilla, Mint Chocolate Chip, Strawberry, Vanilla)

**Full Circle** - All Natural (Butter Pecan, Chocolate, Neopolitan, Vanilla Bean)

**Gaga** - SherBetter (Chocolate, Lemon, Orange, Rainbow, Raspberry)

**Good Karma** -

Chocolate Covered Bars (Chocolate Chocolate, Very Vanilla)

Organic Rice Divine (Banana Fudge, Carrot Cake, Chocolate Peanut Butter Fudge, Coconut Mango, Mint Chocolate Swirl, Mudd Pie, Very Vanilla)

Sundae Cups (Strawberry Swirl, Vanilla Fudge Swirl)

**Haagen-Dazs** -

Five (Brown Sugar, Coffee, Ginger, Milk Chocolate, Mint, Passion Fruit, Vanilla Bean)

Frozen Yogurt (Coffee, Dulce De Leche, Tart Natural, Vanilla, Vanilla Raspberry Swirl, Wildberry)

Ice Cream

Baileys Irish Cream

Banana Split

Butter Pecan

Caramelized Pear & Toasted Pecan

Cherry Vanilla

Chocolate (Chocolate Chip, Peanut Butter, Regular)

Coffee

Crème Brulée

Dulce De Leche

I

Green Tea
Java Chip
Mango
Mint Chip
Pineapple Coconut
Pistachio
Rocky Road
Rum Raisin
Strawberry
Vanilla (Bean, Chocolate Chip, Honey Bee, Regular, Swiss Almond)
White Chocolate Raspberry Truffle

Ice Cream Bars
Chocolate & Dark Chocolate
Coffee & Almond Crunch
Vanilla (& Almonds, & Dark Chocolate, & Milk Chocolate)

Reserve
Amazon Valley Chocolate
Brazilian Acai Berry Sorbet
Caramelized Hazelnut Gianduja
Fleur De Sel Caramel
Hawaiian Lehua Honey & Sweet Cream
Pomegranate Chip
Toasted Coconut Sesame Brittle

Sorbet
Chocolate
Cranberry Blueberry
Mango
Orchard Peach
Raspberry
Strawberry
Zesty Lemon

**Hawaiian Punch** - Freezer Bars

**Hood** -

Frozen Novelty Items

Citrus Stix

Fudge Stix

Hoodsie (Cups, Pops 6 Flavor Assortment Twin Pops, Sundae Cups)

Hot Pop Stix

Ice Cream Bar

Kids Karnival

Mix Stix

Orange Cream Bar

Frozen Yogurt (All Fat Free Varieties)

Light (Butter Pecan, Chocolate Chip, Coffee, French Silk, Maine Blueberry & Sweet Cream, Martha's Vineyard Black Raspberry, Mint Chocolate Chip, Under The Stars, Vanilla)

Maine Blueberry & Sweet Cream

Martha's Vineyard Black Raspberry

Moosehead Lake Fudge

Mystic Lighthouse Mint

New England Homemade Vanilla

New England Lighthouse Coffee

Sherbert (Black Raspberry, Orange, Rainbow, Wildberry)

Vermont Maple Nut

New England Creamery

Bear Creek Caramel

Boston Vanilla Bean

Cape Cod Fudge Shop

Red Sox (All Flavors)

Regular (Chippedy Chocolaty, Chocolate, Classic Trio, Creamy Coffee, Fudge Twister, Golden Vanilla, Holiday Eggnog, Maple

Walnut, Natural Vanilla Bean, Patchwork, Peppermint Stick, Strawberry)

Sherbet (All Varieties)

**Horizon Organic -** All Varieties

**Hy-Vee -**

Ice Cream Bars

Assorted Twin Pops

Fudge Bars (& Fat Free, No Sugar Added)

Galaxy Reduced Fat (Orange, Regular)

Pops (Cherry, Grape, Orange, Root Beer)

Sundae Cups (Chocolate & Strawberry, Sherbet, Vanilla)

Regular

Butter Crunch

Carmel Pecan

Cherry Nut (Light, Regular)

Chocolate (Chip (Light, Regular), Marshmallow, Regular, Vanilla Flavored)

Dutch Chocolate Light

Fudge Marble

Lime Sherbet

Mint Chip

Neapolitan (Light, Regular)

New York Vanilla

Orange Sherbet

Root Beer Float

Sherbet (Lime, Orange, Pineapple, Rainbow, Raspberry)

Star Tracks

Strawberry

Tin Roof Sundae

Vanilla (Light, Regular)

**Icee -** Freezer Bars

**It's Soy Delicious**
- Almond Pecan●
- Awesome Chocolate●
- Black Leopard●
- Carob Peppermint●
- Chocolate (Almond●, Peanut Butter●)
- Espresso●
- Green Tea●
- Mango Raspberry●
- Pistachio Almond●
- Raspberry●
- Tiger Chai●
- Vanilla●
- Vanilla Fudge●

**Jelly Belly** - Freezer Bars/Pops

**Kool Pops** - Freezer Bars

**Lowes Foods Brand** -
- Bars (Fudge, Ice Cream, Orange Cream)
- Cups (Swirls, Vanilla)
- Lite (Chocolate, Neapolitan, Vanilla)
- Novelties (Banana Jr. Pops)
- Regular
  - Butter Pecan
  - Chocolate
  - French Vanilla
  - Fudge Swirl
  - Mint Chocolate Chip
  - Neopolitan
  - Vanilla (Bean, Regular)
- Sherbet (Lime, Orange, Raspberry, Triple Treat)

**Lucerne -**

    Creamery Fresh (Butter Pecan, Mint Chocolate Chip, Vanilla)

    Ice Cream Bars

        Fudge

        Kreme Coolers

        Root Beer Float

        Toffee Brittle

        Vanilla (Regular, Sherbet, Sundae)

    Regular

        Chocolate

        Chocolate Chip

        Golden Nut Sundae

        Low Fat Vanilla

        Mint

        Neapolitan

        Ranch Pecan

        Real Vanilla

        Strawberry

    Vanilla Sundae Ice Cream Cups & Bars

**Meijer Brand -**

    Awesome Strawberry

    Black Cherry

    Brr Bar

    Butter Pecan (Gold Georgian Bay, Lite No Sugar Added w/Splenda, Original)

    Candy Bar Swirl

    Caramel Pecan (Fat Free No Sugar Added)

    Chocolate (Bordeaux Cherry, Carb Conquest, Chip, Peanut Butter Fudge, Thunder, Double Nut Chocolate, Mint, Original)

        Combo Cream

    Cotton Candy

Dream Bars

Dulce De Leche

Fudge Bars (No Sugar Added, Original)

Fudge Swirl

Gold (Caramel Toffee Swirl, Peanut Butter Fudge Swirl, Peanut Butter Fudge Tracks, Thunder Bay Cherry)

Heavenly Hash

Ice Cream Bars

Juice Stix

Mackinaw Fudge

Neapolitan (Lite, Original)

Novelties (Gold Bar, Toffee Bar)

Orange Glider

Party Pops (No Sugar Added Assorted, Orange/Cherry/Grape, RB/B/BR)

Peppermint

Praline Pecan

Red White & Blue Pops

Scooperman

Sherbet (Cherry, Lemonberry Twist, Lime, Orange, Pineapple, Rainbow, Raspberry)

Tin Roof

Toffee Bars

Twin Pops

Vanilla (Carb Conquest, Fat Free No Sugar Added w/Splenda, Gold Victorian, Golden, Lite No Sugar Added w/Splenda, Original)

**Midwest Country Fare** - Chocolate (Chip, Regular), Neapolitan, New York Vanilla, Vanilla (Light, Regular)

**Minute Maid** - Juice Bars

**Natural Choice** - Full of Fruit Bars, Sorbets

**North Star**

## ice cream

Bars (Dream, English Toffee, Fudge, Health Wise No Sugar Added Fudge Bar, Ice Cream, Lotta, Old Recipe Ice Cream, Star Lite, Sugar Free Fudge, Sweet Wise No Sugar Added)

Lotta Pops (Bars, Crème, Fruit, Fudge, Juice, Regular, Sugar Free)

Pops (Assorted Twin, Banana Twin, Blue Raspberry Twin, Cherry Twin, Health Wise Sugar Free, Melon, Patriot Junior)

Shakes (Strawberry, Tornado Twister, Vanilla)

Specialty (Banana Blast, Banana Crème Junior, Chocolate Cherry Nuggets, Double Chocolate Ice Cream Nuggets, Frog Spit Turbo, Peppermint Stars, Totally Tubular Orange Sherbert Push Treat, Tropical Cooler Junior, Rootbeer Float, Vanilla Slice, Yogurt Smooth Bites)

Sundae Ice Cream Cups (Chocolate, Chocolate Strawberry, Club, Strawberry, Vanilla)

**Otter Pops** - Freezer Bars (Plus, Regular)

**Philly Swirl**

Fruit & Cream Stix

Fudge Swirl Stix

Philly Swirl Sorbet/Italian Ice

Original Swirl Stix

Sugar Free Swirl Stix

**Pop Ice** - Freezer Bars

**Prairie Farms** -

Frozen Yogurt (Chocolate, Strawberry, Vanilla)

Homestyle Churn (Cappuccino Supreme, Caramel Treat, Chocolate Silk, Mint Chip, Roasted Butter Pecan, Vanilla)

Ice Cream

Black Walnut

Butter Pecan

Cherry Vanilla

Chocolate (Chip, Fat Free, Regular)

Fat Free Caramel Pecan Crunch

French Vanilla

Mint Chocolate Chip
No Sugar Added (Butter Pecan, Vanilla)
Rocky Road
Spumoni
Toffee Crunch
Vanilla (Chocolate Strawberry, Fat Free, Regular)
Old Recipe
Belgian Chocolate
Butter Pecan
Caramel Coyote
French Vanilla
Heavenly Hash
Moose Tracks
Roadrunner Raspberry
Strawberry (Avalanche, N Crème)
Turtle Tracks
Vanilla (Regular, Storm)
Sherbet - Lemon, Lime, Orange, Rainbow, Raspberry
**Prestige** - Chocolate, Chocolate Almond, Neapolitan, Strawberry, Vanilla
**Publix** -
Creamy Churned Style
Butter Pecan (No Sugar Added, Regular)
Chocolate (No Sugar Added, Regular)
Chocolate Almond Fudge
Vanilla (No Sugar Added, Regular)
Ice Cream
Chocolate (Regular)
Fudge Royal
Neapolitan
Vanilla
Low Fat Frozen Yogurt

Black Jack Cherry
Butter Pecan
Chocolate
Peach
Peanut Butter Cup
Pina Colada
Road Runner Raspberry
Strawberry
Toffee Candy Crunch
Vanilla
Low Fat Ice Cream
Chocolate
Fudge Royal
Neapolitan
Vanilla
Novelties
Banana Pops
Fudge (Bar, Swirl Cups)
Ice Cream (Bar, Squares)
Junior Ice Pops (Cherry, Grape, Orange)
No Sugar Added (Fudge Bars), Ice Cream (Bars, Squares), Ice Pop)
Toffee Bar
Vanilla Cups
Premium Homemade Ice Cream
Butter Pecan
Vanilla
Premium Ice Cream
Banana Split
Bear Claw
Black Jack Cherry
Butter Pecan

Cherry Nut

Chocolate (Almond, Cherish Passion, Chip, Moose Tracks, Regular, Trinity)

Dulce De Leche

French Vanilla

Heavenly Hash

It's Your Birthday Cake

Mint Chocolate Chip

Neapolitan

Otter Paws

Peanut Butter Goo Goo

Strawberry

Vanilla

Premium Limited Editon Ice Cream

French Silk Duo

Maple Walnut

Peppermint Stick

Rum Raisin

Strawberry Lemonade Slide

Sherbet

Citrus Berry Blast

Cool Lime

Exotic Fruit Medley

Peach Mango Passion

Rainbow Dream

Raspberry Blush

Sunny Orange (No Sugar Added, Regular)

Tropic Pineapple

Tropical Twist

**Purely Decadent -**
Bars (Purely Vanilla●, Vanilla Almond●)
Dairy Free Ice Cream
Belgian Chocolate●
Blueberry Cheesecake●
Cherry Nirvana●
Chocolate Coconut Milk●
Chocolate Obsession●
Chocolate Peanut Butter Swirl
Coconut (Craze●, Regular●)
Cookie Dough●
Dulce De Leche●
Key Lime Pie●
Mint Chip●
Mint Chocolate Chip●
Mocha Almond Fudge●
Passionate Mango●
Peanut Butter Zig Zag●
Pomegranate Chip●
Praline Pecan●
Purely Vanilla●
Rocky Road●
Snickerdoodle●
So Very Strawberry●
Turtle Trails●
Vanilla Bean●
**Rice Dream -**
Non Dairy Frozen Desserts
Carob Almond
Cocoa Marble Fudge
Neapolitan

Orange Vanilla Swirl

Strawberry

Vanilla

**Safeway Select -**

Churned (Butter Pecan, Caramel Caribou, Chocolate Moose Tracks, French Vanilla, Mint Chocolate Chip, Mocha Almond Fudge, Moose Tracks, Neapolitan, Peppermint, Rocky Road, Strawberry, Vanilla, Vanilla Bean)

Premium (Black Walnut, Butter Pecan, Chocolate, Chocolate Chip, Coconut Pineapple, Dolce De Leche, French Vanilla, Green Tea, Mango, Neapolitan, Pecan Praline, Rocky Road, Spumoni, Vanilla, White Chocolate Raspberry)

Regular

Caribou Caramel Ice Cream Bars

Fruit Bars (Lemonade, Lime, Mandarine Orange, Strawberry)

Moose Tracks (Chocolate, Extreme, Mint)

Sorbet (Chocolate, Lemon, Mango, Peach, Pomegranate, Raspberry, Strawberry, Tropical)

**Shamrock Farms -**

Ice Cream

Carmelback Mountain

Grand Butter Pecanyon

Peppermint Stick Forest

Rocky Route 66

Show Low Carb Butter Pecan

Snowbowl Vanilla

Tombstone Trail

**So Delicious Coconut Milk -** Bar (Coconut Almond, Vanilla)

**So Delicious Dairy Free**

Kidz (Assorted Fruit Pops●, Fudge Pops●)

Organic

Butter Pecan●

Chocolate (Peanut Butter●, Velvet●)

I

    Creamy Vanilla●

    Dulce De Leche●

    Mint Marble Fudge●

    Mocha Fudge●

    Neapolitan●

    Strawberry●

Organic Creamy Bars (Fudge Bar●, Orange●, Raspberry●, Vanilla●, Vanilla & Almonds●)

Sugar Free Bar (Fudge, Vanilla)

**Soy Dream -**

Non Dairy Frozen Desserts

    Butter Pecan

    Chocolate

    French Vanilla

    Green Tea

    Mocha Fudge

    Strawberry Swirl

    Vanilla (Fudge, Regular)

**Spartan Brand -**

Ice Cream

    Black Cherry

    Butter Pecan

    Chocolate

    French Vanilla

    Golden Vanilla

    Imitation Chocolate Chip

    Lowfat Vanilla

    Moose Tracks

    Neapolitan

    Peanut Butter Cup

    Vanilla

**Sweet Nothings** - Non Dairy (Fudge Bars●, Mango Raspberry●)

**Tampico** - Freezer Bars

**The Skinny Cow** - Low Fat Fudge Bars, Minis Fudge Pops

**Trader Joe's** -

Gone Bananas Chocolate Dipped Bananas

Ice Cream Bars (Blissful, Mango Vanilla, Raspberry Vanilla)

Mangolicious Fruit Blend

Sorbet (All)

Soy Creamy (Cherry Chocolate Chip, Organic Chocolate, Organic Vanilla)

Super Premium Ice Cream (French Vanilla, Mint Chocolate, Ultra Chocolate)

**Wegmans Brand** -

Black Raspberry

Chocolate (Almond, Marshmallow, Peanut Butter Swirl, Regular, Vanilla)

Extra Churned (Peanut Butter, Strawberry)

French (Roast Coffee, Vanilla)

Heavenly Hash

Ice Cream Bars (Cherry w/Dark Chocolate, Fudge (No Sugar Added, Regular), Regular, Vanilla & Dark Chocolate Premium)

Ice Cream Cups (Orange Sherbert, Peanut Butter Candy, Peanut Butter Cup, Regular, Vanilla & Chocolate, Vanilla & Chocolate Swirl)

Ice Pops Twin Stick

Low Fat (Cappuccino Chip, Chocolate Indulgence, Creamy (Black Raspberry, Vanilla), Mint Chip, Praline Pecan, Raspberry Truffle, Vanilla)

Neapolitan

Orange Sherbert Cups

Peak Of Perfection (Black Cherry, Blueberry, Mango, Peach)

Peanut Butter (Cup, Sundae, Swirl)

Pistachio Vanilla Swirl

Premium (Butter Pecan, Chocolate, Chocolate Caramel, Coconut Mango, Creamy Caramel, Jamocha Almond Fudge, Mint Chocolate Chip, Organic Dark Chocolate, Peanut Butter Cup, Pistachio, Rum Raisin, Strawberry, Vanilla)

Sorbet (Lemon, Pink Grapefruit, Green Apple, Vanilla Raspberry)

Strawberry

Super Premium Dark Chocolate

Vanilla (& Chocolate, Orange, Raspberry Sorbet, Regular, w/Orange Sherbet)

**WholeSoy & Co.** - All Frozen Yogurts

**Winn Dixie** - Banana Pops, Classic (Chocolate, Neapolitan, Strawberry, Vanilla), Fudge Bars, Fun Pops, Ice Cream Bars, Orange Cream Bars

**Wyler's** - Italian Ice Freezer Bars

**Ice Cream Cones... see Cones**

**Ice Cream Toppings... see also Syrup**

**Hershey's** - Chocolate Syrup (Lite, Regular)

**Smucker's** -

Magic Shell (Caramel, Cherry, Chocolate, Chocolate Fudge, Cupcake)

Microwaveable Ice Cream Topping Hot Fudge

Sundae Syrups (Butterscotch, Caramel, Chocolate, Strawberry)

Toppings (Andes Chocolate Mint, Apple Cinnamon, Butterscotch, Caramel, Chocolate Fudge, Hot Caramel, Hot Fudge, Marshmallow, Pecans In Syrup, Pineapple, Pumpkin Spice, Strawberry, Walnuts In Syrup)

Special Recipe (Butterscotch Caramel, Dark Chocolate, Hot Fudge, Triple Berry)

**Iced Tea/Iced Tea Mix... see Tea**

**Icing... see Baking Decorations & Frostings**

**Instant Coffee... see Coffee**

**Italian Dressing... see Salad Dressing**

# J J

**Jalapenos...** *All **Fresh** Fruits & Vegetables Are **Gluten-Free***

    **Chi-Chi's** - Red

    **Great Value Brand (Wal-Mart)** - Sliced Jalapenos En Rodajas, Whole Jalapenos

    **Old El Paso** - Slices (Pickled)

    **Ortega**

    **Safeway Brand** - Sliced

    **Winn Dixie**

**Jalfrazi**

    **Seeds of Change** - Jalfrezi Sauce

    **Tamarind Tree** - Vegetable Jalfrazi

**Jam/Jelly**

    **Albertsons** - All (Jam, Jellies, Preserves)

    **Baxters** - Jelly (Cranberry, Mint, Red Currant)

    **Bionaturae** - Fruit Spread (Apricot, Bilberry, Peach, Plum, Red Raspberry, Sicilian Orange, Sour Cherry, Strawberry, Wild Berry, Wild Blackberry)

    **Bramley's** - Jelly & Preserves

    **Cascadian Farm** - Organic Fruit Spreads (Apricot, Blackberry, Blueberry, Concord Grape, Raspberry, Strawberry)

    **Eden Organic** - Butter (Apple, Cherry)

    **Fischer & Wieser -**

        Jelly Texas (Hot Red Jalapeno, Mild Green Jalapeno)

        Marmalade (Apricot Orange, Whole Lemon Fig)

        Preserves

            Cinnamon Orange Tomato

            Old Fashioned Peach

            Rhubarb Strawberry

            Texas (Amaretto Peach Pecan, Jalapeach)

        Texas Pecan (Apple Butter, Peach Butter)

**J**

**Food Club Brand -** Organic Fruit Spread (Apricot, Raspberry, Strawberry, Wild Blueberry), Grape Jam, Grape Jelly, Preserves (Apricot, Peach, Strawberry)

**Full Circle -** Fruit Spread (Raspberry, Strawberry)

**Great Value Brand (Wal-Mart) -** All (Jellies, Preserves)

**Hannaford Brand -** Jelly (Apple, Currant, Grape, Strawberry), Orange Marmalade, Preserves (Apricots, Blueberry, Grape, Red Raspberry)

**Hy-Vee -**

Jelly (Apple, Blackberry, Cherry, Grape, Plum, Red Raspberry, Strawberry)

Orange Marmalade

Preserves (Apricot, Cherry, Concord Grape, Peach, Red Raspberry, Strawberry)

**Kroger Brand -** All Jams, Jellies, Preserves

**Laura Lynn -**

Grape Jam

Jelly (Apple, Grape)

Orange Marmalade

Peanut Butter & (Grape Jelly Spread, Strawberry Jelly Spread)

Preserves (Apricot, Peach, Red Raspberry, Strawberry)

**Lowes Foods Brand -** Jam (Grape), Jelly (Apple, Grape), Preserves (Strawberry)

**Meijer Brand -** Fruit Spread (Apricot, Blackberry Seedless, Red Raspberry, Strawberry), Jam (Grape), Jelly (Grape), Preserves (Apricot, Blackberry Seedless, Marmalade Orange, Peach, Red Raspberry, Red Raspberry w/Seeds, Strawberry)

**Midwest Country Fare -** Grape Jelly, Strawberry

**Nature's Promise -** Organic (Grape Jelly, Raspberry Fruit Spread, Strawberry Fruit Spread)

**O Organics -** Preserves (Apricot, Blackberry, Blueberry, Raspberry, Strawberry)

**Polaner -** All (Jam, Jellies, Preserves)

**Publix -** All (Jam, Jellies, Preserves)

**J**

**Safeway Brand** - All (Jams, Jellies, Preserves)

**Safeway Select** - All (Jams, Jellies, Preserves)

**Smucker's** - All (Jams, Jellies, Marmalades, Preserves)

**Spartan Brand** - Jam (Grape), Jelly (Apple, Currant, Grape, Strawberry), Orange Marmalade, Preserves (Apricot, Blackberry, Cherry, Peach, Red Raspberry, Strawberry)

**Stop & Shop Brand -**

Concord Grape Jelly (Spreadable, Squeezable)

Jelly (Apple, Currant, Mint)

Orange Marmalade

Preserves (Apricot, Grape, Peach, Pineapple, Red Raspberry, Seedless Blackberry, Strawberry)

Simply Enjoy (Red Pepper Jelly, Roasted Garlic & Onion Jam)

Simply Enjoy Preserves (Balsamic Sweet Onion, Blueberry, Raspberry Champagne Peach, Spiced Apple, Strawberry)

Spread (Apricot, Blueberry, Strawberry)

Squeezable Grape Jelly

Sugar Free Preserves (Apricot, Blackberry, Red Raspberry, Strawberry)

**Taste Of Inspirations** - Honey Apple Butter, Hot Pepper Jelly, Mango Pepper Jelly, Mint Jelly, Raspberry Peach Fruit Spread, Roasted Red Pepper Spread, Strawberry Pomegranate Fruit Spread

**Trader Joe's** - All (Jams, Jellies, Preserves), Wild Maine Blueberry Fruit Sauce

**Walden Farms** - Spread (Apple Butter, Apricot, Blueberry, Grape, Orange Marmalade, Raspberry, Strawberry)

**Wegmans Brand -**

Fruit Spread

Apricot/Peach/Passion Fruit

Blueberry/Cherry/Raspberry

Raspberry/Strawberry/Blackberry

Strawberry/Plum/Raspberry

Sugar Free Raspberry/Wild Blueberry/Blackberry

Jelly (Apple, Cherry, Concord Grape, Currant, Mint, Red Raspberry, Strawberry)

Nature's Marketplace Organic Fruit Spread (Jammin' Red Raspberry, Jammin' Strawberry)

Preserves (Apricot, Cherry, Concord Grape, Peach, Pineapple, Red Raspberry, Seedless Blackberry, Strawberry)

Sugar Free Fruit Spread

Apricot/Peach/Passion Fruit

Raspberry/Wild Blueberry/Blackberry

Strawberry/Plum/Raspberry

**Welch's -** All Jams, Jellies & Preserves

**Jello... see Gelatin**

**Jerky/Beef Sticks**

**Applegate Farms -** Joy Stick

**Blackwing -** Organic Beef Jerky (Peppered)

**Buffalo Guys -** Buffalo Jerky (Mild, Old Style)

**Dietz & Watson -** Dried Beef

**Gary West**

Buffalo & Elk Strips

Certified Angus Beef Steak Strips - All Varieties *(Except Teriyaki)*

Original Steak Strips - All Varieties *(Except Teriyaki)*

Silver Fork Natural Steak Strips

**Hormel -** Dried Beef

**Hy-Vee -** Jerky (Original, Peppered)

**Lowes Foods Brand -** Beef Jerky (Honey, Original, Peppered)

**Old Wisconsin -** Snack Sticks (Beef, Pepperoni, Spicy, Turkey) *(Beef Jerky Is NOT Gluten-Free)*

**Organic Prairie -** Organic Beef Jerky 2 oz. (Prairie Classic, Smoky Chipotle, Spicy Hickory)

**Shelton's -** Beef Jerky, Turkey Jerky (Hot Turkey, Regular)

**Wellshire Farms -** Snack Sticks (Hot N' Spicy, Matt's Beef Pepperoni, Turkey Tom Tom)

**J** Juice... see Drinks/Juice
Juice Mix... see Drink Mix

**K**

## K

Kale... *All **Fresh** Fruits & Vegetables Are **Gluten-Free***
  Pictsweet - Cut Leaf
Kasha
  Bob's Red Mill▲ - Organic
  Shiloh Farms - Organic
  Wolff's
Kefir
  Lifeway - All Varieties
  Nancy's - All Cultured Products
  Trader Joe's
Ketchup
  Annie's Naturals - Organic
  Food Club Brand
  Full Circle - Organic (Squeeze Bottle, Upside Down)
  Great Value Brand (Wal-Mart)
  Hannaford Brand
  Heinz - Hot & Spicy, No Sodium Added, Organic, Reduced Sugar, Regular
  Home Harvest Brand
  Hy-Vee - Squeezable Thick & Rich Tomato, Thick & Rich Tomato
  Kurtz
  Lowes Foods Brand - Squeeze, Squeeze Upside Down Bottle
  Meijer Brand - Regular, Squeeze, Tomato Organic
  Midwest Country Fare
  Muir Glen - Organic Tomato Ketchup
  O Organics

**Organicville** - Organic
**Publix**
**Publix GreenWise Market** - Organic
**Safeway Brand**
**Spartan Brand**
**Trader Joe's** - Organic
**Walden Farms**
**Wegmans Brand** - Organic
**Winn Dixie** - Organic, Regular
**Woodstock Farms** - Organic
**Kielbasa... see Sausage**
**Kipper Snacks**
    **Crown Prince** - Natural Naturally Smoked, Regular Naturally Smoked
    **Ocean Prince** - In Mustard, Naturally Smoke
**Kiwi...** *All Fresh Fruits & Vegetables Are Gluten-Free*
**Kohlrabi...** *All Fresh Fruits & Vegetables Are Gluten-Free*
**Korma**
    **Amy's** - Indian Vegetable
    **Patak's**
    **Seeds of Change** - Korma Sauce
    **Sharwood's** - Chicken Korma
    **Tamarind Tree** - Navratan
    **Tasty Bite** - Vegetable Korma
    **Trader Joe's** - Korma Simmer Sauce

# L

**Lamb...** *All Fresh Meat Is Gluten-Free (Non-Marinated, Unseasoned)*
    **Trader Joe's** - Seasoned Rack of Lamb
**Lasagna/Lasagne**
    **Amy's** - Garden Vegetable

**L**

Conte's Pasta - Cheese, Meat, Vegetable

Everybody Eats▲ - Beef

Foods By George▲ - Cheese Lasagna

Lasagna/Lasagne Noodles... see Pasta

Lemonade... see Drinks/Juice

Lemons... *All **Fresh** Fruits & Vegetables Are **Gluten-Free***

Sunkist

Trader Joe's - Lemon Curd

Lentils... see also Beans

365 Organic Every Day Value - Organic

Manischewitz - Lentil Pilaf Mix

Tasty Bite - Bengal, Jaipur, Jodphur, Madras

Trader Joe's - Curried Lentils w/Basmati Rice, Steamed Lentils

Lettuce... *All **Fresh** Fruits & Vegetables Are **Gluten-Free***

Licorice... see Candy/Candy Bars

Limeade... see Drinks/Juice

Limes... *All **Fresh** Fruits & Vegetables Are **Gluten-Free***

Liquid Aminos

Bragg - Liquid Aminos

Liverwurst

Dietz & Watson - Liverwurst AC

Farmer John - Lunchmeat (Original Premium Liverwurst, Premium Braunschweiger, Premium Liverwurst w/Bacon)

Five Star Brand - Natural Casing Braunschweiger (Chubs, Regular)

Jones Dairy Farm

Chub Braunschweiger Liverwurst (Bacon & Onion●, Light●, Mild & Creamy●, Original●)

Chunk Braunschweiger (Light●, Original●)

Sliced Braunschweiger●

Stick Braunschweiger●

Old Wisconsin - Spreadable Pate (All Varieties)

Wellshire Farms - Liverwurst (Pork, Turkey)

**Lobster...** *\*All **Fresh** Seafood Is **Gluten-Free** (Non-Marinated, Unseasoned)*

**Lunch Meat... see Deli Meat**

**M**

**Macaroni & Cheese**

    **Amy's** - Rice Mac & Cheese

    **Annie's ▲** - Rice Pasta & Cheddar

    **Blue Chip Group** - Gluten Free Macaroni & Cheese

    **Gluten Free & Fabulous▲** - Macaroni & Cheese●

    **Ian's** - Wheat Free Gluten Free Mac & No Cheese

    **Mrs. Leeper's** - Mac & Cheese Dinner

    **Namaste Foods▲** - Say Cheez

    **Pastariso▲** - Dolphin Rice Macaroni & Yellow Cheese, Elephant Rice Macaroni & White Cheese, Gorilla Rice Mini Shells & White Cheese, Rhino Rice Mini Shells & Yellow Cheese

    **Pastato▲** - Potato Mac & Cheese (Orangutan, Panda)

    **Road's End Organics** - Dairy Free (Mac & Cheese Alfredo, Penne & Cheese)

    **Trader Joe's** - Rice Pasta & Cheddar

**Macaroons... see Cookies**

**Mackerel...see Fish...** *\*All **Fresh** Fish Is **Gluten-Free** (Non-Marinated, Unseasoned)*

    **Chicken Of The Sea** - All Mackerel Products

    **Crown Prince** - Fillet of Mackerel In Soybean Oil, Jack Mackerel

**Mahi Mahi...see Fish...** *\*All **Fresh** Fish Is **Gluten-Free** (Non-Marinated, Unseasoned)*

**Makhani**

    **Tamarind Tree** - Dal Makhani

**Mandarin Oranges...** *\*All **Fresh** Fruits & Vegetables Are **Gluten-Free***

    **Albertsons**

**M**

**Del Monte -**
    Canned/Jarred Fruit (All Varieties)
    Fruit Snack Cups (Metal, Plastic)
**Dole -** All Fruits (Bowls, Canned, Dried, Frozen, Jars) *(Except Real Fruit Bites)*
**Food Club Brand**
**Great Value Brand (Wal-Mart) -** In Light Syrup
**Hy-Vee -** Light Syrup, Orange Gel Cups, Regular Cups
**Kroger Brand -** Fruit (Canned, Cups)
**Lowes Foods Brand -** In Lite Syrup
**Meijer Brand -** Light Syrup
**Publix -** In Light Syrup
**Spartan Brand -** Fruit Cups
**Trader Joe's -** In Light Syrup
**Wegmans Brand -** Regular, Whole Segment In Light Syrup
**Winn Dixie**

**Mango...** *All **Fresh** Fruits & Vegetables Are **Gluten-Free***
**Del Monte -**
    Canned/Jarred Fruit (All Varieties)
    Fruit Snack Cups (Metal, Plastic)
**Meijer Brand -** Frozen (Chunks, Sliced)
**Native Forest -** Organic Mango Chunks
**Stop & Shop Brand -** Mango
**Trader Joe's -** Mangolicious Fruit Blend
**Winn Dixie -** Frozen Mango Chunks
**Woodstock Farms -** Organic Frozen Mango

**Maple Syrup... see Syrup**

**Maraschino Cherries... see Cherries**

**Margarine... see Spread and/or Butter**

**Marinades**
    **Annie's Naturals -** Baja Lime

**M**

**Consorzio -** Roasted Garlic & Balsamic

**Drew's All Natural -**

Buttermilk Ranch

Classic Italian

Green Olive & Caper

Honey Dijon

Poppy Seed

Raspberry

Roasted Garlic & Peppercorn

Romano Caesar

Rosemary Balsamic

Smoked Tomato

**Food Club Brand -** 30 Minute Marinades (Herb & Garlic, Lemon Pepper, Mesquite)

**Hy-Vee -** Citrus Grill, Herb & Garlic, Lemon Pepper, Mesquite

**Jack Daniel's EZ Marinader -** Honey Teriyaki, Slow Roasted Garlic & Herb

**Ken's Steak House -** Buffalo Wing Sauce

**Lawry's -** Baja Chipotle, Caribbean Jerk, Havana Garlic & Lime, Herb & Garlic, Lemon Pepper, Louisiana Red Pepper, Mesquite, Tequila Lime

**McCormick -**

Grill Mates

Baja Citrus Marinade

Chipotle Pepper Marinade

Garlic Herb & Wine

Hickory BBQ Marinade

Mesquite Marinade

Mojito Lime

Montreal Steak Marinade (25% Less Sodium, Original)

Peppercorn & Garlic Marinade

Southwest Marinade

Tomato Garlic & Basil Marinade

**M**

**Meijer Brand** - Garlic & Herb, Lemon Pepper, Mesquite

**Moore's Marinade** - Original, Teriyaki

**Mr. Spice Organic** - Sauce & Marinade (Garlic Steak, Ginger Stir Fry, Honey BBQ, Honey Mustard, Hot Wing, Indian Curry, Sweet & Sour, Thai Peanut)

**Safeway Brand** - Carribean Jerk, Lemon Garlic

**San-J** - Gluten Free (Sweet & Tangy, Szechuan, Teriyaki, Thai Peanut)

**Taste Of Inspirations** - Cajun, Roasted Garlic

**Weber Grill Creations** - Chipotle Marinade

**Wegmans Brand** -

    Chicken BBQ

    Citrus Dill

    Fajita

    Greek

    Honey Mustard

    Italian

    Lemon & Garlic

    Mojo

    Peppercorn Marinade

    Rosemary Balsamic

    Santa Fe Medium

    Steakhouse Peppercorn

    Tangy

    Zesty (Savory, Thai)

**Winn & Lovett** - Argentina, Cilantro Lime, Citrus, Garlic, Red Chili & Thyme

**Winn Dixie** - Mojo

**Marmalade... see Jam/Jelly**

**Marsala**

    **Wegmans Brand** - Mushroom Marsala Sauce

**Marshmallow Dip**

    **Marshmallow Fluff** - Original, Raspberry, Strawberry

**Walden Farms** - Calorie Free Marshmallow Dip

Marshmallows

**Albertsons** - Mini, Regular

**AllerEnergy**

**Food Club Brand** - Mini, Regular

**Great Value Brand (Wal-Mart)** - Marshmallow Crème, Marshmallows (Flavored, Miniature, Regular)

**Hannaford Brand** - Miniature, Regular

**Hy-Vee** - Colored Miniatures, Miniatures, Regular

**Jet-Puffed** - Chocomallows, Miniatures, Regular

**Kroger Brand** - Colored, Cream, Large, Miniature

**Laura Lynn**

**Lowes Foods Brand** - Mini, Regular

**Lunar Mallows** - Big, Mini

**Manischewitz**

**Marshmallow Fluff** - Original, Raspberry, Strawberry

**Meijer Brand** - Mini, Mini Flavored, Regular

**Publix**

**Safeway Brand** - Large, Mini

**Spartan Brand** - Minature, Regular

**Winn Dixie** - Mini, Regular

Masala

**A Taste of India** - Masala Rice & Lentils

**Ethnic Gourmet** - Chicken

**Loyd Grossman** - Tikka Masala

**Patak's** - Tikka Masala

**Seeds of Change** - Tikka Masala

**Sharwood's** - Saag

**Tamarind Tree** - Channa Dal Masala

**Tasty Bite** - Beans Masala & Basmati Rice, Channa

**Trader Joe's** - Channa, Chicken, Masala Simmer Sauce, Paneer Tikka

**M** Mashed Potatoes

 **Alexia** - Red Potatoes w/Garlic & Parmesan, Yukon Gold Potatoes & Sea Salt

 **Edward & Sons** - Organic (Chreesy, Home Style, Roasted Garlic)

 **Harris Farms**

 **Kroger Brand** - Plain Instant

 **Laura Lynn** - Herb & Garlic, Regular, Roasted Garlic, Sour Cream & Chives

 **Meijer Brand** - Instant Mashed Potatoes

 **Ore-Ida** - Steam N' Mash (Cut Red, Cut Russet, Cut Sweet, Garlic Seasoned, Three Cheese)

 **Safeway Brand** - Instant Mashed Potatoes (Herb Butter, Regular, Roasted Garlic)

 **Spartan Brand** - Butter & Herb, Instant, Roasted Garlic

 **Trader Joe's** - Garlic Mashed Potatoes

Mayonnaise

 **Albertsons**

 **Bakers & Chefs** - Extra Heavy

 **Best Foods** - All (Canola, Light, Real, Reduced Fat)

 **Cain's** - All Natural, Fat Free, Light, Sandwich Spread

 **Di Lusso** - Sandwich Spread

 **Dietz & Watson** - Sandwich Spread

 **Enlighten**

 **Follow Your Heart** - Expeller Pressed, Grapeseed Oil, Organic, Original, Reduced Fat

 **Food Club Brand**

 **Great Value Brand (Wal-Mart)**

 **Hannaford Brand** - Lite, Regular, Squeeze

 **Hellmann's** - All (Canola, Light, Real, Reduced Fat)

 **Hy-Vee** - Regular, Squeezable

 **Laura Lynn** - Fat Free, Regular

 **Lowes Foods Brand** - Light, Regular, Southern Style, Squeeze Bottle

**Meijer Brand -** Lite, Regular

**Miracle Whip -** Light, Regular

**Nasoya -** Nayonaise (Fat Free, Original)

**Portmann's**

**Publix**

**Safeway -** Light, Regular

**Simply Delicious -** Organic Mayonnaise (Garlic, Lemon, Original)

**Smart Balance -** Omega Plus Light

**Spartan Brand -** Regular Squeeze

**Spectrum -** All Mayonnaise Products

**Trader Joe's -** Real, Reduced Fat, Wasabi Mayo

**Walden Farms -** Mayo

**Wegmans Brand -** Classic, Light

## Meals

**A Taste of China -** Sweet & Sour Rice, Szechuan Noodles

**A Taste of India -** Quick Meals (Masala Rice & Lentils, Spiced Rice w/Raisins)

**A Taste Of Thai -** Quick Meal (Coconut Ginger Noodles, Pad Thai Noodles, Peanut Noodles, Red Curry Noodles, Vermicelli Rice Noodles, Wide Rice Noodles, Yellow Curry Noodles)

**Amy's -** Kids Meals Baked Ziti

**Chi-Chi's -** Fiesta Plates (Creamy Chipotle, Salsa, Savory Garlic)

**Del Monte -** Harvest Selections Heat & Eat (Chili & Beans, Santa Fe Style Rice & Beans)

**Dinty Moore -** Microwave Meals (Rice w/Chicken, Scalloped Potatoes & Ham)

**Gillian's Foods▲ -** Chicken Cordon Bleu, Chicken Cutlets

**Gluten Free Café -** Frozen Meals (Asian Noodles●, Fettuccini Alfredo●, Lemon Basil Chicken●, Pasta Primavera●)

**Glutino▲ -** Frozen Meals (Chicken Penne Alfredo, Chicken Ranchero, Duo Mushroom Penne, Pad Thai w/Chicken, Penne Alfredo, Pomodoro Chicken)

**M**

**Hormel** - Compleats (Santa Fe Style Chicken), Compleats Microwave 10 oz. Meals (Chicken & Rice, Santa Fe Chicken & Rice)

**Ian's** - Wheat Free Gluten Free (Mac & Meat Sauce, Mac & No Cheese)

**Kid's Kitchen** - Beans & Wieners

**Lowes Foods Brand** - Taco Dinner Kit

**Mayacamas** - Skillet Toss (Black Olive Pesto, Dried Tomato, Garden Style, Green Olive Pesto, Mushroom Sauce, Seafood Recipe, Spicy Style)

**Mixes From The Heartland▲** - Meal Mix (BBQ Beef N' Pasta●, Baked Chicken Salad●, Beef Skillet●, Cheeseburger Pie●, Garden Meat Loaf●, Green Chili●, Green Chili Spaghetti●, Italian Meat Pie●, Mexican Chicken N' Rice●, Mexican Meat Pie●, Mexican Rice Bake●, Tex Mex Meat Loaf●)

**Mrs. Leepers** -

Beef (Lasagna Dinner, Stroganoff Dinner)

Cheeseburger Mac Dinner

Chicken Alfredo Dinner

Creamy Tuna Dinner

Mac & Cheese Dinner

**My Own Meals** - Beef Stew, Chicken & Black Bean, Mediterranean Chicken Meal, My Kind Of Chicken, Old World Stew

**Namaste Foods▲** - Pasta Meals (Pasta Pisavera, Say Cheez, Taco)

**Old El Paso** - Dinner Kit (Stand 'N Stuff Taco, Taco)

**Orgran▲** - Pasta Ready Meal (Tomato & Basil, Vegetable Bolognese), Spaghetti In A Can

**Ortega** - Dinner Kit (12 Count Taco, 18 Count Taco, Pizza Grande)

**Smart Ones** - Frozen Entrees (Broccoli & Cheddar Potatoes, Chicken Santa Fe, Creamy Tuscan Chicken, Fiesta Chicken, Grilled Chicken In Garlic Herb Sauce, Home Style Chicken, Lemon Herb Chicken Piccata, Santa Fe Rice & Beans)

**Tasty Bite** -

Aloo Palak

Beans Masala & Basmati Rice

Beans Paneer & Basmati Rice

Bombay Potatoes

Jaipur Vegetables

Kashmir Spinach

Madras Lentils

Mushroom Takatak

Peas Paneer & Basmati Rice

Punjab Eggplant

Spinach Dal & Basmati Rice

Sprouts Curry & Basmati Rice

Vegetable Supreme & Basmati Rice

**Thai Kitchen -**

Noodle Carts (Lemon & Chili, Pad Thai, Thai Peanut, Toasted Sesame)

Stir Fry Rice Noodle Meal Kit (Lemongrass & Chili, Original Pad Thai, Thai Peanut)

Take Out Box (Ginger & Sweet Chili, Original Pad Thai, Thai Basil & Chili)

**Trader Joe's -** Chicken Masala, Chicken Tandoori Rice Bowl, Peruvian Style Chimichurri Rice w/Vegetables, Roasted Poblano Peppers w/Shrimp Rice & Cheese, Indian Fare Meals (All)

## Meatballs

**Aidells -** Buffalo Style, Chipotle, Sun Dried Tomato & Parmesan Cheese

Melon... *All **Fresh** Fruits & Vegetables Are **Gluten-Free***

## Milk

**Albertsons -** All Varieties (Instant & Powdered), 1%, 2%, Evaporated, Fat Free, Half & Half, Lactose Free (Reduce Fat, w/Calcium), Sweetened Condensed

**Borden Eagle Brand -** Sweetened Condensed Milk

**Carnation -** Evaporated (Fat Free, Low Fat, Regular), Instant Nonfat Dry, Sweetened Condensed Milk

**Coburn Farms -** Evaporated Milk

**M**

**Dairy Ease** - Lactose Free Milk

**Dari Free** - Non Dairy Milk Alternative (Chocolate, Original)

**Food Club Brand** - 1%, 2%, Chocolate, Condensed Milk, Evaporated Milk, Skim, Vitamin D

**Friendship**

**Full Circle** - Organic (1%, 2%, Skim, Whole)

**Garelick** - Fresh Extra Heavy Whipping Cream, Naturals Colossal Coffee Low Fat Milk, Ultimate Chocolate Low Fat Milk

**Great Value Brand (Wal-Mart)** -

Evaporated Milk

Fat Free Milk (Evaporated Skimmed, Sweetened Condensed)

Half & Half

Heavy Whipping Cream

Non Fat Dry Milk

Sweetened Condensed Milk

**Health Market Organic** -

1% Low Fat

2% Reduced Fat

Skim

Whole

**Hood** - All Creams, All Fluid Milk (All Fat Levels), All Chocolate (Full Fat, Low Fat, All Sizes), Buttermilk, Calorie Countdown (All Varieties)

**Horizon Organic** - All Varieties

**Hy-Vee** -

½%

1% Low Fat

2% Reduced Fat

Chocolate Soy

Enriched (Original Rice, Vanilla Rice)

Evaporated

Fat Free (Evaporated, Skim)

Instant Nonfat Dry

Original Soy

Refrigerated Soy (Chocolate, Original, Vanilla)

Skim

Sweetened Condensed

Vanilla Soy

Vitamin D

**Kemps** - All Varieties

**Kroger Brand** - Liquid, Powdered

**Lactaid** - All Varieties

**Laura Lynn** - Evaporated, Half & Half, Instant Dry, Lactose Reduced, Sweetened Condensed

**Lowes Foods Brand** - Half & Half, Half & Half Fat Free, Whipping Cream (Heavy, Light, Regular)

**Lucerne** - Buttermilk (Fat Free, Low Fat, Regular), Chocolate, Half & Half, Lactose Free Fat Free

**Meijer Brand** -

½% Lowfat

1% Lowfat

2% Reduced Fat

Chocolate (1% Lowfat, Regular)

Evaporated (Lite Skimmed, Small, Tall)

Fat Free

Instant

Lactose Free Milk (2% w/Calcium, Fat Free w/Calcium)

Milk Sweetened Condensed

Strawberry Milk

Ultra Pasteurized Heavy Half & Half

Vitamin D

**Nature's Promise** - Chocolate Soymilk, Organic (1%, 2%, Chocolate Soymilk, Fat Free, Soymilk, Vanilla Soymilk, Whole), Ricemilk (Regular, Vanilla)

**Nesquik** - Ready To Drink (All Flavors)

**O Organics** - All Varieties

**Organic Valley** -

Buttermilk

Chocolate 2%

Eggnog

Fat Free/Nonfat/Skim

Half & Half

Heavy Whipping Cream

Lactose Free

Lowfat 1%

Powder (Buttermilk Blend, Nonfat Dry Milk)

Reduced Fat 2%

Shelf Stable Liters (Chocolate 2%, Half & Half, Whole)

Shelf Stable Single Serves (Chocolate, Lowfat, Strawberry, Vanilla)

**Pet** - Evaporated

**Prairie Farms** -

Flavored Milk (1 % Chocolate, 1% Strawberry, 1% Vanilla, 2% Chocolate, Chocolate)

Half & Half (Fat Free, Heavy Whipping, Regular, Ultra Pasteurized, Ultra Pasteurized Heavy Whipping Cream, Whipped Cream Aerosol)

White Milk (1% Low Fat, 2% Low Fat, 2% Reduced Fat, Fat Free, Vitamin D)

Regular Egg Nog

**Publix** - Chocolate, Evaporated, Fat Free (Plus, Regular), Low Fat (Chocolate, Regular), Reduced Fat, Sweetened Condensed, Whole

**Publix GreenWise Market** - Organic Milk (Fat Free, Reduced Fat, Whole)

**Safeway Brand** -

1%

2%

Buttermilk

Evaporated

Fat Free

Half & Half (Reduced Fat, Regular)

Instant

Lactose Free (Fat Free, Whole)

Milk Drinks (Chillin' Chocolate, Marvelous, Mocha Cappuccino, Vanilla, Very Berry Strawberry)

Sweetened Condensed

Table Cream

Whole

**Shamrock Farms -**

Buttermilk

Chocolate Milk (1%, Regular)

Milkshakes (Chocolate, Dulce De Leche, Strawberry, Vanilla)

Regular (1%, 2%, Fat Free, Fat Free Plus Calcium, Sweet Acidophilus)

**Simply Smart -** Chocolate Fat Free, Half & Half Fat Free, Milk (Fat Free, Low Fat)

**Spartan Brand -**

.5%

1% Chocolate

1% Low Fat

2% Reduced Fat

Evaporated (Milk, Skim)

Half & Half

Instant Powdered

Skim

Sweetened Condensed

**Stonyfield Farms -** All Varieties ●

**Stop & Shop Brand -**

Half & Half (Fat Free, Pasteurized, Ultra Pasteurized)

Lactose Free (Calcium Fortified Fat Free, Whole)

**M**

    Low Fat

    Skim

    Ultra Pasteurized Cream (Heavy Whipping, Light, Sweetened Whipped Light, Whipping)

    Whole

**Wegmans Brand -**

    1% (Low Fat, Regular)

    2% (Reduced Fat, Regular)

    Evaporated (Fat Free, Regular)

    Fat Free Skim (Regular, Rich Calcium Fortified)

    Half & Half (Fresh, Ultra)

    Heavy Cream

    Lactose Free (Fat Free, Low Fat, Reduced Fat, Regular)

    Low Fat Chocolate

    Organic (1%, 2%, Fat Free, Vitamin D)

    Sweetened Condensed

    Vitamin A & D Added

    Vitamin D

**Winn Dixie -** Fat Free, Instant Nonfat Dry, Low Fat (1%, 2%), Organic (1% Low Fat, 2% Low Fat, Fat Free, Whole), Soy (Chocolate, Plain, Unsweetened, Vanilla), Whole

**Woodstock Farms -** Organic Milk (1%, 2%, Fat Free, Whole)

**Yoo-Hoo -** All Varieties

**Millet**

**Arrowhead Mills -** Hulled Millet, Millet Flour

**Bob's Red Mill▲ -** Flour, Grits/Meal, Hulled Millet

**Mints**

**Altoids -** Curiously Strong Mints Large Tins (Creme De Menthe, Peppermint, Wintergreen) *(Smalls Contain Gluten)*

**Andes -** Crème de Menthe

**Lowes Foods Brand -** Starlight Mints

**Safeway Brand -** Dessert, Star Light

**Vermints -** Café Express, Chai, Cinnamint, Gingermint, Peppermint, Wintermint

## Miso

**Eden Organic -** Organic Miso (Genmai, Shiro)

**Edward & Sons -** Miso Cup Savory Soup w/Seaweed

**South River -** Azuki Bean, Dandelion Leek, Garlic Red Pepper, Golden Millet, Hearty Brown Rice, Sweet Tasting Brown Rice, Sweet White

## Mixed Fruit... *All *Fresh* Fruits & Vegetables Are **Gluten-Free**

**Cascadian Farm -** Organic Frozen Tropical Fruit Blend

**Del Monte -**

Canned/Jarred Fruit (All Varieties)

Fruit Snack Cups (Metal, Plastic)

**Dole -** All Fruits (Bowls, Canned, Dried, Frozen, Jars) *(Except Real Fruit Bites)*

**Food Club Brand -** Frozen Berry Medley, Triple Cherry Mixed Fruit (Fruit Cups)

**Great Value Brand (Wal-Mart) -**

Canned (Triple Cherry Fruit Mix in Natural Flavored Cherry Light Syrup, Tropical Fruit Salad in Light Syrup & Fruit Juices)

Frozen (Berry Medley)

**Home Harvest Brand**

**Hy-Vee -** Fruit Cups (Mixed, Tropical), Mixed Fruit (Lite Chunk, Regular)

**Laura Lynn -** Canned

**Lowes Foods Brand -** Canned Fruit Cocktail (In Heavy Syrup, In Juice)

**Meijer Brand -** Frozen Tropical Fruit Blend, Mixed Fruit (Individually Quick Frozen, Regular)

**Publix -**

Canned (Chunky Mixed Fruit In Heavy Syrup, Fruit Cocktail In Heavy Syrup, Lite Chunky Mixed Fruit in Pear Juice)

Frozen (Mixed Fruit)

**S&W -** All Canned/Jarred Fruits

**Spartan Brand -** Frozen (Berry Medley, Mixed Fruit), In Heavy Syrup

**M**

**Stop & Shop Brand** - Fruit Mix In Heavy Syrup, Mixed Fruit, Very Cherry Fruit Mix In Light Syrup

**Wegmans Brand** - Fruit Cocktail (In Heavy Syrup, In Pear Juice, Regular)

**Winn Dixie** - Canned Chunky Mixed Fruit (Heavy Syrup, Light Syrup), Frozen (Berry Medley, Mixed Fruit), Fruit Cocktail (Heavy Syrup, Light Syrup)

**Woodstock Farms** - Tropical Fruit Mix

**Mixed Vegetables...** *All Fresh Fruits & Vegetables Are Gluten-Free*

**Albertsons** - Canned, Frozen *(Except Sweet Onion Rounds)*

**Birds Eye** - All Plain Frozen Vegetables *(Except With Sauce)*

**C & W** - All Plain Frozen Vegetables

**Cascadian Farm** - Organic Frozen (California Style Blend, Gardener's Blend Mixed Vegetables)

**Del Monte** - All Canned Vegetables

**Food Club Brand** - Canned Mixed Vegetables, Frozen (California Style, Florentine Style, Italian Style, Mixed Vegetables)

**Freshlike** - Frozen Plain Vegetables *(Except Pasta Combos and Seasoned Blends)*

**Full Circle** - Organic Frozen 4 Vegetable Blend

**Grand Selections** - Frozen Vegetables (Caribbean Blend)

**Great Value Brand (Wal-Mart)** -

Canned (Mixed Vegetables, Vegetable Medley)

Frozen Vegetable Mix (California Style, Italian Style)

**Green Giant** -

Frozen

Garden Vegetable Medley Seasoned

Mixed Vegetables

Simply Steam (Baby Vegetable Medley, Garden Vegetable Medley)

**Hannaford Brand** - Mixed Vegetables

**Home Harvest Brand** - Mixed Vegetables (Canned, Frozen)

## mixed vegetables

**M**

**Hy-Vee -**
- Canned Mixed Vegetables
- Frozen
  - California Mix
  - Country Trio
  - Feast Blend
  - Mixed Vegetables
  - Oriental Vegetables
  - Stew Vegetables

**Kroger Brand -** All Plain Vegetables (Canned, Frozen)

**Laura Lynn** - #2 Frozen Vegetables *(Except Breaded Okra, Hushpuppies, Onion Rings)*, Mixed Vegetables (No Salt, Regular)

**Lowes Foods Brand -** Frozen (California Blend, Fajita Blend, Italian Blend, Mixed Vegetables, Peking Stir Fry, Vegetables For Soup)

**Meijer Brand -**
- Canned Mixed
- Frozen
  - California Style
  - Fiesta
  - Florentine
  - Italian
  - Mexican
  - Mixed Vegetables (Organic, Regular)
  - Oriental
  - Parisian Style
  - Stew Mix
  - Stir Fry

**Midwest Country Fare -** Canned, Frozen (California Blend, Mixed Vegetables, Winter Mix)

**O Organics -** Frozen (California Style Vegetables, Mixed Vegetable Blend)

**Pictsweet -** All Plain Vegetables (Frozen)

**M** Publix -
 Canned Mixed
 Frozen Blends
  Alpine
  California
  Del Oro
  Gumbo
  Italian
  Japanese
  Mixed Vegetable
  Peas & Carrots
  Roma
  Soup Mix w/Tomatoes
  Succotash

**S&W** - All Canned Vegetables

**Safeway Brand** - Frozen Blends (Asian Style, California Style, Santa Fe Style, Stew Vegetables, Stir Fry, Tuscan Style Vegetables, Winter Blend), Mixed Vegetables (Canned, Frozen)

**Spartan Brand** - Canned Mixed Vegetables, Frozen (Baby Corn Blend, Baby Pea Blend, California Vegetables, Fiesta Vegetables, Italian Vegetables, Mixed Vegetables, Oriental Vegetables, Pepper Stirfry, Stew Mix Vegetables, Vegetables For Soup, Winter Blend)

**Stop & Shop Brand** -
 Blend (Country, Latino)
 Mixed Vegetables (No Added Salt, Regular)
 Stew Vegetables

**Tasty Bite** - Jaipur Vegetables, Kerala Vegetables, Vegetable Korma, Vegetable Supreme & Basmati Rice

**Trader Joe's** - All Plain Vegetables (Frozen)

**Wegmans Brand** -
 Mix (Santa Fe, Southern, Spring)
 Mixed Vegetables (Canned, Frozen)

**Winn Dixie -** Canned No Salt Added, Frozen Mixed Vegetables (Organic, Regular)

**Woodstock Farms -** Organic Frozen Plain Mixed Vegetables

## Mochi

**Grainaissance -** All Varieties

## Molasses

**Brer Rabbit -** Molasses (Blackstrap, Full Flavor, Mild)

**Grandma's -** Original, Robust

**Publix**

## Mousse

**Orgran▲ -** Chocolate Mousse Mix

## Muffins/Muffin Mix

**1-2-3 Gluten Free▲ -** Meredith's Marvelous Muffin/Quickbread Mix●

**365 Everyday Value -** Gluten Free (Cornbread & Muffin Mix, Muffin Mix)

**Andrea's Fine Foods▲ -** Banana, Blueberry, Carrot Spice, Chocolate Chunk, Pumpkin

**Aunt Gussie's▲ -** English Muffins (Cinnamon Raisin, Plain)

**Authentic Foods▲ -** Blueberry Muffin Mix, Chocolate Chip Muffin Mix

**Breads From Anna▲ -** Pancake & Muffin Mix (Apple, Cranberry, Maple)

**Cause You're Special ▲ -** Classic Muffin & Quickbread Mix, Lemon Poppy Seed Muffin Mix, Sweet Corn Muffin Mix

**Celiac Specialties▲ -** English, Mini Lemon Poppy, Mini Pumpkin Chocolate, Pumpkin

**Ener-G ▲ -** Brown Rice English Muffins w/ Flax, English Muffins

**Flax4Life -** Flax Muffins (Chunky Chocolate Chip●, Faithfull Carrot Raisin●, Hawaiian Pineapple Coconut●, Tantalizing Cranberry & Orange●, Wild Blueberry●)

**Flour Nut -** Muffin Mix (Austin's Maple Cinnamon, Maple Walnut)

**Foods By George▲ -** Muffins (Blueberry, Cinnamon Currant English, Corn, English, No-Rye Rye English)

**Gluten Free Life▲ -** Apple Pie, Blueberry, Carrot Cake, Chocolate Chip, The Ultimate Gluten Free Cake Muffin & Brownie Mix

**M**

**Gluten-Free Creations**▲ - English Muffins●, Chocolate Zucchini●, Cinnamon Rolls●, Cranberry Orange Pecan●, Lemon Poppyseed●, Pecan Sticky Rolls●

**Gluten-Free Essentials**▲ - Lemon Poppy Seed Bread & Muffin Mix●, Spice Cake & Muffin Mix●

**Gluten-Free Pantry**▲ - Muffin & Scone Mix, Quick Mix

**Glutino**▲ - Premium English Muffins

**Good Juju Bakery** ▲- Banana Nut Muffins

**Hodgson Mill**▲ - Apple Cinnamon Muffin Mix

**Kinnikinnick**▲ - Blueberry, Carrot, Chocolate Chip, Cranberry, Cornbread & Muffin Mix, Muffin Mix, Tapioca Rice English Muffin

**Madwoman Foods**▲ - Tea Cakes (Banana Chocolate, Banana Cinnamon, Blueberry, Chocolate Cherry, Cocoa Mocha, Lemon Poppyseed, Orange Chocolate, Orange Cranberry, Pecan Cocoa Mocha)

**Midge's Muffins** - Banana, Cherry Apple, Chocolate Chip, Cranberry, Blueberry, Pumpkin

**Mixes From The Heartland**▲ - Muffin Mix (Apple Cinnamon●, Blueberry●, Cinnamon Raisin●, Corn N' Cranberry●, Spring●, Zuchini●)

**Namaste Foods**▲ - Muffin Mix, Sugar-Free

**Only Oats** - Muffin Mix (Cinnamon Spice●, Decadent Chocolate●)

**Orgran**▲ - Muffin Mix (Chocolate, Lemon & Poppyseed)

**Pitter Patties** - Cheezini, Pasghetti, Spinach Patch, Viva Vegan, Yammy Chicken

**Really Great Food Company**▲ - Apple Spice Muffin Mix, Cornbread Muffin Mix, English Muffin Mix, Maple Raisin Muffin Mix, Sweet Muffin Mix, Vanilla Muffin Mix

**Skye Foods** - Muffins (Blueberry●, Chocolate Chunk●)

**Whole Foods Market Gluten Free Bakehouse** ▲ - Blueberry Muffins, Cherry Almond Streusel Muffins, Lemon Poppyseed, Morning Glory Muffins

**Mushrooms...** *All **Fresh** Fruits & Vegetables Are **Gluten-Free***

**Albertsons** - Pieces & Stems (No Salt, Regular)

**M**

**Birds Eye** - All Plain Frozen Vegetables *(Except With Sauce)*

**Cara Mia** - Marinated

**Eden Organic** - Maitake (Dried), Shiitake (Dried Sliced, Dried Whole)

**Food Club Brand** - Canned (Pieces & Stems, Whole)

**Great Value Brand (Wal-Mart) -** Canned Mushrooms (Pieces & Stems, Sliced)

**Green Giant** - Canned Mushrooms (Pieces & Stems, Sliced, Whole)

**Hannaford Brand** - Stems & Pieces (No Salt, Regular)

**Hy-Vee -** Sliced, Stems & Pieces

**Laura Lynn** - All Mushrooms

**Lowes Foods Brand -** Jar (Sliced, Whole)

**Meijer Brand** - Canned (Sliced, Whole), Canned Stems & Pieces (No Salt, Regular)

**Midwest Country Fare** - Mushrooms & Stems (No Salt Added, Regular)

**Pennsylvania Dutchman** - Sliced, Stems & Pieces, Whole

**Publix -** Sliced, Stems & Pieces

**Publix GreenWise Market -** Organic (Mushrooms, Portabella, Sliced Portabella)

**Safeway Brand -** Canned (Button Sliced)

**Trader Joe's -** Marinated w/Garlic

**Wegmans Brand -** Button, Pieces & Stems, Sliced

**Woodstock Farms -** Organic Frozen (Mixed, Shiitake)

Mustard

**Annie's Naturals -** Organic (Dijon, Honey, Horseradish, Yellow)

**Best Foods -** Deli Brown, Dijonnaise, Honey

**Bone Suckin'**

**Di Lusso -** Chipotle, Cranberry Honey, Deli Style, Dijon, Honey, Jalapeno

**Dietz & Watson -** Champagne Dill, Cranberry Honey, Jalapeno, Stone Ground, Sweet & Hot, Wasabi, Whole Grain Dijon

**Dorothy Lane Market -** Champagne, Classic Dijon, Honey

**Eden Organic -** Organic (Brown, Yellow)

**Emeril's** - Dijon (Kicked Up Horseradish, NY Deli Style, Smooth Honey, Yellow)

**Fischer & Wieser** - Smokey Mesquite, Sweet Heat, Sweet Sour & Smokey Sauce

**Food Club Brand** - Dijon, Honey, Regular, Regular w/White Wine, Spicy Brown, Yellow

**French's** - Classic Yellow, Honey, Honey Dijon, Horseradish, Spicy Brown

**Frontera** - Chipotle Honey Mustard Grilling Sauce

**Full Circle** - Organic (Spicy Brown, Yellow)

**Great Value Brand (Wal-Mart)** - Coarse Ground, Honey, Prepared Dijon, Prepared Mustard, Southwest Spicy Sweet & Hot Mustard, Spicy Brown

**Grey Poupon** - Country Dijon, Deli, Dijon, Harvest Coarse Ground, Hearty Spicy Brown, Mild & Creamy, Savory Honey

**Guldens**

**Hannaford Brand** - Dijon, Honey, Spicy Brown, Yellow

**Heinz** - All Varieties

**Hellmann's** - Deli Brown, Dijonnaise, Honey

**Home Harvest Brand** - Prepared

**Hy-Vee** - Dijon, Honey, Regular, Spicy Brown

**Jack Daniel's** - Hickory Smoke, Honey Dijon, Horseradish, Old No.7, Spicy Southwest, Stone Ground Dijon

**Laura Lynn** - All Varieties

**Lou's Famous** - Hot Mustard w/Horseradish

**Meijer Brand** - Dijon Squeeze, Honey Squeeze, Horseradish Squeeze, Hot & Spicy, Salad Squeeze, Spicy Brown Squeeze

**Mr. Spice Organic** - Honey Mustard Sauce & Marinade

**O Organics** - Coarse Ground Dijon, Dijon, Honey, Spicy Brown, Stone Ground w/Horseradish, Sweet & Spicy, Yellow

**Publix** - Classic Yellow, Deli Style, Dijon, Honey, Spicy Brown

**Publix GreenWise Market** - Creamy Yellow, Spicy Yellow, Tangy Dijon

**M**

**N**

**Safeway Brand** - Coarse Ground Dijon, Dijon, Honey Mustard, Spicy Brown, Stone Ground Horseradish, Sweet & Spicy

**Spartan Brand** - Dijon, Honey, Prepared, Spicy Brown, Sweet & Hot

**Stop & Shop Brand** - Creamy Dijon, Deli, Dijon, Honey, Old Grainy, Raspberry Grainy, Spicy Brown, Tarragon Dijon, Yellow

**Taste of Inspirations** - Cranberry, Honey, Maine Maple, Raspberry Honey, Wasabi Ginger

**Texas Pete** - Honey Mustard

**Trader Joe's** - Dijon, Organic Yellow

**Wegmans Brand** - Classic Yellow, Dijon (Traditional, Whole Grain), Honey, Horseradish, Smooth & Tangy, Spicy Brown

**Winn Dixie** - Dijon, Honey, Horseradish, Spicy Brown, Yellow

**Woodstock Farms** - Dijon, Stone Ground, Yellow

Mutter

**Tamarind Tree** - Dhingri Mutter

# N

Nayonaise

**Nasoya** - Dijon Style, Fat Free, Original

Nectars

**Bionaturae** - Organic (Apple, Apricot, Bilberry, Carrot Apple, Peach, Pear, Plum, Sicilian Lemon, Sour Cherry, Strawberry, Wildberry)

Neufchatel... see Cream Cheese

Noodles

**A Taste Of Thai** - Rice Noodles (Regular, Thin, Wide)

**Annie Chun's** - Rice Noodles (Original, Pad Thai Basil)

**Blue Chip Group** - Gluten Free Rice Noodles

**Manischewitz** - Passover Noodles

**Mixes From The Heartland▲** - Noodle Mix (Creamy Italian●, Plain●, Spinach●)

**N**

**Seitenbacher** - Gourmet Noodles Gluten Free Golden Ribbon, Gluten Free Rigatoni

**Sharwood's** - Rice Noodles

**Thai Kitchen** -

Instant Noodle Bowls (Bangkok Curry, Garlic & Vegetable, Lemongrass & Chili, Mushroom, Roasted Garlic, Spring Onion, Thai Ginger)

Noodle Carts (Pad Thai, Roasted Garlic, Thai Peanut, Toasted Sesame)

Rice Noodles (Stir-Fry Rice Noodles, Thin Rice Noodles)

Stir Fry Rice Noodle Meal Kit (Lemongrass & Chili, Original Pad Thai, Thai Peanut)

Take Out Boxes (Ginger & Sweet Chili, Original Pad Thai, Thai Basil & Chili)

**Thai Pavilion** - Rice Noodles (Green Curry, Pad Thai, Spicy Pad Thai, Thai Peanut)

**Trader Joe's** - Rice Noodles

**Nut Beverage**

**Blue Diamond** - Almond Breeze (Chocolate, Original, Vanilla), Almond Breeze Unsweetened (Chocolate, Original, Vanilla)

**MimicCreme** - Sugar Free Sweetened, Sweetened, Unsweetened

**Pacific Natural Foods** - All Natural Hazelnut Original, Organic Almond (Chocolate, Original, Vanilla)

**Nut Butter... see Peanut Butter**

**Nutritional Supplements**

**Boost Drink** - All Varieties *(Except Chocolate Malt)*

**Carnation** - All Instant Breakfast Powders *(Except Classic Chocolate Malt)*

**Ensure** - All Liquid Products

**Gatorade** - Nutrition Shakes (All Varieties)

**Glucerna** - All Shakes

**Hannaford Brand** - Strawberry, Vanilla, Vanilla Plus

**N**

**Hy-Vee -** Nutritional Supplement (Chocolate (Plus, Regular), Strawberry (Plus, Regular), Vanilla (Plus, Regular))

**MLO -** Brown Rice Protein Powder

**Meijer Brand -**

Diet Quick Extra Thin (Chocolate, Strawberry, Vanilla)

Gluco Burst (Arctic Cherry, Chocolate Diabetic Nutritional Drink, Strawberry DND, Vanilla DND)

**Nutripals -** Balanced Nutrition Drinks (Chocolate, Strawberry, Vanilla)

**Odwalla -** All Drinks *(Except Super Protein Vanilla Al Mondo & Superfood)*

**Pedialyte -** All Flavors

**Pediasure -** Drinks (Banana Cream, Berry Cream, Chocolate, Strawberry, Vanilla, Vanilla w/Fiber)

**Ruth's -** Organic Hemp Protein Powder (E3Live & Maca, Hemp Protein Power, Hemp w/Sprouted Flax & Maca)

**Safeway Brand -** All Flavors of Nutritional Shakes (Plus, Regular)

**Salba●**

**Worldwide Pure Protein -** Banana Crèam, Chocolate, Strawberry Cream, Vanilla

## Nuts

**Albertsons -** Cashews (Halves & Pieces, Lightly Salted, Whole), Mixed Nuts (Deluxe, Lighty Salted, Regular), Peanuts (Dry Roasted, Dry Roasted Unsalted, Honey Roasted, Lightly Salted, Lightly Salted Party, Party)

**Andrea's Fine Foods▲ -** Glazed Pecans (Butter Toffee, Dark Chocolate, Milk Chocolate, Sesame Toffee)

**Back To Nature -** All Natural Nantucket Blend

**Eden Organic -** Tamari Dry Roasted Almonds

**Emerald -**

Glazed Walnuts (Apple Cinnamon, Butter Toffee, Chocolate Brownie, 'N Almonds, Original)

Glazed Pecans (Original, Pecan Pie)

**N**

On The Go Canisters (Cashew Halves & Pieces, Cocktail Peanuts, Cocoa Roast Almonds, Deluxe Mix Nuts, Dry Roasted Almonds, Dry Roated Peanuts, Mixed Nuts, Seasalt & Pepper Cashews, Smoked Almonds, Whole Cashews)

**Food Club Brand** - Almonds (Natural, Roasted & Salted), Cashews (Halves & Pieces, Lightly Salted Halves & Pieces, Whole), Dry Roasted Peanuts (Honey Roasted, Lightly Salted, Original, Unsalted), Honey Roasted Peanuts, Mixed Nuts (Deluxe, Less Than 50% Peanuts), Party Peanuts (Lightly Salted, Original), Redskin Spanish, Smoked Almonds

**Frito Lay -**

Cashews

Deluxe Mixed Nuts

Honey Roasted (Cashews, Peanuts)

Hot Peanuts

Praline Pecans

Salted (Almonds, Peanuts)

Smoked Almonds

**Great Value Brand (Wal-Mart)** - Cashew (Pieces, Whole), Deluxe Mixed, Honey Roasted, Mixed, Party Peanuts

**Hannaford Brand** - Walnut Halves & Pieces

**Harrison Select Brand** - Dry Roasted Peanuts

**Home Harvest Brand** - Peanuts (Dry Roasted, Oil Roasted Spanish)

**Hy-Vee -**

Almonds (Dry Roasted, Honey Roasted, Natural, Raw, Roasted, Roasted & Salted)

Black Walnuts

Cashews (Halves & Pieces, Honey Roasted, Sea Salted, Whole, Whole Lightly Salted, w/Almonds)

English Walnut Pieces

English Walnuts

Macadamia

Mixed Nuts (Deluxe Lightly Salted, Deluxe No Peanuts, Lightly Salted, Regular, w/Pistachios)

Natural Almonds (Regular, Sliced)

Peanuts (Butter Toffee, Dry Roasted, Dry Roasted Unsalted, Honey Roasted, Party)

Pecan (Pieces, Regular)

Raw Spanish Peanuts

Salted Peanuts (Blanched, Spanish)

Slivered Almonds

**Katy Sweet▲** - Nuts (Bar-B-Que●, Double Dip Chocolate Nuts●, Glazed Pecans●, Holy Mole●, Pecan Krunch●, Pecan Quartets●, Peppered Pecans●, Roasted & Salted Pecans●, Smokin'Chipotle Pecans●, Sugar & Spice Pecans●)

**Laura Lynn -**

Almonds (Roasted, Smoked)

Cashew Halves

Deluxe Mixed Nuts

Dry Roast Nuts

Light Salt (Cashews, Dry Roast Nuts, Mixed Nuts, Peanuts)

Mixed Nuts

Peanuts (Honey Roast, Party, Spanish)

Unsalted Dry Roast Nuts

Whole Cashews

**Mareblu Naturals -**

Crunch (Almond, Almond Coconut, Cashew Coconut, Cashew, CranMango Cashew, Dark Chocolate Cashew, Pecan Cinnamon, Pistachio, Pistachio Pumpkin Seed)

Trail Mix Crunch (Blueberry Pomegranate, Cranberry Pomegranate, Cranblueberry Trail, Cranstrawberry Trail, Pecan Trail, Pistachio Trail, Regular)

**Meijer Brand -**

Almonds (Blanched Sliced, Blanched Slivered, Natural Sliced, Slivered, Whole)

Cashews (Halves w/Pieces, Halves w/Pieces Lightly Salted, Whole)

Mixed (Deluxe, Lightly Salted, Regular)

**N**

Nut Topping

Peanuts

    Blanched (Regular, Slightly Salted)

    Butter Toffee

    Dry Roasted (Lightly Salted, Regular, Unsalted)

    Honey Roasted

    Hot & Spicy

    Spanish

Pecan (Chips, Halves)

Pine

Walnuts (Black, Chips, Halves & Pieces)

**Nut Harvest -**

Natural

    Honey Roasted Peanuts

    Lightly Roasted Almonds

    Nut & Fruit Mix

    Sea Salted (Peanuts, Whole Cashews)

**Planters -** Cashews Halves & Pieces, Dry Roasted Peanuts, Extra Large Virginia Peanuts, Fancy Whole Cashews, Honey Roasted Peanuts, Mixed Nuts, Pistachio Lovers Mix

**Publix -**

Almonds (Chocolate Covered, Natural Whole, Salted, Sliced, Smoked)

Cashews (Dry Roasted, Halves & Pieces, Halves & Pieces Lightly Salted, Honey Roasted, Premium Salted Jumbo, Whole)

Macadamia

Mixed (Deluxe, Lightly Salted, Regular)

Peanuts (Dry Roasted Lightly Salted, Dry Roasted Salted, Dry Roasted Unsalted, Honey Roasted, Oil Roasted, Premium Salted Jumbo, Salted Party)

Pecan Halves

Walnuts

**N**

**Sabritas** - Picante Peanuts, Salt & Lime Peanuts

**Safeway Brand -**
    Almonds (Roasted & Salted, Smoked Flavored, Whole Natural)
    Butter Toffee
    Honey Roasted Party Peanuts
    Mixed (Deluxe, Regular)
    Nuts Cashews (Halves, Pieces, Whole)

**Spartan Brand -**
    Cashews (Halves w/Pieces, Whole)
    Mixed (Fancy w/Macadamias, Lightly Salted, Nature, Regular)
    Peanuts (Blanched Roasted, Butter Toffee, Dry Roasted (Honey, Regular, Salted), Honey Roasted, Lightly Salted Dry Roasted, No Salt Dry Roasted, Spanish)

**Sunkist** - Gourmet Oven Roasted Almonds, Pistachios (Dry Roasted, Kernels)

**Trader Joe's -**
    All Raw & Roasted Nuts
    Almond Nut Meal
    Cinnamon Almonds
    Marcona Almonds

**True North** - Almond (Clusters, Cranberry Vanilla Clusters, Pistachios Walnut Pecans), Peanut Clusters (Pecan Almond, Regular)

**Wegmans Brand -**
    Cashews (Salted, Unsalted)
    Dry Roasted (Macadamias, Seasoned Peanuts, Seasoned Sunflower Kernels, Unsalted Peanuts)
    Honey Roasted (Peanuts, Whole Cashews)
    Natural Whole Almonds
    Party Peanuts (Roasted Lightly Salted, Salted)
    Peanuts (Salted In The Shell, Unsalted In The Shell)
    Peanuts Dry Roasted (Lightly Salted, Seasoned, Unsalted)

**N**

Pine Nuts Italian Classics

Roasted

    Almonds (Salted)

    Cashew Halves & Pieces Salted

    Deluxe Mixed Nuts w/Macadamias Salted

    Jumbo (Cashew Mix w/Almonds Pecans & Brazils, Cashews)

    Mixed Nuts w/Peanuts (Lightly Salted)

    Party Mixed Nuts w/Peanuts (Salted, Unsalted)

    Party Peanuts (Salted, Lightly Salted)

    Spanish Peanuts Salted

    Whole Cashews (Salted, Unsalted)

    Virginia Peanuts (Chocolate Covered, Salted)

**Woodstock Farms -**

Organic Nuts (Almonds (Chocolate (Dark, Milk) Covered w/Evaporated Cane Juice, Regular), Brazil, Cashews (Large Whole (Regular, Roasted & Salt), Pieces), Pecan Halves, Pine, Pistachios (No Salt, Roasted & Salt), Soy Nuts (No Salt, Roasted), Walnuts Halves & Pieces)

Almonds (Non Pareil, Roasted & No Salt, Roasted & Salt, Supreme, Tamari, Thick Sliced)

Brazil

Cashew (Large Whole (Regular, Roasted))

Cocoa Dusted Dark Chocolate Almonds

Deluxe Mixed Nuts Roasted

Extra Fancy Mixed Nuts

Hazelnut Filberts

Peanuts Honey Roasted

Pecan Halves

Pine

Soynuts Roasted (No Salt, Regular)

Walnuts Halves & Pieces

Yogurt Covered Almonds w/Evaporated Cane Juice

# O  O

## Oatmeal

**GlutenFreeda▲** - Instant Oatmeal (Apple Cinnamon w/Flax, Banana Maple w/Flax, Maple Raisin w/Flax)

## Oats

**Bob's Red Mill▲** - Gluten Free Rolled Oats

**Chateau Cream Hill Estates** - Lara's Rolled Oats●

**Gifts of Nature▲** - Old Fashioned Rolled Oats, Whole Oat Groats

**Gluten-Free Oats▲** - Old Fashioned Rolled Oats●

**Montana Monster Munchies** - Whole Grain (Grab & Go●, Quick Oats●, Rolled Oats●)

**Only Oats** - Oat Flakes (Quick, Regular), Steel Cut Oat Pearls●

## Oil

**365 Every Day Value** - Expeller Pressed Canola Oil, Extra Virgin Olive Oil (Italian, Regular)

**365 Organic Every Day Value** - Expeller Pressed Canola Oil, Olive Oil Imported

**Albertsons** - Olive Oil, Canola Oil

**Annies Naturals** -

Olive Oil (Basil, Dipping, Roasted Pepper)

Olive Oil Extra Virgin (Roasted Garlic)

**Authentic Food Artisan (AFA)** - Lapas Organic Extra Virgin Olive Oil, McEvoy Olive Oil, Nunez de Prado Organic Olive Oil

**Bakers & Chefs** - 100% Pure Clear Frying Oil

**Bertolli** - All Olive Oils

**Bionaturae** - Organic Extra Virgin Olive Oil

**Bragg** - All Varieties

**Carapelli** - Olive Oil

**Crisco** - Oil (100% Pure Extra Virgin Olive, Frying Blend, Light Olive, Natural Blend, Pure (Canola, Corn, Olive, Peanut, Vegetable), Puritan Canola w/Omega 3DHA)

**Eden Organic -**

> Olive Oil Spanish Extra Virgin
>
> Organic (Hot Pepper Sesame Oil, Safflower Oil, Sesame Oil Extra Virgin, Soybean Oil)
>
> Toasted Sesame Oil

**Food Club Brand** - Canola, Corn, Vegetable

**Full Circle** - Organic (Canola, Extra Virgin Olive Oil)

**Grand Selections** - 100% Pure & Natural Olive Oil, Extra Light, Extra Virgin Olive Oil, Olive Oil (Basil, Chili, Garlic, Lemon)

**Great Value Brand (Wal-Mart)** - Canola Oil Blend, Olive Oil (Extra Virgin, Light Tasting), Pure Oil (Canola, Corn, Vegetable)

**Hannaford Brand** - Canola Oil, Corn Oil, Olive (Extra Virgin, Extra Virgin Imported, Light, Pure), Vegetable Oil

**Home Harvest Brand** - Blended, Corn, Vegetable

**House of Tsang** - Oil (Hot Chili Sesame, Mongolian Fire, Sesame, Wok)

**Hy-Vee -**

> 100% Pure Oil (Canola, Corn, Vegetable)
>
> Natural Blend Oil
>
> Vegetable (Oil Shortening, Shortening Butter Flavor)

**Kroger Brand** - Canola, Corn, Olive, Sunflower, Vegetable

**Laura Lynn** - Blended, Canola, Corn, Peanut, Vegetable

**Lee Kum Kee** - Oil (Blended Sesame, Chili, Pure Sesame, Sesame)

**Lowes Foods Brand** - 100% Pure, Canola, Corn, Extra Virgin, Peanut, Vegetable

**Manischewitz** - Vegetable

**Manitoba Harvest** - Hemp Seed Oil (Organic, Regular)

**Mazola** - All Oils

**Meijer Brand** - Blended Canola/Vegetable, Canola, Corn, Olive (100% Pure Italian Classic, Extra Virgin (Italian Classic, Regular), Italian Select Premium Extra Virgin, Milder Tasting, Regular), Oil Olive Infused (Garlic & Basil Italian, Roasted Garlic Italian, Spicy Red Pepper Italian), Sunflower, Peanut, Vegetable

**Member's Mark** - 100% Pure Olive Oil

O

**Midwest Country Fare** - 100% Pure Vegetable Oil, Vegetable Oil

**Newman's Own Organics** - Extra Virgin Olive Oil

**Nutiva** - Organic (Extra Virgin Coconut Oil, Hemp Oil)

**O Organics** - Extra Virgin

**Odell's** - Popcorn Popping Oil

**Oskri Organics** - Extra Virgin Olive Oil, Flaxseed Oil, Grapeseed Oil, Omega 3 Olive Oil, Sesame Seed Oil

**Publix** - Oil (Canola, Corn, Extra Virgin, Light Olive, Olive, Peanut, Pure Italian Olive, Vegetable)

**Ruth's** - Certified Organic Hemp Oil

**Safeway Brand** - Canola, Canola Vegetable Blend, Corn, Vegetable

**Safeway Select** - Olive Oil (Extra Light, Extra Virgin, Regular)

**Simply Enjoy** - Apulian Regional Extra Virgin Olive Oil (Apulian, Sicilian, Tuscan, Umbrian)

**Spartan Brand** - Blended, Canola, Corn, Olive (Extra Virgin, Regular), Vegetable

**Spectrum Organic Products** -

Almond Refined

Apricot Kernel Refined

Avocado Refined

Canola (High Heat, Organic Refined, Regular)

Coconut Organic (Refined, Unrefined)

Corn Unrefined

Grapeseed Refined

Olive Oil (All Varieties)

Peanut Unrefined

Safflower (Organic High Heat Refined, Regular High Heat, Unrefined)

Sesame (Organic Unrefined, Organic Unrefined Toasted, Refined, Regular, Unrefined Toasted)

Soy Organic Refined

Sunflower Organic High Heat Refined

Walnut Refined

**Star** - Extra (Light, Virgin), Originale

**Stop & Shop Brand** - Blended, Canola, Corn, Extra Light Olive,
  MiCasa (Corn, Vegetable), Pure Olive, Soybean, Vegetable

**Tassos** - Olive Oil (Extra Virgin, Fine, Organic Extra, Peza Crete Extra)

**Trader Joe's** - Oils (All)

**Wegmans Brand** -

  Basting w/Garlic & Herbs

  Canola

  Corn

  Extra Virgin (Black Truffle, Campania Style, Regular, Sicilian
    Lemon, Sicilian Style, Tuscany Style)

  Grapeseed

  Mild Olive

  Organic (Extra Virgin, Sunflower Oil)

  Peanut

  Pumpkin Seed

  Pure

  Submarine Sandwich

  Sunflower Oil

  Vegetable

**Winn & Lovett** - Olive Oil (Balsamic, Extra Virgin, Garlic, Mediterranean,
  Roasted Garlic, Zesty Italian)

**Winn Dixie** - Canola, Corn, Olive, Peanut, Vegetable

**Okra...** *All **Fresh** Fruits & Vegetables Are **Gluten-Free***

  **365 Every Day Value** - Cut Okra

  **Albertsons** - Frozen (Cut, Whole)

  **Lowes Foods Brand** - Cut

  **Meijer Brand** - Frozen (Chopped, Whole)

  **Pictsweet** - All Vegetables (Frozen)

  **Publix** - Frozen (Cut, Whole Baby)

  **Safeway Brand** - Frozen

**O**

**Spartan Brand** - Cut, Whole

**Trappey** - Okra

**Winn Dixie** - Frozen (Cut, Diced, Whole)

**Woodstock Farms** - Organic Frozen Cut Okra

**Olive Oil... see Oil**

**Olives**

**Albertsons**

**B&G** - Black, Green

**Di Lusso** - Green Ionian, Mediterranean Mixed

**Food Club Brand** - Pitted (Large, Medium)

**Great Value Brand (Wal-Mart)** -

Chopped Ripe

Large Pitted Ripe

Medium Pitted Ripe

Minced Pimento Stuffed (Manzanilla, Queen)

Sliced Ripe

**Hannaford Brand** - Pitted Ripe (Extra Large, Large, Medium, Small),
Sliced Ripe, Sliced Salad, Stuffed (Manzanilla, Queen)

**Hy-Vee** -

Chopped Ripe

Manzanilla Olives

Medium Ripe Black

Queen

Ripe Black (Jumbo, Large)

Sliced (Ripe Black, Salad)

**Krinos** - Imported Kalamata Olives

**Kroger Brand** - Black (Not Stuffed), Green (Not Stuffed), Green
Pimento Stuffed

**Laura Lynn** - All Olives (Green, Ripe)

**Lowes Foods Brand** - Chopped Ripe, Manzanilla Stuffed, Plain
Queen, Salad Sliced, Ripe Pitted (Jumbo, Large, Medium, Small),
Sliced (Buffet Ripe, Ripe)

**O**

**Meijer Brand -** Manzanilla Stuffed (Placed, Thrown, Tree), Queen (Stuffed Placed, Whole Thrown), Ripe (Large, Medium, Pitted Jumbo, Pitted Small, Sliced), Salad, Salad Sliced

**Midwest Country Fare -** Large Ripe Black, Sliced Ripe Black

**Peloponnese -** Kalamata Olives

**Publix -** Colossal, Green, Large, Ripe, Small

**Safeway Brand -** Black Olives, Manzanilla

**Santa Barbara Olive Co. -** Garlic Stuffed

**Spartan Brand -** Ripe Pitted Olives (Jumbo, Large, Medium, Sliced, Small)

**Star -** Spanish Olives (Manzanilla, Queen)

**Stop & Shop Brand -**

Manzanilla Olives (Sliced, Stuffed)

Pitted Black Ripe Olives Chopped

Stuffed Queen

Whole & Sliced (Jumbo, Large, Medium, Small)

**Tassos -** Black Olives In Extra Virgin Olive Oil & Red Wine Vinegar, Blonde Olives In Extra Virgin Olive Oil & Red Wine Vinegar, Evian Olives In Sea Salt Brine, Kalamata In Tassos Extra Virgin Olive Oil & Red Wine Vinegar, Stuffed Almond In Sea Salt Brine

**Trader Joe's -**

Colossal Olives Stuffed w/(Garlic Cloves, Jalapeño Peppers)

Pitted Kalamata

Stuffed Queen Sevillano

**Wegmans Brand -**

Greek Mix

Kalamata (Pitted, Whole)

Pitted Ripe (Colossal, Extra Large, Medium)

Ripe (Pitted Colossal, Pitted Extra Large, Pitted Medium, Sliced)

Spanish (Manzanilla, Queen, Salad)

Stuffed w/ (Almonds, Garlic, Red Peppers)

**Winn Dixie -** Green (All Varieties), Ripe (All Varieties)

**O**

**Onions...** *All **Fresh** Fruits & Vegetables Are **Gluten-Free***

    **Birds Eye -** All Plain Frozen Vegetables *(Except With Sauce)*

    **Harry Ramsdens -** Pickled Silverskin Onions In Spirit Vinegar

    **Lowes Foods Brand -** Frozen Diced

    **Meijer Brand -** Frozen Chopped

    **Publix -** Frozen (Diced, Chopped)

    **Trader Joe's -** All Plain Vegetables (Frozen)

    **Wegmans Brand -** Whole Onions In Brine

    **Winn Dixie -** Frozen Pearl Onions

**Orange Juice... see Drinks/Juice**

**Oranges...** *All **Fresh** Fruits & Vegetables Are **Gluten-Free***

    Sunkist

**Oyster Sauce**

    **Lee Kum Kee -** Panda Oyster Flavored Sauce (5 Gal, 55 Gal)

    **Panda Brand -** Green Label Oyster Flavored Sauce, Lo Mein Oyster Flavored Sauce

    **Wok Mei -** All Natural Oyster Flavored Sauce

**Oysters...** *All **Fresh** Seafood Is **Gluten-Free (Non-Marinated, Unseasoned)***

    **Bumble Bee -** Smoked, Whole

    **Chicken Of The Sea  -** Regular, Smoked (In Oil, In Water), Whole

    **Crown Prince -** Whole Boiled, Smoked In Cottonseed Oil

    **Crown Prince Natural -**

        Smoked In Pure Olive Oil

        Whole Boiled In Water

    **Great Value Brand (Wal-Mart) -** Canned Smoked Oysters

    **Ocean Prince -**

        Fancy Whole Smoked In Cottonseed Oil

        Whole Boiled

    **Trader Joe's -** Whole Smoked Oysters In Olive Oil

# P P

## Pancakes/Pancake Mix & Waffles/Waffle Mix

**1-2-3 Gluten Free**▲ - Allie's Awesome Buckwheat Pancake Mix●

**365 Everyday Value** - Gluten Free Pancake & Waffle Mix

**Arrowhead Mills** - Gluten Free Pancake & Waffle Mix, Wild Rice Pancake & Waffle Mix

**Authentic Foods**▲ - Pancake & Baking Mix

**Blue Chip Baker** - Gluten Free Pancake Mix

**Bob's Red Mill**▲ - Gluten Free Pancake Mix

**Breads From Anna**▲ - Pancake & Muffin Mix (Apple, Cranberry, Maple)

**Celiac Specialties**▲ - Pancake Mix (Buttermilk, Plain & Flaxseed)

**Cherrybrook Kitchen** - Gluten Free Pancake Mix *(Box Must Say Gluten-Free)*

**El Peto**▲ - Pancake Mix

**Food-Tek Fast & Fresh** - Minute Waffle Mix

**Gluten Free Sensations** - Pancake & Waffle Mix

**Gluten-Free Creations**▲ - Buckwheat Pancake Mix●, Mighty Mesquite Pancake Mix●

**Gluten-Free Essentials**▲ - Pancake & Waffle Mix●

**Gluten-Free Pantry**▲ - Brown Rice Pancake Mix

**Glutino**▲ - Pancake Mix

**Grandma Ferdon's**▲ - Pancake/Waffle Mix●

**Hodgson Mill**▲ - Gluten Free Pancake & Waffle Mix

**Hol Grain** - Pancake & Waffle Mix

**Kinnikinnick**▲ - Pancake & Waffle Mix

**Larrowe's** - Instant Buckwheat Pancake Mix

**Laurel's Sweet Treats** ▲- Bulk Pancake Mix, Pancake & Waffle Mix

**Linda's Gourmet Latkes** - Potato Pancake Latkes

**Manischewitz** - Pancake Mix (Potato, Sweetened Potato)

**Maple Grove Farms of Vermont** - Gluten Free Pancake Mix

**P**

**Mixes From The Heartland▲** - Pancake Mix (Apple Cinnamon●, Cornmeal●, Country●)

**Namaste Foods▲** - Waffle & Pancake Mix

**Nature's Path** - Frozen Organic Waffles (Buckwheat Wildberry, Homestyle Gluten Free, Mesa Sunrise Omega 3)

**Only Oats** - Whole Oat Pancake Mix●

**Orgran▲** - Apple & Cinnamon Pancake Mix, Buckwheat Pancake Mix, Plain Pancake Mix (w/Sorghum)

**Pamelas Products▲** - Baking & Pancake Mix

**Really Good Foods** - Classic Pancake Mix

**Ruby Range** - Southwest Pancakes Gluten Free Baking Mix●

**Sylvan Border Farm** - Pancake & Waffle Mix

**Toro▲** - Waffle & Pancake Mix

**Trader Joe's** - Gluten Free Homestyle Pancakes, Gluten Free Pancake & Waffle Mix, Wheat Free Toaster Waffles

**Van's All Natural** - Apple Cinnamon, Blueberry, Buckwheat, Flax, French Toast Sticks, Homestyle, Mini

## Paneer

**Amy's** - Indian Mattar Paneer (Light In Sodium, Regular), Indian Palak Paneer

**Tamarind Tree** - Palak Paneer

**Tasty Bite** - Peas Paneer, Peas Paneer & Basmati Rice

**Trader Joe's** - Paneer Tikka Masala

## Papaya... *All **Fresh** Fruits & Vegetables Are **Gluten-Free***

**Native Forest** - Organic Papaya Chunks

**Woodstock Farms** - Organic Frozen Papaya Chunks

## Pappadums

**Patak's** - Pappadums (Black Peppercorn, Garlic, Plain)

**Sharwood's** - Indian Puppodums (Crushed Garlic & Corriander, Plain)

## Paprika... see Seasonings

## Parmesan Cheese... see Cheese

**P** Pasta

**Allegaroo**▲ - Chili Mac, Spaghetti, Spyglass Noodles

**Ancient Harvest Quinoa** - Elbows, Garden Pagodas, Linguine, Rotelle, Shells, Spaghetti, Veggie Curls

**Annie Chun's** - Rice Noodles (Original, Pad Thai)

**Aproten** - Fettuccine, Fusilli, Penne, Rigatini, Spaghetti, Tagliatelle

**Berreta** - Gluten Free Rice Pasta (Fusilli, Penne, Spaghetti)

**Bi-Aglut** - Fusilli, Lasagne, Maccheroncini, Penne, Sedani, Spaghetti, Tagliatelle

**Bionaturae**▲ - Organic Gluten Free (Elbow, Fusilli, Penne, Spaghetti)

**Conte's Pasta** - Cheese Stuffed Shells, Gnocchi, Pierogies (Potato Cheese Onion, Potato Onion), Ravioli (Cheese, Cheese Spinach)

**Cornito** - Elbow Macaroni, Mystic Flames Noodles, Rainbow Rotini, Rigatoni, Rotini, Sea Waves, Spaghetti

**DeBoles** -

Corn Pasta (Elbow Style, Spaghetti)

Gluten Free Rice (Angel Hair & Golden Flax, Elbow Style Pasta & Cheese, Shells & Cheddar, Spirals & Golden Flax)

Gluten Free Multi Grain (Penne, Spaghetti)

Rice Pasta (Angel Hair, Fettuccini, Lasagna, Penne, Spaghetti, Spirals)

**Eden Organic** - Bifun, Kuzu, Mung Bean

**Ener-G** ▲ - White Rice (Lasagna, Macaroni, Small Shells, Spaghetti, Vermicelli)

**Gillian's Foods**▲ - Fetuccini, Fusilli, Penne, Spaghetti

**Glutano**▲ - Fusilli, Penne, Spaghetti

**Glutino**▲ - Brown Rice (Fusilli, Macaroni, Penne, Spaghetti)

**Grandma Ferdon's**▲ - Brown Rice (Chow Mein Noodles●, Elbows●, Fettuccini●, Lasagna●, Spaghetti●)

**Hodgson Mill**▲ - Gluten Free Brown Rice (Angel Hair Pasta, Elbows, Linguine, Penne, Spaghetti)

**Lundberg**▲ - Organic Brown Rice Pasta - Elbow, Penne, Rotini, Spaghetti

**P**

**Manischewitz** - Passover Noodles

**Mrs. Leepers** - Corn Pasta (Elbows, Rotelli, Spaghetti, Vegetable Radiatore), Dinners (Beef Lasagna, Beef Stroganoff, Cheeseburger Mac, Creamy Tuna, Chicken Alfredo, Mac & Cheese), Rice Pasta (Alphabets, Elbows, Kids Shapes, Penne, Spaghetti, Vegetable Twists)

**Namaste Foods▲** - Pasta Meals (Pasta Pisavera, Say Cheez, Taco)

**Notta Pasta** - Fettuccine, Linguine, Spaghetti

**Orgran▲** -

Buckwheat Spirals

Buontempo Rice Pasta (Penne, Shells, Spirals)

Canned (Alternative Grain Spaghetti, Spaghetti In Tomato Sauce, Spirals In Tomato Sauce)

Corn & Vegetable Pasta Shells

Corn Pasta Spirals

Corn & Spinach Rigati

Essential Fibre (Penne, Spirals)

Garlic & Parsley Rice Pasta Shells

Italian Style Spaghetti

Pasta & Sauce (Tomato Basil)

Pasta Ready Meals (Tomato & Basil, Vegetable Bolognese)

Rice & Corn (Herb Pasta, Macaroni, Mini Lasagne Sheets, Penne, Risoni Garlic Herb, Spaghetti, Spirals, Tortelli, Vegetable Animal Shapes, Vegetable Corkscrews)

Rice & Millet Spirals

Rice Pasta Spirals

Super Grains Multigrain Pasta (w/Amaranth, w/Quinoa)

Tomato & Basil Corn Pasta

Vegetable Rice (Penne, Spirals)

**Pastariso▲** - Organic Brown Rice (Angel Hair, Elbows, Fettuccine, Lasagna, Linguine, Penne, Rotini, Spaghetti, Vermicelli), Spinach Spaghetti, Vegetable Rotini

**P** **Pastato▲** - Elbows, Shells, Spaghetti

**Rizopia** -

Brown Rice (Elbows, Fettuccine, Fusilli, Lasagne, Penne, Shells, Spaghetti, Spirals)

Organic Brown Rice (Elbows, Fantasia, Fettuccine, Fusilli, Penne, Spaghetti)

Organic Wild Rice (Elbows, Fusilli, Penne, Radiatore, Shells, Spaghetti)

Spinach Brown Rice Spaghetti

Vegetable Brown Rice Fusilli

White Rice Spaghetti

**Rustichella** - Gluten Free Pasta (Corn Fusillotti, Corn Spaghetti, Rice Penne, Rice Spaghetti)

**Sam Mills ▲** - Corn Pasta (Conchiliette, Cornetti Rigati, Fusilli, Lasagna, Penne Rigate, Rigatoni, Tubetti Rigati)

**Schar▲** - Anellini, Fusilli, Multigrain Penne Rigate, Penne, Spaghetti, Tagliatelle

**Seitenbacher** - Gourmet Noodles Gluten Free Golden Ribbon, Gluten Free Rigatoni

**Tinkyada▲** -

Brown Rice (Elbows, Fettuccini, Fusilli, Grand Shells, Lasagne, Little Dreams, Penne, Shells, Spaghetti, Spirals)

Organic Brown Rice (Elbows, Lasagne, Penne, Spaghetti, Spirals)

Spinach Brown Rice Spaghetti

Vegetable Brown Rice Spirals

White Rice Spaghetti

**Trader Joe's** - Organic Brown Rice Pasta (All), Rice Pasta & Cheddar, Rice Sticks Rice Pasta

**Westbrae** - Corn Angel Hair Pasta

**Pasta Sauce... see Sauces**

**Pastrami**

**Boar's Head** - All Varieties

**Dietz & Watson** - Pastrami Brisket, Spiced Beef Pastrami

**Hormel** - Deli Sliced Cooked

**Hy-Vee** - Thin Sliced
**Jennie-O Turkey Store** - Refrigerated Dark Turkey
**Meijer Brand** - Sliced Chipped Meat
**Norwestern** - Deli Turkey Pastrami
**Perdue** - Deli Dark Turkey Pastrami Hickory Smoked
**Wellshire Farms** - Pastrami (Brisket, Round, Sliced Beef)

**Pastry Mix**

**Orgran▲** - All Purpose

**Pate**

**Kootenay Kitchen** - Vege Pate (Curry, Herb, Jalapeno)
**Old Wisconsin** - Spreadable Pate (All Varieties)
**Tartex** - Pate (Herb Meadow, Mushroom, Original)

**Pea Pods... sea also Peas**

**Meijer Brand** - Frozen (Chinese)

**Peaches...** *All **Fresh** Fruits & Vegetables Are **Gluten-Free***

**Albertsons** - All Canned Peaches, Frozen
**Cascadian Farm** - Organic Frozen Sliced Peaches
**Del Monte** -
　Canned/Jarred Fruit (All Varieties)
　Fruit Snack Cups (Metal, Plastic)
**Dole** - All Fruits (Bowls, Canned, Dried, Frozen, Jars) *(Except Real Fruit Bites)*
**Food Club Brand** - Fruit Cups Diced Peaches, Frozen Peaches, Halves In Heavy Syrup, Sliced In Heavy Syrup, Sliced Lite
**Great Value Brand (Wal-Mart)** -
　Frozen
　No Sugar Added Yellow Cling Peach Halves In Pear Juice From Concentrate & Water
　No Sugar Added Yellow Cling Sliced Peaches
　Yellow Cling Sliced Peaches in Heavy Syrup
**Home Harvest Brand** - Yellow Cling Peaches (In Light Syrup, Sliced)

**P**

Hy-Vee -
Diced
Diced Fruit Cups
Halves
Lite (Diced, Halves, Slices)
Peaches in Strawberry Gel
Slices

**Kroger Brand** - Fruit (Canned, Cups)

**Laura Lynn** - Canned

**Lowes Foods Brand** - Slices (In Heavy Syrup, In Juice)

**Meijer Brand** -
Cling Halves (In Heavy Syrup, In Juice Lite, In Pear Juice Lite)
Cling Sliced (In Heavy Syrup, In Juice, In Pear Juice Lite)
Frozen (Organic, Sliced)
Yellow Sliced in Heavy Syrup

**Midwest Country Fare** - Lite Peaches (Halves, Slices), Slices

**Publix** -
Canned (Lite Yellow Cling Peaches in Pear Juice Halves & Slices,
Yellow Cling Peaches in Heavy Syrup Halves & Slices)
Frozen Sliced Peaches

**S&W** - All Canned/Jarred Fruits

**Safeway Brand** - Canned Peaches (Halves, Halves Lite, Sliced, Sliced
Lite), Frozen

**Spartan Brand** - Cling Halves (Heavy Syrup, Regular), Diced (Heavy
Syrup, Light Syrup), Frozen, Lite Cling Halves, Sliced Cling Peaches
In Pear, Yellow Cling Sliced

**Thrifty Maid** - Yellow Cling Halves & Slices

**Wegmans Brand** - Halved Yellow Cling, Sliced Yellow Cling (In Heavy
Syrup, In Pear Juice, Regular)

**Winn Dixie** - Frozen Sliced, Yellow Cling Halves & Slices (Heavy
Syrup, Light Syrup)

**Woodstock Farms** - Organic Frozen Peach Slices

## Peanut Butter

**P**

**Albertsons** - Creamy, Crunchy, Reduced Fat (Creamy, Crunchy)

**Arrowhead Mills** -

Almond Butter (Creamy, Crunchy)

Cashew Butter (Creamy, Crunchy)

Honey Sweetened Peanut Butter (Creamy, Crunchy)

Organic Valencia Peanut Butter (Creamy, Crunchy)

Valencia Peanut Butter (Creamy, Crunchy)

**Bee's Knees** - All Varieties

**Earth Balance** - Creamy Natural Almond Butter, Natural Peanut Butter (Creamy, Crunchy)

**Food Club Brand** - Creamy, Crunchy

**Full Circle** - Organic Creamy

**Great Value Brand (Wal-Mart)** - Peanut Butter (Creamy, Crunchy)

**Hannaford Brand** - Creamy, Crunchy

**Hy-Vee** - Creamy, Crunchy, Reduced Fat

**I.M. Healthy** -

Soy Nut Butter

Chocolate

Honey (Chunky, Creamy)

Original (Chunky, Creamy)

Unsweetened (Chunky, Creamy)

**Jif** - Creamy, Extra Crunchy, Jif To Go, Peanut Butter & Honey, Reduced Fat Creamy, Reduced Fat Crunchy, Simply Jif

**Kroger Brand** - Creamy, Crunchy, Natural (Creamy, Crunchy), Reduced Fat (Creamy, Crunchy)

**Laura Lynn** - Peanut Butter & Grape Jelly Spread, Peanut Butter & Strawberry Jelly Spread

**Lowes Foods Brand** - Creamy, Crunchy

**MaraNatha** - All Varieties

**Meijer Brand** - Creamy, Crunchy, Natural (Creamy, Crunchy)

**P**

**Midwest Country Fare** - Creamy, Crunchy

**O Organics** - Old Fashioned (Creamy, Crunchy)

**Panner** - Peanut Butter

**Peanut Butter & Co.** - All Varieties

**Publix** - All Natural (Creamy, Crunchy), Creamy, Crunchy, Reduced Fat Spread (Creamy, Crunchy)

**Safeway Brand** - Creamy, Crunchy, Reduced Fat (Creamy, Crunchy)

**Santa Cruz** - Organic Dark Roasted (Creamy, Crunchy), Organic Light Roasted (Creamy, Crunchy)

**Skippy** - Creamy, Extra Crunchy Super Chunk, Natural (Creamy, Super Chunk), Reduced Fat (Creamy, Super Chunk), Roasted Honey Nut (Creamy, Super Chunk)

**Smart Balance** - Omega (Chunky, Creamy)

**Smucker's** - Goober (Grape, Strawberry), Natural (Chunky, Creamy, Honey, No Salt Added Creamy, Reduced Fat)

**Spartan Brand** - Crunchy, Smooth

**Stop & Shop Brand** -

All Natural Smooth Peanut Butter (No Added Salt, Reduced Fat, Regular)

Peanut Butter (Creamy, Crunchy, Smooth)

**Trader Joe's** - All Nut Butters, Pumpkin, Sunflower Seed

**Walden Farms** - Creamy Peanut Spread (Sugar Free)

**Wegmans Brand** -

Natural Peanut Butter (Creamy, Crunchy)

Organic Natural Peanut Butter w/Peanut Skins (Creamy, Crunchy)

Organic No Stir (Creamy, Crunchy)

Peanut Butter (Creamy, Crunchy, Reduced Fat Spread)

**Woodstock Farms** -

Non-Organic Nut Butters

Almond Butter (Crunchy Unsalted, Smooth Unsalted)

Cashew Butter Unsalted

Raw Almond

Tahini Unsalted

Organic Nut Butters

Almond Butter (Crunchy Unsalted, Smooth Unsalted)

Classic Peanut Butter (Crunchy Salted, Smooth Salted)

Easy Spread Peanut Butter (Crunchy (Salted, Unsalted), Smooth (Salted, Unsalted))

Peanut Butter (Crunchy (Salted, Unsalted), Smooth (Salted, Unsalted))

Raw Almond

Tahini Unsalted

**Peanut Sauce**

**A Taste Of Thai** - Peanut Satay Sauce, Peanut Sauce Mix

**Lee Kum Kee** - Satay Sauce

**Mr. Spice Organic** - Thai Peanut Sauce & Marinade

**San-J** - Gluten Free Thai Peanut Marinade & Dipping Sauce

**Thai Kitchen** - Peanut Satay

**Peanuts... see Nuts**

**Pears...** *All **Fresh** Fruits & Vegetables Are **Gluten-Free***

**Albertsons** - Canned

**Del Monte -**

Canned/Jarred Fruit (All Varieties)

Fruit Snack Cups (All Varieties)

**Dole** - All Fruits (Bowls, Canned, Dried, Frozen, Jars) *(Except Real Fruit Bites)*

**Food Club Brand** - Fruit Cups (Diced Pears), Sliced

**Full Circle** - Organic (Halves In Juice, Sliced In Juice)

**Great Value Brand (Wal-Mart) -**

Bartlett Pear Halves In Heavy Syrup

Bartlett Sliced Pears In Heavy Syrup

No Sugar Added Bartlett (Chunky Mixed Fruits, Fruit Cocktail, Pear Halves) in Pear Juice From Concentrate & Water

**P**

**Home Harvest Brand** - Whole Pears (In Light Syrup, Regular)

**Hy-Vee** - Bartlett Pears (Halves, Sliced), Diced Bartlett Pears Cups, Lite Pears

**Kroger Brand** - Fruit (Canned, Cups)

**Laura Lynn** - Canned Pears

**Lowes Foods Brand** - Halves (In Heavy Syrup, In Juice)

**Meijer Brand** - Halves (Heavy Syrup, In Juice, In Juice Lite, Lite), Slices (Heavy Syrup, In Juice Lite)

**Midwest Country Fare** - Bartlett Pear Halves In Light Syrup

**Native Forest** - Organic Sliced Asian Pears

**Publix** - Canned (Barlett Pears in Heavy Syrup (Halves, Slices), Lite Barlett Pear Halves In Pear Juice)

**S&W** - All Canned/Jarred Fruits

**Safeway Brand** - Canned Pears (Halves, Halves Lite, Sliced, Sliced Lite)

**Spartan Brand** - Halves (Heavy Syrup, In Juice, Lite Syrup), Slices (Heavy Syrup, In Juice)

**Stop & Shop Brand** - Bartlett Pear Halves (Heavy Syrup, Light Syrup, Pear Juice, Splenda)

**Thrifty Maid** - Bartlett Halves & Slices

**Wegmans Brand** - Halves (Heavy Syrup, Regular), Sliced (Heavy Syrup, Regular)

**Winn Dixie** - Bartlett Halves & Slices (Heavy Syrup, Light Syrup)

Peas... *All **Fresh** Fruits & Vegetables Are **Gluten-Free***

**Albertsons** - Canned, Frozen

**Birds Eye** - All Plain Frozen Vegetables *(Except With Sauce)*

**Bush's Best** - All Varieties

**C & W** - All Plain Frozen Vegetables

**Cascadian Farm** - Organic Frozen (Garden Peas, Peas & Carrots, Peas & Pearl Onions, Purely Steam Petite Sweet Peas , Sugar Snap Peas, Sweet Peas)

**Del Monte** - All Canned Vegetables

**Food Club Brand** - Canned Sweet, Frozen (Green Peas, Peas & Carrots, Sugar Snap)

**P**

**Freshlike** - Select (Petite Sweet Peas, Sweet Peas & Tiny Onions), Sweet Peas & Carrots, Tender Garden

**Full Circle** - Organic Frozen Peas, Organic Sweet Peas

**Grand Selections** - Frozen (Petite Green, Sugar Snap)

**Great Value Brand (Wal-Mart)** - Canned (Blackeye Peas, No Salt Added Sweet Peas, Sweet Peas), Frozen Sweet Peas, Microwaveable Plastic Cups Sweet Peas

**Green Giant** -

Canned Sweet Peas

Frozen

Baby Sweet Peas & Butter Sauce

Simply Steam (Baby Sweet Peas, Sugar Snap Peas)

Sweet Peas

**Halstead Acres** - Blackeye Peas

**Hannaford Brand** - No Salt, Petite, Sweet

**Health Market Organic** - Sweet

**Home Harvest Brand** - Canned Sweet, Frozen

**Hy-Vee** - Black Eyed, Dry Green Split, Frozen Sweet, Steam In A Bag Frozen Peas, Sweet

**Kroger Brand** - All Plain Vegetables (Canned, Frozen)

**Laura Lynn** - Canned Blackeye Peas, Sweet Peas, Tiny June Peas

**Lowes Foods Brand** - Black Eyed, Frozen (Crowder, Field Peas, Green, Peas, Peas & Carrots, Tiny Green), Split Green Peas

**Meijer Brand** -

Canned (Blackeye, Peas & Sliced Carrots, Small, Sweet, Sweet No Salt, Sweet Organic)

Frozen Peas (Green, Green Petite, Organic Green, Peas & Sliced Carrots)

**Midwest Country Fare** - Frozen Green, Sweet

**O Organics** - Frozen Sweet Peas

**Pictsweet** - All Plain Vegetables (Frozen)

**P** Publix -

Canned Sweet Peas (No Salt Added, Regular, Small)

Frozen (Butter, Green, Field Peas w/Snap, Original, Peas & Carrots, Petite)

**Publix GreenWise Market** - Organic Canned Sweet Peas

**S&W** - All Canned Vegetables

**Safeway Select** - Frozen (Blackeyed, Green, Peas & Carrots, Petite), Steam In Bag (Pod, Peas & Onions, Petite Green)

**Spartan Brand** - Canned (Green, Sweet), Dried (Blackeyed, Green Split), Frozen (Blackeyed, Crowder, Peas, Peas & Carrots, Peas w/Snaps, Petite, Sugar Snap, w/Snaps)

**Tasty Bite** - Agra Peas & Greens

**Trader Joe's** - All Plain Vegetables (Frozen)

**Wegmans Brand** - Blackeye, Petite In Butter Sauce, Regular, Small Sweet, Sugar Snap Frozen, Sweet (No Salt Added, Regular), Sweet Petite Frozen, w/Pearl Onions Frozen

**Winn Dixie** -

Canned Green Peas (Large, Medium, No Salt Addded, Small, Tiny)

Frozen (Butter, Crowder, Field w/Snaps, Green, Organic Green, Petite Green, Peas & Carrots, Purple Hull)

**Woodstock Farms** - Organic Frozen (Green Peas, Peas & Carrots, Petite Peas, Sugar Snap)

**Wylwood** - Blackeye Peas

Pepper Rings... see also Peppers

**Meijer Brand** - Banana Pepper Rings (Hot, Mild)

**Publix** - Banana Pepper Rings Mild

**Spartan Brand** - Pepper Rings (Mild, Hot)

Pepper Sauce... see Chili Sauce and/or Hot Sauce

Pepperoni... see Sausage

Peppers... *All **Fresh** Fruits & Vegetables Are **Gluten-Free***

**B&G** -

Giardiniera

Hot Cherry Peppers (Red & Green, Regular, w/Oregano & Garlic)

**P**

Hot Chopped Peppers (Regular, Roasted)

Hot Jalapenos

Hot Pepper Rings

Pepperoncini

Roasted (w/Balsamic Vinegar, w/Oregano & Garlic)

Sweet (Bell, Fried, Hot Jalapenos, Pepper Strips, Red, Red & Green, Salad w/Oregano & Garlic)

**Birds Eye** - All Plain Frozen Vegetables *(Except With Sauce)*

**Cara Mia** - Roasted Piquillo Peppers

**Di Lusso** - Roasted Red

**Hannaford Brand** - Whole Pepperoncini

**Heinz** - All Varieties

**Hy-Vee** - Diced Green Chilies, Green Salad Pepperoncini, Hot Banana Peppers, Mild Banana Peppers, Salad Peppers, Sliced Hot Jalapenos, Whole Green Chilies

**La Victoria** - Diced Jalapenos, Nacho Jalapenos Sliced

**Meijer Brand** - Diced Mild Mexican Style Chilies, Frozen Green Peppers Chopped

**Peloponnese** - Roasted Sweet Peppers

**Publix** - Frozen Green Peppers (Diced)

**Safeway Select** - Fire Roasted, Frozen Pepper Strips

**Spartan Brand** - Jalapeno

**Stop & Shop Brand** - Chopped Green

**Trader Joe's** -

All Plain Vegetables (Frozen)

Artichoke Red Pepper Tapenade

Fire Roasted Red (Regular, Sweet & Yellow)

Marinated Red

Red Pepper Spread w/Garlic & Eggplant

**Trappey** - Peppers

**Vlasic** - Peppers

**P**  **Wegmans Brand** - Clean and Cut Peppers & Onions (Diced, Sliced), Pepper & Onions Mix, Roasted Red Peppers Whole

**Winn Dixie** - Pepperoncini, Sliced Banana Peppers

**Woodstock Farms** - Organic Frozen Tri Colored Peppers

Pesto

   **Classico** - All Varieties

   **Member's Mark** - Pesto

   **Santa Barbara** - Basil, Chipotle Basil, Spinach Cilantro, Sun Dried Tomato

   **Sauces 'N Love** - Mint, Pesto, Pink

   **Trader Joe's** - Pesto Alla Genovese Basil Pesto

Picante Sauce

   **Albertsons** - Medium, Mild, Regular

   **Chi-Chi's**

   **Laura Lynn** - All Varieties

Pickled Beets... see Beets

Pickles... *All **Fresh** Fruits & Vegetables Are **Gluten-Free***

   **Albertsons** - All Varieties

   **B&G** -

      Bread & Butter

      Hamburger Dill

      Kosher Dill (Baby Gherkins, Gherkins, Original)

      Midget Gherkins

      NY Deli Dill

      Pickle In A Pouch

      Sour

      Sweet (Gherkins, Mixed, Mixed Pickles)

      Tiny Treats

      Unsalted (Bread & Butter, Kosher Dill)

      Zesty Dill

   **Boar's Head** - All Varieties

   **Easton Pickles**

**P**

**Food Club Brand** - All Varieties

**Great Value Brand (Wal-Mart)** -

Bread & Butter

Dill Spears

Garlic Dill Slices

Hamburger Dill Chips

Kosher Baby Dill

Kosher Dill Spears

Sweet (Gherkin, Pickle Relish)

Whole Sweet

**Hannaford Brand** - Bread & Butter (Chips, Sandwich Slices), Dill Relish, Hot Dog Relish, Kosher (Baby Dills, Dill, Dill Sandwich Slices, Dill Spears, Petite), Polish Dill Spears, Sour Dill, Sugar Free Bread & Butter (Chips, Spears), Sweet (Gherkins, Mixed Chips), Sugar Free Sweet Gherkins, Sweet (Midgets, Relish, Relish Squeeze)

**Harry Ramsdens** - Pickled Gherkins In Vinegar

**Heinz** - All Varieties

**Home Harvest Brand** - Dill Hamburger Slices, Kosher Dill (Pickles, Spears), Sweet Cucumber Chips

**Hy-Vee** -

Bread & Butter (Sandwich Slices, Sweet Chunk Pickles, Sweet Slices)

Dill (Kosher Sandwich Slices, Relish)

Fresh Pack Kosher Baby Dills

Hamburger Dill Slices

Kosher (Baby Dills, Cocktail Dills, Dill Pickles, Dill Spears)

Polish Dill (Pickles, Spears)

Refrigerated Kosher Dill (Halves, Sandwich Slices, Spears, Whole Pickles)

Special Recipe (Baby Dills, Bread & Butter Slices, Hot & Spicy Zingers, Hot & Sweet Zinger Chunks, Jalapeno Baby Dills, Sweet Garden Crunch)

**P**

Sweet Gherkins

Whole (Dill, Sweet)

Zesty (Kosher Dill Spears, Sweet Chunks)

**Laura Lynn -** All Pickles

**Lowes Foods Brand -** Bread & Butter Chips, Dill (Hamburger, Kosher, Kosher Spears), Kosher (Baby Dill, Sandwich Slices, Whole Petite), Sweet Midgets

**Meijer Brand -** Bread & Butter (Chips (Regular, Sugar Free), Sandwich Slice), Dill (Hamburger, Kosher (Baby, Spears, Whole), Polish, Sandwich Slice (Polish), Spears (No Garlic, Polish, Zesty), Whole), Kosher (Baby Dill, Sandwich Slices, Whole), Sweet (Gherkin, Midgets, Sugar Free, Whole)

**Midwest Country Fare -** Dill, Hamburger Dill Pickle Slices, Kosher Dill, Whole Sweet

**Mrs. Renfro's -** Green Tomato Pickles

**Patak's -** Pickles (Chilli, Lime, Mango, Hot Mango)

**Publix -** All Varieties

**Safeway Brand -** All Varieties

**Sharwood's -** Lime

**Spartan Brand -**

Bread & Butter Pickle (Slices, Sticks)

Hamburger Dill Slices

Kosher Dill (Baby, Slices, Spears, Whole)

Plain Baby Dills

Polish Dill (Regular, Spears)

Sweet (Gherkin Whole, Regular, Slices)

**Trader Joe's -** All Varieties

**Vlasic -** All Varieties

**Wegmans Brand -**

Hamburger Dill Slices

Kosher Dill (Baby Dills, Slices, Spears, Spears Reduced Sodium, Whole)

Polish Dill (Spears, Whole)

**P**

    Refrigerated Kosher Dills (Halves, Mini, Sandwich Slices, Spears, Whole)

    Sweet (Gherkins, Midgets)

    Sweet Bread & Butter Chips (No Salt Added, Regular)

    Sweet Sandwich Slices

    Whole (Kosher Dills, Polish Dills)

**Winn Dixie** - Dill (All Varieties), Sweet Pickles (All Varieties), Sweet Relish

**Woodstock Farms** - Organic (Kosher Dill (Baby, Sliced, Whole), Sweet Bread & Butter)

## Pie

**Amy's** - Organic Mexican Tamale Pie, Shepherd's Pie (Light In Sodium, Regular)

**Andrea's Fine Foods▲** - Pecan, Pumpkin, Strawberry Almond Cheesecake

**Cedarlane** - Three Layer Enchilada Pie

**El Peto▲** - Apple, Blueberry, Cherry, Peach, Strawberry Rhubarb, Walnut

**Foods By George▲** - Pecan Tarts

**Gillian's Foods▲** - Apple, Pumpkin

**Mixes From The Heartland▲** - Pie Mix (Impossible Coconut●, Impossible Pumpkin●)

**Skye Foods** - Pie Tarts (Apple●, Cherry●, Pumpkin●)

**Trader Joe's** - Shepherd's Pie (Beef)

**Whole Foods Market Gluten Free Bakehouse ▲**- Apple, Cherry, Pumpkin, Southern Pecan

## Pie Crust/Pie Crust Mix

**Andrea's Fine Foods▲** - Pie Crust

**Authentic Foods▲** - Pie Crust Mix

**Blue Chip Group** - GF Pie Crust

**Breads From Anna▲** - Piecrust Mix

**Deerfields Bakery▲** - Frozen Pie Crust

**El Peto▲** - Pie Dough, Perfect Pie Dough Mix

**P**   Gillian's Foods▲ - Pie Shell

  Gluten-Free Creations▲ - Graham Cracker Crumb Mix●

  Gluten-Free Pantry▲ - Perfect Pie Crust

  Kinnikinnick▲ - Pastry & Pie Crust Mix

  Mixes From The Heartland▲ - Pie Crust Mix●

  Namaste Foods▲ - Biscuits Piecrust & More Mix

  Whole Foods Market Gluten Free Bakehouse▲ - Pie Shells

**Pie Filling**

  **Comstock** - All Varieties

  **Full Cover Brand** - Apple, Blueberry, Cherry, Peach

  **Gold Leaf** - Apple, Blueberry, Cherry, Peach

  **Great Value Brand (Wal-Mart)** - Apple, Blueberry, Cherry, No Sugar Added (Apple, Cherry)

  **Hy-Vee** - More Fruit Pie Filling/Topping (Apple, Cherry)

  **Jell-O** -

    Regular Cook N Serve

      Banana Cream

      Butterscotch

      Chocolate (Fudge, Regular)

      Coconut Cream

      Fat Free Tapioca

      Lemon

      Vanilla

    Regular Instant Pudding & Pie Filling

      Banana Cream

      Butterscotch

      Cheesecake

      Chocolate (Caramel Chip, Fudge, Mint Chip, Regular)

      Coconut Cream

      Devil's Food

      French Vanilla

    Lemon

    Pistachio

    Pumpkin Spice

    Vanilla (Chocolate Chip, Regular)

    White Chocolate

  Sugar Free Fat Free Cook N Serve (Chocolate, Vanilla)

  Sugar Free Fat Free Instant Pudding & Pie Filling

    Banana Cream

    Butterscotch

    Cheesecake

    Chocolate

    Lemon

    Pistachio

    Vanilla

    White Chocolate

**Kroger Brand** - Canned Pie Filling

**Lowes Foods Brand** - Apple, Blueberry, Cherry

**Lucky Leaf** - Apple, Apricot, Banana Crème, Blueberry, Cherries Jubilee, Cherry, Chocolate Crème, Coconut Crème, Dark Sweet Cherry, Key Lime Pie Crème, Lemon, Lemon Crème, Lite (Apple, Cherry), Peach, Pineapple, Premium (Apple, Blackberry, Blueberry, Cherry, Red Raspberry), Raisin, Strawberry

**Meijer Brand** - Apple, Blueberry, Cherry, Cherry Lite, Peach

**Midwest Country Fare** - Apple, Cherry

**Musselman's** - Apple, Banana Crème, Blueberry, Cherries Jubilee, Cherry, Chocolate Crème, Coconut Cream, Key Lime Crème Pie, Lemon, Lemon Crème, Strawberry, Vanilla Entrée

**My T Fine** - Lemon, Vanilla

**Spartan Brand** - Apple, Blueberry, Cherry (Lite, Regular)

**Wilderness** - All Varieties

**Winn Dixie** - Apple, Blueberry, Cherry

**P** Pilaf

    **Manischewitz** - Lentil Pilaf Mix Lentil

    **Trader Joe's** - Quinoa Pilaf w/Shrimp & Vegetables, Thai Style Lime, Wild & Basmati Rice

Pimentos

    **Meijer Brand** - Pieces, Sliced

Pineapple... *All **Fresh** Fruits & Vegetables Are **Gluten-Free***

    **Albertsons** - All Varieties

    **Del Monte** -

        Canned/Jarred Fruit (All Varieties)

        Fruit Snack Cups (Metal, Plastic)

    **Dole** - All Fruits (Bowls, Canned, Dried, Frozen, Jars) *(Except Real Fruit Bites)*

    **Food Club Brand** - Chunks, Crushed, Sliced, Tidbits

    **Great Value Brand (Wal-Mart)** - Chunks, Pineapple In Unsweetened Pineapple Juice (Crushed, Slices), Tidbits

    **Hy-Vee** - Chunk, Crushed, In Lime Gel, Sliced, Tidbit Fruit Cup

    **Kroger Brand** - Fruit (Canned, Cups)

    **Laura Lynn** - Canned

    **Lowes Foods Brand** - Chunks In Juice, Crushed In Juice, Sliced In Juice

    **Meijer Brand** - Chunks (Heavy Syrup, In Juice), Crushed (Heavy Syrup, In Juice), Frozen Chunks, Sliced In (Heavy Syrup, Juice)

    **Midwest Country Fare** - Chunks, Crushed, Slices, Tidbits

    **Native Forest** - Organic (Chunks, Crushed, Slices)

    **Publix** - Canned All Styles

    **Safeway Brand** - Chunks, Crushed, Sliced

    **Spartan Brand** - Chunks, Crushed, Tidbits

    **Stop & Shop Brand** - Frozen Pineapple

    **Wegmans Brand** - Chunk, Crushed, Sliced (In Heavy Syrup, Regular), Tidbits

    **Winn Dixie** - Chunks, Crushed, Sliced, Tidbits

Pistachio Nuts... **see Nuts**

**P**

## Pizza

**Amy's -** Rice Crust Pizza (Cheese, Non Dairy Cheese, Spinach)

**Andrea's Fine Foods▲ -** Cheese, Pepperoni, Sausage, Spinach Artichoke

**Celiac Specialties▲ -** French Bread Pizza, Pizza (6" Pizza, 12" Pizza)

**Conte's Pasta -** Margherita, Mushroom Florentine

**Di Manufacturing -** Gluten Free Pizza

**Everybody Eats▲ -** Tomato Mozzarella Pizza

**Foods By George▲ -** Cheese Pizza

**Gluten Free & Fabulous▲ -** Cheese●, Pepperoni●

**Glutino▲ -** Frozen Pizza (3 Cheese Pizza w/Brown Rice Crust, Duo Cheese, Spinach & Feta, Spinach Soy Cheese Pizza w/Brown Rice Crust)

**Ian's -** Wheat Free Gluten Free Recipe French Bread Pizza

**Madwoman Foods▲ -** Cheese, Greek, Veggie

**Miller's Gluten Free Bread Co.▲-** Thin Crust Pizza

## Pizza Crust/Pizza Mix

**365 Everyday Value -** Gluten Free Pizza Crust Mix

**Andrea's Fine Foods▲ -** Pizza Crust (6", 12")

**Arrowhead Mills -** Gluten Free Pizza Crust Mix

**Authentic Foods▲ -** Pizza Crust Mix

**Blue Chip Group -** GF Pizza Dough, GF Pizza/Pasta Spice Mix

**Bob's Red Mill▲ -** GF Pizza Crust Mix

**Celiac Specialties▲ -** Pizza (6" Pizza Crust, 12" Pizza Crust)

**Chebe▲ -** Pizza Mix, Pizza Frozen Dough

**Dad's -** Gluten Free Pizza Crust

**Domata -** Gluten Free Pizza Crust●

**Ener-G ▲ -** Rice Pizza Shell (6", 10"), Yeast Free Rice Pizza Shell (6", 10")

**Everybody Eats▲ -** Pizza Shells

**Food-Tek Fast & Fresh -** Dairy Free Minute Pizza Crust Mix

**Foods By George▲ -** Pizza Crusts

**French Meadow Bakery -** Gluten-Free Pizza Crust●

**P**  Gillian's Foods▲ - Deep Dish Pizza Crust, Pizza Dough Mix

Gluten Free & Fabulous▲ - Pizza Crust●

Gluten-Free Creations▲ - Italian Seasoned Crust●, Simply Pizza Crust●, Whole Grain Crust●

Gluten-Free Pantry▲ - French Bread & Pizza Mix

Glutino▲ - Frozen Pizza (Duo Cheese, Spinach & Feta), Premium Pizza Crust

Katz Gluten Free▲ - Pizza Crust

Kinnikinnick▲ - Pizza Crust (7", 10"), Pizza Crust Mix

Laurel's Sweet Treats ▲- Pizza Dough Mix

Namaste Foods▲ - Pizza Crust Mix

Orgran▲ - Pizza & Pastry Multi Mix

Rose's Bakery▲ - All Varieties●

Rustic Crust▲ - Gluten Free Napoli Herb Pizza Crust●

Schar▲ - Pizza Crusts

Tastefully Gluten Free ▲- Pizza Crust Mix

Whole Foods Market Gluten Free Bakehouse ▲- Pizza Crust

Pizza Sauce... see also Sauce

Contadina - All Pizza Sauces

Del Pino's -

Eden Organic - Organic Pizza Pasta Sauce

Great Value Brand (Wal-Mart)

Hannaford Brand

Hy-Vee

Lowes Foods Brand

Meijer Brand

Muir Glen

Sauces 'N Love - Marinara Fresh

Spartan Brand - w/Basil

Trader Joe's - Fat Free

Ukrop's

**Wegmans Brand** - Chunky

**Winn Dixie**

## Plum Sauce

**Lee Kum Kee** - Gold Label Plum Sauce, Plum Stir Fry & Dipping Sauce

**Sharwood's**

**Winn Dixie**

**Wok Mei** - All Natural Plum Sauce

## Plums... *All Fresh Fruits & Vegetables Are Gluten-Free*

**Stop & Shop Brand** - Whole Plums In Heavy Syrup

**Wegmans Brand** - Dried Plums

**Winn Dixie** - Canned Whole Plums

## Polenta

**Bob's Red Mill▲** - Gluten Free Corn Grits/Polenta

**Food Merchants Brand** - Ready Made Organic (Ancient Harvest Quinoa, Basil & Garlic, Chili Cilantro, Mushroom & Onion, Sun Dried Tomato, Traditional)

**San Gennaro Foods** - Basil & Garlic, Sundried Tomato & Garlic, Traditional

**Trader Joe's** - Organic Polenta

## Pop... see Soda Pop/Carbonated Beverages

## Popcorn

**Cape Cod Popcorn** - Sweet Cream Butter, Sweet Salty, White Cheddar

**Chester's** - Butter Flavored Puffcorn Snacks, Cheddar Cheese Flavored Popcorn, Cheese Flavored Puffcorn Snacks

**Cracker Jack** - Original Caramel Coated Popcorn & Peanuts

**Eden Organic** - Organic Popping Kernels

**Farmer Steve's** - Kernels, Organic Microwave

**Food Club Brand** - Popcorn Microwave (Butter, Butter Crazy, Light Butter)

**Full Circle** - Organic Microwave (Butter, Natural)

**Herr's** - Light, Original, White Cheddar Ranch

**P** **Home Harvest Brand** - Cheese, Microwave (Butter, Kettle Corn, Lite Butter, Natural Lite Butter), White, Yellow

**Hy-Vee -**

Microwave

94% Fat Free Butter

Butter

Caramel Fresh Pop

Cheese

Extra Butter (Lite, Regular)

Kettle

Light Butter

Lightly Salted

Natural Flavor

No Salt

Regular

White Cheddar

Regular (White, Yellow)

**Jolly Time -**

Microwave

America's Best

Better Butter

Blast O Butter (Light, Minis, Regular)

ButterLicious (Light, Regular)

Crispy N White (Light, Regular)

Healthy Pop (Butter Flavor, Caramel Apple, Regular)

Mallow Magic

Sassy Salsa

The Big Cheez

White & Buttery

Kernel Corn (American's Best, Organic Yellow, White, Yellow)

**Kroger Brand** - Plain Popcorn Kernels

**Laura Lynn** - All Items

**LesserEvil** - Kettle Corn (Black & White, Class Kettle)

**Lowes Foods Brand** - Microwave (Butter, Butter 94% Fat Free, Extra Butter, Light Butter Mini Bags, Light Natural, Natural), Popcorn (Butter Flavor, White Cheddar Flavor), Yellow Bag

**Meijer Brand** -

Microwave

75% Fat Free Butter

94% Fat Free

Butter (GP, Regular)

Extra Butter (GP, Lite, Regular)

Hot N' Spicy

Kettle Sweet & Salty

Natural Lite

Regular (White, Yellow)

**Newman's Own** -

Microwave

100 Calorie Natural (Mini Bags)

94% Fat Free

Butter (Boom, Light, Low Sodium, Reduced Sodium, Regular)

Natural

Tender White Kernels Natural

Regular (Raw Popcorn)

**Newman's Own Organics** - Microwave Pop's Corn (94% Fat Free, Butter, Light Butter)

**O Organics** - Microwave Popcorn (Butter Flavor, Regular)

**Odell's** - Movie Theatre Popcorn Kit

**Old Dutch** - Popcorn Twists

**Pop Secret**

Microwave

1 Step Cheddar

Butter (94% Fat Free, Regular)

**P**

    Cheddar

    Extra Butter

    Homestyle

    Jumbo Pop (Butter, Movie Theater Butter)

    Kettle Corn

    Light Butter

    Movie Theater Butter

**Publix -** Microwave (Butter, Kettle, Light Butter, Movie Theater, Natural)

**Pirate's Booty -**

    Aged White Cheddar

    Barbeque

    Bermuda Onion

    Caramel

    Sea Salt & Vinegar

    Veggie

**Safeway Brand -** Kettle, Microwave (All Varieties), Yellow

**Skeete & Ike's -** All Organic Popcorn Varieties

**Smartfood -** White Cheddar Cheese Flavored (Reduced Fat, Regular)

**Snyder's Of Hanover -** Butter Flavored Popcorn

**Spartan Brand -** Microwave (94% Fat Free, Butter, Extra Butter, Lite Butter), Regular

**Stop & Shop Brand -**

    Microwave Popcorn

        94% Fat Free Butter

        Butter (Flavored, Light)

        Kettle Corn

        Movie Theatre Butter Flavored

        Natural Light

        Sweet & Buttery

        Yellow Popcorn

**Trader Joe's -**

    Cranberry Nut Clusters

Fat Free Caramel

Gourmet White

Kettle

Lite Popcorn 50% Less Salt

Microwave (94% Fat Free, Natural Butter)

Organic w/Olive Oil

White Cheddar

**UTZ** - Popcorn (Butter, Cheese, White Cheddar)

**Wegmans Brand** -

Microwave

94% Fat Free Butter Flavor

Butter Flavor

Kettle Corn

Light Butter Flavor

Movie Theater Butter

Organic

Regular - Yellow

**Wise** - Popcorn (Butter Flavored, Hot Cheese, Reduced Fat Butter Flavored, Reduced Fat White Cheddar, White Cheddar Cheese)

**Pork...** *All Fresh Meat Is Gluten-Free (Non-Marinated, Unseasoned)*

**Always Tender** -

Flavored Fresh Pork

Adobo Pork Cubes

Apple Bourbon

Citrus

Fajita Pork Strips

Honey Mustard

Lemon Garlic

Mesquite

Mojo Criollo

Onion Garlic

**P**

Original

Peppercorn

Portabella Mushroom

Raspberry Chipotle

Roast Flavor

Sun Dried Tomato

Non Flavored Fresh Pork

**Dietz & Watson -** Barbecue Roast of Pork, Boneless Pork Chops w/Natural Juices, Italian Style Roast Pork, Panchetta Sweet, Pork Cello Butt, Roast Sirloin Of Pork

**Ejay's So. Smokehouse -** All Natural Salt Pork

**Farmer John -**

California Natural Pork (Back Ribs, Bone In Butt Roast, Bone In Pork Loin, Bone In Pork Picnic, Boneless Loin, Boneless Pork Butt, Boneless Pork Picnic, Boneless Pork Shoulder, Boneless Pork Sirloin, Case Ready Pork Chops, Ground Pork, Pork Cushion, Spareribs, St. Louis Style Spareribs, Tenderloins

Carefree Cookin' Pork (Boneless Leg, Boneless Pork Loin, Picnics, Pork Boneless Sirloin, Pork Cushion, Riblets, Ribs, Spareribs, St. Louis Style Spareribs, Tenderloins)

**Homestyle Meals -** Pork Baby Back Ribs w/BBQ Sauce, Shredded Pork in BBQ Sauce, Whole Bulk St. Louis Ribs w/BBQ Sauce

**Hormel -**

Pickled (Pigs Feet, Pork Hocks, Tidbits)

Pork Rib Tips In Barbecue Sauce (Party Tray)

Pork Roast Au Jus (Fully Cooked Entrée)

**Jones Dairy Farm**

All Natural

Hearty Pork Sausage Links●

Little Link Pork Sausage●

Light Pork Sausage & Rice Links●

Pork Sausage Patties●

Maple Sausage Patties●

Original Pork Roll Sausage●

All Natural Golden Brown Fully Cooked & Browned Sausage Patties (Maple●, Mild●)

All Natural Golden Brown Fully Cooked & Browned Turkey●

All Natural Golden Brown Light Fully Cooked & Browned Sausage & Rice Links●

All Natural Golden Cooked & Browned Sausage Links Pork & Uncured Bacon Fully●

**Lloyd's -** Pork or Beef Ribs w/Original BBQ Sauce, Original BBQ Sauce w/Cocktail Smokies, Restaurant Style Smoked Pork Chops, Shredded Pork In Original Barbecue Sauce

**Organic Prairie -** Fresh Organic (Ground Pork 1 lb., Pork Loin, Pork Ribs, Pork Chops, Pork Loin Roast), Frozen Organic Pork Chops 12 oz.

**Publix -**

All Natural Fresh Pork

Deli Pre Pack Sliced Lunch Meats (Spanish Style Pork)

**Publix GreenWise Market -** Boston Butt Roast (Boneless, Regular), Butterfly Porkchop, Cajun Pork Sausage, Center Cut Pork (Loin Chop, Loin Roast Boneless, Rib Chop, Roast), Cubed Steak, Ground, Pork Back Ribs, Pork Chop Boneless, Pork For Stew, Pork For Stir Fry, Pork Ham Rump Portion, Pork Ham Shank Portion, Pork Ham Whole, Pork Kabobs, Pork Loin Crown Roast, Pork Picnic, Pork Sage Sausage, Pork Shoulder Country Ribs, Pork Spare Ribs, Pork Steak, Pork Steak Boneless, Romano Pork Sausage, Sirloin Cutlets, St. Louis Pork Spare Ribs, Whole Pork Tenderloin

**Saz's -** Barbecue Pork Meat Tub, Barbecued Baby Back Ribs

**Trader Joe's -** Refrigerated (BBQ Shredded Pork, Baby Back Pork Ribs, Pork in Barbecue Sauce)

**Ukrop's -** Pork Tenderloin w/Apple Smoked Bacon

**Wegmans Brand -** Canned Pork & Beans In Tomato Sauce

**Wellshire Farms -** Whole Smoked Boneless Pork Loin

**P** Potato Chips... see Chips

Potato Crisps... see Crisps

Potato Puffs... see Snacks

**Potato Salad**

> **Publix** - Potato Salad (German, Greek, Homestyle, New York Style, Southern Style)

**Potatoes...** *All Fresh Fruits & Vegetables Are Gluten-Free*

> **Albertsons** - French Fries, Hash Browns (Country, Southern), Potato Rounds (Tator Tots), Potatoes O'Brien, Steak Fries
>
> **Alexia Foods** -
>> Crispy Potatoes w/Seasoned Salt Waffle Fries
>>
>> Julienne Fries Spicy Sweet Potato
>>
>> Julienne Fries Sweet Potato
>>
>> Julienne Fries w/Sea Salt Yukon Gold
>>
>> Mashed Potatoes (Red Potatoes w/Garlic & Parmesan, Yukon Gold Potatoes w/Sea Salt)
>>
>> Olive Oil & Sea Salt Oven Fries
>>
>> Olive Oil Rosemary & Garlic Oven Fries
>>
>> Olive Oil Parmesan & Roasted Garlic Oven Reds
>>
>> Olive Oil Sun Dried Tomatoes & Pesto Oven Reds
>>
>> Organic (Classic Oven Crinkles, Oven Crinkles Onion & Garlic, Oven Crinkles Salt & Pepper, Seasoned Salt Hashed Browns, Yukon Gold Julienne Fries w/Sea Salt)
>>
>> Yukon Gold Potatoes w/Seasoned Salt Potato Nuggets
>
> **Andrea's Fine Foods▲** - Hash Brown Potato Casserole
>
> **Cascadian Farm** - Organic Frozen (Country Style Potatoes, Crinkle Cut French Fries, Hash Browns, Shoe String Fries, Spud Puppies, Straight Cut French Fries, Wedge Cut Oven Fries)
>
> **Chester's** - Flamin' Hot Flavored Fries
>
> **Food Club Brand** - Canned (Sliced, Whole), Frozen Potatoes (Crinkle Cut Fries, Hash Browns, Potato Crowns, Potatoes O'Brien, Shoestring Fries, Steak Fries, Southern Style Hashbrowns, Tater

Treats), Instant Potatoes, Potato Classics Hash Browns

**Funster** - Natural Potato Letters (BBQ Lite, Original)

**Great Value Brand (Wal-Mart)** - Canned (Diced, Sliced, Whole New), Frozen (Crinkle, French Fries Regular, Tator), Instant (4 Cheese, Creamy Butter, Herb & Butter, Sour Cream & Chive, Roasted Garlic), Potatoes Au Gratin

**Hannaford Brand** - Diced, Instant (Butter & Herb, Regular, Roasted Garlic, Sliced, Sweet Potatoes, Whole

**Home Harvest Brand** - Canned White (Sliced, Whole), Frozen French Fries, Instant Mashed Potatoes

**Hy-Vee** - Canned (Sliced, Whole), Frozen (Country Style Hash Brown Potatoes, Crinkle Cut Fries, Criss Cut Potatoes, Curly Cut, Potatoes O'Brien, Regular, Steak Fries), Instant Hash Browns

**Ian's** - Alphatots

**Jimmy Dean**

    Breakfast Skillets

        Bacon

        Ham

        Sausage

        Smoked Sausage

        Southwest Style

**Kroger Brand** - Plain Frozen Salted, Plain Instant

**Laura Lynn** - All Frozen Potatoes *(Except Seasoned Fries)*, Cut Sweet Potatoes, Sliced, Whole

**Linda's Gourmet Latkes** - Potato Pancake Latkes

**Lowes Foods Brand** -

    Canned Sweet Potatoes Cut

    Frozen

        French Fries (Crinkle Cut, Shoestring, Steak Cut)

        Hash Browns (Country Style, Regular)

        Tater Treats

    Instant Mashed

**P**   **Manischewitz** - Potato Mix (Homestyle Latke, Kugel, Mini Knish, Pancake, Sweetened Pancake)

**Meijer Brand -**

Canned White (Sliced, Whole)

Frozen French Fries (Crinkle Cut, Original, Quickie Crinkles, Shoestring, Steak Cut)

Frozen Hash Browns (Original, Shredded, Southern Style, Western Style)

Potatoes (Crinkle Cut, Tater Tots, Tater Treats)

Regular Hash Browns

**Midwest Country Fare -** Whole White Potatoes

**Mixes From The Heartland▲ -** Texas Style Potatoes●

**O'Day's -** French Fried Potato Tater Puffs

**Ore-Ida -**

Frozen

ABC Tater Tots

Cottage Fries

Country Style Steak Fries

Crispers

Extra Crispy (Crinkle Cut, Fast Food Fries, Seasoned Crinkle Cut)

Fast Food Fries

Golden (Crinkles, Crinkles 8 lb. *(Costco Only, Sam's Club Only)*, Fries)

Hash Browns (Country Style, Nine Count Golden Patties, Original, Southern Style)

Pixie Crinkles

Potato Wedges w/Skins

Potatoes O'Brien

Seasoned French Fries *(8 lb. Sam's Club Only)*

Shoestrings

Steak Fries

Steam N' Mash (Cut Russet, Cut Sweet, Garlic Seasoned, Three Cheese)

Tater Tots (All Varieties)

Waffle Fries

Zesties

**Publix -**

Canned (Sliced & Whole, White)

Deli Side Dishes (Garlic Redskin Smashed Potatoes)

Frozen (Crinkle Cut Fries, Extra Crispy Fries, Golden Fries (Fast Food Style, Regular), Original Cut Fries, Shoestring Fries, Southern Style Hash Browns, Steak Fries, Tater Bites)

**S&W -** All Canned Vegetables

**Safeway Brand -**

Crinkle Cut

French Fries

Hashbrowns Southern Style

Instant Mashed Potatoes (Herb Butter, Roasted Garlic)

Instant Potatoes

Restaurant Style Crinkle Cut

Shoestring

Steak Cut

Twice Baked (Cheddar, Sour Cream & Chives)

**Shiloh Farms -** Potato Flakes

**Smart Ones -** Frozen Entrée (Broccoli & Cheddar Potatoes)

**Spartan Brand -** Frozen Shoestring, Mashed Potatoes (Butter & Herb, Instant, Roasted Garlic), White (Sliced, Whole Sliced)

**Stop & Shop Brand -**

Cut Sweet Potatoes In Light Syrup

French Fries (Crinkle Cut, Straight Cut)

Fries (Crispy, Extra Crispy Crinkle Cut, Shoestring, Steak)

Frozen Natural Wedges Potatoes

Latkes

# potatoes

Puffs w/Onions

Shredded Hash

Southwestern Style Hash Browns

Twice Baked Potatoes (Butter, Cheddar Cheese, Sour Cream & Chive)

Whole Potatoes (No Added Salt, Regular)

**Tasty Bite** - Aloo Palak, Bombay, Mushroom Takatak

**Trader Joe's -**

Frozen

Crinkle Wedge Potatoes

Organic French Fries

Garlic Mashed Potatoes

**Wegmans Brand -**

Frozen (Crinkle Cut, Steak Cut, Straight Cut, Tater Puffs)

Frozen Hash Browns (Country Style, Hash Browns O'Brien, Regular)

White Potatoes (Peeled, Sliced)

**Winn Dixie -** Canned (Diced White, No Salt Added White, Sliced White, Sweet, Whole White), Instant Potato Flakes, Frozen Crinkle Cuts

**Woodstock Farms -** Organic Frozen (Crinkle Cut Oven Fries, Shredded Hash Browns, Tastee Taters

Preserves... see Jam/Jelly

Pretzels

**Barkat -** Pretzels (Sesame, Sticks, Regular)

**Better Balance -** Cinnamon Toast Pretzel Sticks, Golden Butter Twists, Jalapeno Honey Mustard Pretzel Sticks

**Ener-G ▲ -** Crisp Pretzels, Sesame Pretzel Rings, Wylde Pretzels (Poppy Seed, Regular, Sesame)

**Dutch Country -** Soft Pretzel Mix

**Glutano▲ -** Pretzels

**Glutino▲ -** Family Bag (Sticks, Twists), Sesame Ring, Snack Pack, Sticks, Twists, Unsalted Twists

## Protein

**Beneprotein** - Instant Protein Powder

**Bob's Red Mill▲** - Hemp Protein Powder, TSP (Textured Soy Protein), TVP (Textured Vegetable Protein)

**Living Harvest** - Organic Hemp Protein Powder (Original, Vanilla Spice)

**MLO** - Brown Rice Protein Powder

**Nutiva** - Hemp Protein Shake (Amazon Acai, Berry Pomegrate, Chocolate), Protein Powder (Hemp, Hemp & Fiber)

**Odwalla** - All Drinks *(Except Super Protein Vanilla Al Mondo & Superfood)*

**PaleoMeal** - Organic Whey Protein

**Ruth's** - Organic Hemp Protein Powder (E3Live & Maca, Hemp Protein Power, Hemp w/Sprouted Flax & Maca)

**Safeway Brand** - Nutritional Shakes (Plus, Regular) (All Flavors)

**Trader Joe's** - All Protein Powders *(Except Whey Quick Dissolve (Chocolate, Vanilla))*

**Worldwide Pure Protein** - Banana Crèam, Chocolate, Strawberry Cream, Vanilla

## Protein Shakes... see Shakes &... see Protein

## Prunes

**Great Value Brand (Wal-Mart)** - Pitted Prunes

**Meijer Brand** - Pitted (Canister, Carton)

**Spartan Brand** - Prunes Pitted

## Pudding

**Albertsons** - Cups (Butterscotch, Chocolate, Tapioca, Vanilla)

**Bakers & Chefs** - Chocolate, Vanilla

**Echo Farms** - All Puddings

**Food Club Brand** -

Pudding (Cook & Serve Chocolate & Vanilla, Instant Chocolate & Vanilla)

Pudding Cups (Banana, Butterscotch, Chocolate, Fat Free Chocolate, Tapioca, Vanilla)

**P** **Great Value Brand (Wal-Mart)** -
   Instant
      Banana Cream (Regular)
      Chocolate (Regular, Sugar Free)
      French Vanilla (Regular, Sugar Free)
      Pistachio (Regular)
      Vanilla (Regular)

**Hannaford Brand** -
   Pudding Cook & Serve - Chocolate, Vanilla
   Pudding Instant (Banana Cream, Butterscotch, Chocolate, Chocolate Fudge, Pistachio, Vanilla)
   Pudding Snacks (Banana, Butterscotch, Chocolate, Fudge, Tapioca, Vanilla)

**Hunt's** -
   Pudding Snack Packs
      Banana Cream Pie
      Butterscotch
      Caramel Cream
      Chocolate (Mud Pie, Regular)
      Chocolate & Vanilla Triples
      Fat Free (Chocolate, Vanilla)
      Ice Cream Sandwich
      Lemon
      No Sugar Added (Chocolate, Vanilla)
      Swirls (Milk Chocolate Variety)
      ~~Tapioca (*Except Fat Free Tapioca*)~~
      Vanilla

**Hy-Vee** -
   Cooked Pudding (Chocolate, Vanilla)
   Instant Pudding (Butterscotch, Chocolate (Fat Free/Sugar Free, Regular), Lemon, Pistachio, Vanilla (Fat Free/Sugar Free, Regular))

Pudding Cups (Butterscotch, Chocolate (Fat Free, Fudge, Regular),
Strawberry Banana, Tapioca, Vanilla)

**Jell-O -**

Regular Cook N Serve

Banana Cream

Butterscotch

Chocolate (Fudge, Regular)

Coconut Cream

Fat Free Tapioca

Lemon

Vanilla

Regular Instant Pudding & Pie Filling

Banana Cream

Butterscotch

Cheesecake

Chocolate (Caramel Chip, Fudge, Mint Chip, Regular)

Coconut Cream

Devil's Food

French Vanilla

Lemon

Pistachio

Pumpkin Spice

Vanilla (Chocolate Chip, Regular)

White Chocolate

Sugar Free Fat Free Cook N Serve (Chocolate, Vanilla)

Sugar Free Fat Free Instant Pudding & Pie Filling

Banana Cream

Butterscotch

Cheesecake

Chocolate

Lemon

**P**

Pistachio
Vanilla
White Chocolate
**Kozy Shack** - All Puddings
**Kroger Brand** - Boxed, Snack Cups
**Laura Lynn** - Pudding RTE Dairy (All Items)
**Meijer Brand** -
Cook & Serve (Butterscotch, Chocolate, Vanilla)
Instant
Banana Cream
Butterscotch (Fat Free, Sugar Free)
Chocolate (Fat Free, Sugar Free)
Vanilla (Fat Free, Sugar Free)
Instant Pudding & Pie Filling
Chocolate
Coconut Cream
French Vanilla
Pistachio
Vanilla
Premium (Chocolate Peanut Butter, French Vanilla, Orange Dream)
Snack
Banana
Butterscotch
Chocolate (Fat Free, Fudge, Regular)
Multi Pack Chocolate & Vanilla
Tapioca
Vanilla
**Mixes From The Heartland▲** - Pudding Mix (Apple Cinnamon Rice●, Chocolate Delight●)
**Mori-Nu** - Mates Pudding Mix (Chocolate, Lemon Crème, Vanilla)

**My T Fine** - Lemon, Vanilla

**Publix** - Rice, Sugar Free Chocolate Vanilla Swirl, Tapioca

**Royal** - All Varieties

**Safeway Brand** - All Flavors (Snack Cups)

**Spartan Brand** -

    Cook & Serve (Chocolate, Vanilla)

    Instant

        Banana Cream

        Butterscotch

        Chocolate (Regular, Sugar Free)

        French Vanilla

        Pistachio

        Vanilla (Regular, Sugar Free)

    Snack (Butterscotch, Chocolate, Tapioca, Vanilla)

**Stop & Shop Brand** -

    Butterscotch

    Chocolate (Fudge, Instant Pudding & Pie Filling, Regular, Sugar Free Instant)

    Fat Free (Chocolate, Chocolate/Vanilla)

    Instant Low Calorie Vanilla Pudding & Pie Mix

    Refrigerated (Chocolate, Chocolate/Vanilla)

    Rice

    Tapioca

    Vanilla

**Trader Joe's** - Puddings (Chocolate, Rice, Tapioca)

**Wegmans Brand** -

    Chocolate (Fat Free, Regular, Sugar Free)

    Chocolate Vanilla Swirl (Fat Free, Regular, Sugar Free)

    Homestyle (Chocolate, Rice, Tapioca)

    Vanilla (Fat Free, Regular, Sugar Free)

**ZenSoy** - All Varieties

**P**

**Pumpkin...** *All **Fresh** Fruits & Vegetables Are **Gluten-Free***

    **Libby's** - Canned (100% Pure Pumpkin, Easy Pumpkin Pie Mix)

**Q**

    **Meijer Brand** - Canned

    **Safeway Brand -** Canned

    **Spartan Brand** - Canned

    **Wegmans Brand** - Solid Pack

**Puppodums**

    **Sharwood's** - Indian Puppodums (Crushed Garlic & Coriander, Plain)


# Q

**Queso**

    **Chi-Chi's** - Con Queso

    **Eat Smart** - Salsa Con Queso

    **Great Value Brand (Wal-Mart)** - Salsa Con Queso, White Salsa Con Queso

    **Lowes Foods Brand** - Salsa Con Queso

    **Taco Bell** - Black Bean Con Queso, Chili Con Queso w/Beef, Salsa Con Queso (Medium, Mild)

    **Tostitos** - Monterey Jack Queso, Salsa Con Queso, Spicy Queso Supreme

**Quiche**

    **Andrea's Fine Foods▲** - Ham & Swiss, Spinach & Cheddar

    **Trader Joe's** - Crustless Quiche (Bacon & Feta, Chorizo & Egg)

**Quinoa**

    **Ancient Harvest Quinoa -**

        Inca Red Quinoa

        Quinoa Flakes

        Quinoa Flour

        Quinoa Pasta (Elbows, Garden Pagodas, Linguine, Rotelle, Shells, Spaghetti, Veggie Curls)

        Traditional Quinoa Grain

**Q**

**R**

**Arrowhead Mills** - Quinoa
**Arzu** - Chai●, Original●, Southwest●
**Gluten Free & Fabulous▲** - Bon Appetit! Quinoa w/Marinara●
**Seeds of Change** -
    Amantani Whole Grain Blend Quinoa & Wild Rice
    Cuzco Whole Grain Quinoa Blend
**Shiloh Farms** - Quinoa, Quinoa Flakes, Red Quinoa
**Trader Joe's** - Organic Quinoa, Quinoa Pilaf w/Shrimp & Vegetables

# R

**Radishes...** *All **Fresh** Fruits & Vegetables Are **Gluten-Free***
**Raisins**
    **Albertsons** - Regular
    **Food Club Brand**
    **Full Circle** - Organic (Canister, Regular)
    **Great Value Brand (Wal-Mart)** - California Sun Dried Raisins (100% Natural)
    **Hy-Vee** - California Sun Dried Raisins
    **Lowes Foods Brand** - Canister, Seedless Carton
    **Meijer Brand** - Canister, Seedless (Carton)
    **Publix** - Raisins
    **Spartan Brand** - Regular
    **Sun-Maid** - Raisins (Baking, Golden, Natural California, Regular), Zante Currants
    **Wegmans Brand** - Seedless
    **Winn Dixie** - Raisins
    **Woodstock Farms** - Organic (Chocolate (Dark, Milk) Raisins w/Evaporated Cane Juice, Raisins (Jumbo Thompson, Select Thompson)), Raisin Mania, Raisins (Jumbo Flame), Yogurt Raisins w/Evaporated Cane Juice

R Raspberries... *All **Fresh** Fruits & Vegetables Are **Gluten-Free***

    **Cascadian Farm** - Organic Frozen Raspberries

    **Food Club Brand** - Frozen Red Raspberries

    **Full Circle -** Organic Raspberries

    **Hy-Vee** - Frozen Red Raspberries

    **Meijer Brand** - Frozen (Organic, Regular), Red Individually Quick Frozen

    **Publix -** Frozen

    **Safeway Brand -** Frozen Red Raspberries

    **Spartan Brand** - Frozen Red Raspberries

    **Stop & Shop Brand** - Raspberries, Raspberries In Syrup

    **Wegmans Brand** - Raspberries (Regular, w/Sugar)

    **Winn Dixie** - Frozen Red Raspberries

    **Woodstock Farms** - Organic Frozen Red Raspberries

Raspberry Vinaigrette... see Salad Dressing

Ravioli

    **Conte's Pasta -** Cheese, Spinach & Cheese

    **Everybody Eats▲** - Beef, Chicken, Cheese, Spinach Ricotta

Refried Beans... see Beans

Relish

    **Albertsons** - Sweet

    **B&G** - Dill, Emerald, Hamburger, Hot Dog, India, Piccalilli, Sweet, Unsalted

    **Baxters -** Dipping Relish (Crushed Tomato w/Italian Pesto, Cucumber & Mint w/Diced Shallots, Spice Red Onion w/Chopped Coriander)

    **Food Club Brand** - All Varieties

    **Heinz** - All Varieties

    **Home Harvest Brand** - Sweet

    **Hy-Vee** - Dill, Squeeze Sweet, Sweet

    **Lowes Foods Brand** - Regular, Sweet Pickle

    **Meijer Brand -** Dill Relish, Sweet Relish (Sugar Free)

**R**

**Midwest Country Fare** - Sweet Pickle

**Mrs. Renfro's -** Corn, Hot Chow Chow, Hot Tomato, Mild Chow Chow, Mild Tomato

**Spartan Brand** - Dill, Sweet

**Trader Joe's** - Organic Sweet

**Vlasic -** All Varieties

**Wegmans Brand** - Dill, Hamburger, Sweet

**Woodstock Farms** - Organic (Spicy Chipotle Sweet, Sweet Relish)

Ribs... *All Fresh Meat Is **Gluten-Free (Non-Marinated, Unseasoned)***

**Homestyle Meals** - Pork Baby Back w/BBQ Sauce, Whole Bulk St. Louis Ribs w/BBQ Sauce

**Saz's** - Barbecued Baby Back Ribs

**Trader Joe's** - Baby Back Pork Ribs

Rice

**A Taste of India** - Masala Rice & Lentils, Spiced Rice w/Raisins

**A Taste Of Thai** - Rice (Coconut Ginger, Garlic Basil, Jasmine, Yellow Curry)

**Albertsons -** Boil In A Bag, Brown, White (Instant, Regular)

**Annie Chun's** - Sprouted Brown Rice, Sticky White Rice

**Arrowhead Mills** - Brown Basmati, Long Grain Brown, Short Brown, White Basmati

**Dinty Moore** - Microwave Meal (Rice w/Chicken)

**Eden Organic** -

Organic Canned

Curried Rice & Lentils

Mexican Rice & Black Beans

Moroccan Rice & Garbanzo Beans

Rice & Cajun Small Red Beans

Rice & Caribbean Black Beans

Rice & Garbanzo Beans

Rice & Kidney Beans

**R**

Rice & Lentils

Rice & Pinto Beans

Spanish Rice & Pinto Beans

**Fantastic World Foods** - Arborio, Basmati, Jasmine

**Food Club Brand** - Instant Rice

**Full Circle -** Organic (Basmati Brown, Basmati White, Long Grain Brown, Long Grain White)

**Gluten-Free Essentials▲** - Side Kicks (Exotic Curry●, Italian Herb & Lemon●, Southwest Chipotle & Lime●)

**Go Go Rice** - Organic Steamed Rice Bowls (Brown,White), Organic White Rice

**Golden Star -** Jasmine Rice

**Great Value Brand (Wal-Mart) -** Enriched Long Grain (Instant, Parboiled Rice, Rice Extra Fancy)

**Hannaford Brand -** Enriched Long Grain, Frozen Steam In Bag White Rice, Instant

**Hol Grain -** Artichoke Brown Rice Mix

**Home Harvest Brand** - 50% Broken Long Grain, Instant, Long Grain

**Hormel -**

Compleats Microwaveable Meals

Chicken & Rice

Sante Fe Chicken & Rice

**Hy-Vee -**

Boil In Bag Rice

Enriched Extra Long Grain (Instant, Regular)

Extra Long Grain

Instant Brown

Natural Long Grain Brown

Spanish

**Konriko -**

Original Brown Rice (Bag)

Wild Pecan Rice (Box, Burlap Bag)

**Kraft Minute Rice** - Brown, White

**Laura Lynn** - Boil N' Bag, Flavored Rice (All Items), Instant, Long Grain White

**Lotus Foods** - Forbidden Black

**Lowes Foods Brand** - Boil N Bag, Instant (Brown, White), Long Grain

**Lundberg▲** - All Varieties Of Rice

**Manischewitz** - Lentil Pilaf Mix

**Meijer Brand** - Brown, Instant (Boil In Bag, Brown), Long Grain, Medium Grain

**Midwest Country Fare** - Pre Cooked Instant Rice

**Minute Rice** - Brown, White

**Nishiki** - Sushi Rice

**O Organics -** Long Grain (Brown, Thai Jasmine)

**Ortega** - Saffron Yellow, Spanish

**Publix** -
  Long Grain (Brown, Enriched)
  Medium Grain White
  Pre Cooked Instant (Boil in Bag, Brown, White)
  Yellow Rice Mix

**Royal -** Basmati Rice

**S&W -** Natural Brown, White

**Safeway Brand -** Brown, Instant, Long Grain, Rice Pouch Gently Milled Bran Rice, White

**Seeds of Change -**
  Amantani Whole Grain Blend Quinoa & Wild Rice
  Cuzco Whole Grain Quinoa Blend
  Havana Cuban Style Whole Grain Rice & Beans
  Microwaveable (Dharamsala Aromatic Indian Rice Blend, Rishikesh Whole Grain Brown Basmati Rice, Tapovan White Basmati Rice)
  Velleron French Style Herb Whole Grain Blend

**Shiloh Farms -** Brown Basmati Rice, Brown Rice, California Wild Rice

**R**

**Smart Ones** - Frozen Entrée (Santa Fe Rice & Beans)

**Spartan Brand** - Instant (Boil In Bag, Brown Box, Regular Box), 4% Broken Long Grain

**Stop & Shop Brand** -

Instant Brown

Organic Long Grain (Brown & White)

Simply Enjoy (Butter Chicken, Pad Thai w/Chicken, Tikka Masala)

**Success** - Boil In Bag (Jasmine Rice, Whole Grain Brown Rice, White Rice)

**Tasty Bite** - Basmati Rice & (Beans Masala, Peas Paneer, Spinach Dal, Sprouts Curry, Vegetable Supreme)

**Thai Kitchen** -

Jasmine Rice Mixes

Green Chili & Garlic

Jasmine Rice

Lemongrass & Ginger

Roasted Garlic & Chili

Spicy Thai Chili

Sweet Chili & Onion

Thai Yellow Curry

**Trader Joe's** -

All Grain Rice

Biryani Curried Rice

Chicken Tandoori Rice Bowl (Frozen)

Curried Lentils w/Basmati Rice

Organic (All Grain Rice)

Organic Fully Cooked Brown Rice

Peruvian Style Chimichurri w/Vegetables (Frozen)

Roasted Poblano Peppers w/Shrimp Rice & Cheese

Spanish Style

Sprouted Brown Rice Fully Cooked

**R**

    Thai Style Lime Pilaf
    Wild & Basmati Rice Pilaf

**Uncle Ben's -**
    Boil In Bag
    Fast & Natural Instant Brown Rice
    Instant Rice
    Original Converted Brand Rice
    Ready Rice (Original Long Grain Rice 8.8 oz. & 14.8 oz.)

**Wegmans Brand -**
    Boil In Bag
    Arborio (Italian Style, Regular)
    Basmati
    Enriched (Long, Long Grain White, Medium)
    Instant (Brown, Regular)
    Jasmine
    Long Grain (Brown, Regular)
    Medium Grain White

## Rice Beverages

**365 Organic Every Day Value -** Organic Ricemilk (Original, Unsweetened, Vanilla)

**Full Circle -** Organic (Original, Vanilla)

**Good Karma -** Organic Ricemilk (Chocolate, Original, Vanilla)

**Grainaissance -**
    Almond Shake
    Amazing Mango
    Banana Appeal
    Chocolate (Almond, Chimp)
    Cool Coconut
    Gimme Green
    Go (Go Green, Hazelnuts)
    Oh So Original

**R**     Rice Nog

Tiger Chai

Vanilla (Gorilla, Pecan Pie)

**Kroger Brand -** Rice Drink (Plain, Vanilla)

**Nature's Promise** - Ricemilk (Regular, Vanilla)

**Pacific Foods** - Low Fat Rice Beverage (Plain, Vanilla)

**Rice Dream** - Refrigerated & Shelf Stable Rice Beverages (All Varieties)

**Trader Joe's -** Rice Milk

**Wegmans Brand -** Organic (Original, Vanilla)

**Rice Bread... see Bread**

**Rice Cakes**

**Hy-Vee -** Caramel, Lightly Salted, White Cheddar

**Kroger Brand -** Plain, Salted

**Lundberg▲ -**

Eco Farmed

Apple Cinnamon

Brown Rice (Lightly Salted, Salt Free)

Honey Nut

Sesame Tamari

Toasted Sesame

Organic

Brown Rice (Lightly Salted, Salt Free)

Caramel Corn

Cinnamon Toast

Koku Seaweed

Mochi Sweet

Rice w/Popcorn

Sesame Tamari

Sweet Green Tea w/Lemon

Tamari w/Seaweed

Wild Rice

**R**

**S**

**Publix** - Cheddar, Lightly Salted, Mini (Caramel Fat Free, Cheddar, Ranch), Unsalted

**Spartan Brand** - Caramel, Salt Free, White Cheddar

**Stop & Shop Brand** - Rice Cakes (Multigrain Unsalted, Plain Salted, Plain Unsalted, Sesame Unsalted, Sour Cream & Onion, White Cheddar)

**Trader Joe's** - Lightly Salted Rice Cakes

Rice Crackers... see Crackers

Rice Cream

**Erewhon** - Brown Rice Cream

Rice Noodles... see Noodles

Rice Shakes... see Rice Beverages or Shakes

Rice Snacks... see Snacks

Rice Syrup...see Syrup

Rice Vinegar... see Vinegar

Risotto

**Lundberg▲** -

Eco Farmed (Butternut Squash, Cheddar Broccoli, Creamy Parmesan, Garlic Primavera, Italian Herb)

Organic (Alfredo, Florentine, Tuscan, Wild Porcini Mushroom)

Roast Beef... see Beef

Rolls... see Bread

Rum... *All **Distilled** Alcohol Is **Gluten-Free** [2]

Rusks

**Glutino▲** - Gluten Free Rusks

Rutabaga... *All **Fresh** Fruits & Vegetables Are **Gluten-Free**

# S

Salad... *All **Fresh** Fruits & Vegetables Are **Gluten-Free**

**Mixes From The Heartland▲** - Pasta Salad (Corn N' Pasta●, Dilled●)

**S**  **Publix** -

    Classic Blend

    Cole Slaw Blend

    Deli Pre Made Salads (Carrot, Chicken, Chicken Tarragon, Chunky Chicken, Cranberry Orange Relish, Egg, Ham, Marshmallow Delight, Santa Fe Turkey)

    European Blend

    Italian Blend

    Packaged Blends

    Romaine Lettuce Heart

    Spinach

**Publix GreenWise Market** - Organic Salad (Baby Arugula, Baby Lettuce, Baby Romaine, Baby Spinach, Baby Spinach Blend, Fresh Herb, Mixed Baby Greens, Romaine Hearts, Spinach)

**Safeway Select** - Mediterranean Salad

**Trader Joe's** -

    Baby Spinach Salad

    Chef

    Chicken Caesar *(Except Croutons)*

    Chicken

    Classic Greek

    Cobb

    Egg White

    Eggless Egg

    Garden

    Gorgonzola Walnut

    Greek

    Grilled Chicken w/Orange Vinaigrette

    Marinated Bean

**Salad Dressing**

  **A Taste Of Thai** - Peanut Salad Dressing Mix

**Annie's Naturals -**

Natural Dressings

Artichoke Parmesan

Balsamic Vinaigrette

Basil & Garlic

Caesar

Cowgirl Ranch

Lemon & Chive

Light Italian

Lite Vinaigrette (Honey Mustard, Raspberry)

Roasted Red Pepper Vinaigrette

Tuscany Italian

Organic

Balsamic Vinaigrette

Buttermilk

Caesar

Cowgirl Ranch

Creamy Asiago

French

Green (Garlic, Goddess)

Maple Ginger

Oil & Vinegar

Papaya Poppyseed

Pomegranate Vinaigrette

Red Wine & Olive Oil

Roasted Garlic Vinaigrette

Sesame Ginger w/Chamomile

**Bakers & Chefs -** Italian, Ranch

**Bragg -** Organic (Ginger & Sesame, Healthy Vinaigrette)

**S** Briannas -
  Champagne Caper Vinaigrette
  Dijon Honey Mustard
  New American
  Rich (Poppy Seed, Santa Fe Blend)
  Vinaigrette (Blush Wine, Real French)
  Zesty French
Cardini's -
  Caesar (Fat Free, Light, Original)
  Honey Mustard
  Italian
  Vinaigrette (Balsamic, Light Balsamic, Pear, Raspberry Pomegranate)
Consorzio - Fat Free (Mango, Raspberry & Balsamic, Strawberry & Balsamic)
Drew's All Natural -
  Buttermilk Ranch
  Classic Italian
  Green Olive & Caper
  Honey Dijon
  Poppy Seed
  Raspberry
  Roasted Garlic & Peppercorn
  Romano Caesar
  Rosemary Balsamic
  Smoked Tomato
El Torito - Cilantro Pepita
Emeril's - Caesar, Vinaigrette (Balsamic, House Herb, Italian, Raspberry Balsamic)
Enlighten - Balsamic & Red Wine Vinaigrette, Garden Italian, Honey Mustard, Roasted Sweet Pepper & Garlic Vinaigrette
Fischer & Wieser - Citrus Herb & Truffle Oil Vinaigrette, Creamy Garlic & Chile, Original Roasted Raspberry Chipotle Vinaigrette,

Southwestern Herb & Tomato Vinaigrette, Spicy Lime & Coriander, Sweet Corn & Shallot

**Follow Your Heart** -

Caesar (Regular, w/Aged Parmesan)

Creamy Garlic

Honey Mustard

Lemon Herb

Ranch (Low Fat, Spicy Southwestern)

Sesame (Dijon, Miso)

Thousand Island

**Food Club Brand** - Blue Cheese, California French (Fat Free, Regular), Italian (Fat Free, Regular), Ranch (Fat Free, Regular), Thousand Island, Western Style, Zesty Italian

**Full Circle** - Organic (Buttermilk Ranch, Fat Free Balsamic Vinaigrette, Greek Feta, Pomegranate Vinaigrette, Raspberry Vinaigrette, Tuscan Italian

**Girard's** -

Caesar (Light, Regular)

Champagne (Light, Regular)

Fat Free (Caesar, Balsamic Vinaigrette, Raspberry, Red Wine Vinaigrette)

Honey Dijon Peppercorn

Olde Venice Italian

Original French

Parmesan Peppercorn

Raspberry

Romano Cheese Italian

Spinach Salad Dressing

Vinaigrette (Balsamic Basil, Blue Cheese, Greek, Wasabi Ginger, White Balsamic)

**Hannaford Brand** - Bacon Ranch, Balsamic Vinaigrette, California French Style, Chunky Blue Cheese, Creamy (Dill, Italian, Ranch), Deluxe French, Fat Free (Ranch, Sweet Vinaigrette & Olive Oil),

**S**  Honey Dijon, Light (Caesar, Italian), Old World Greek, Ranch Lite, Raspberry Vinaigrette, Robust Italian, Thousand Island, Vidalia Onion, Whipped, Zesty Italian

**Health Market Organic** - Balsamic, Creamy Caesar, Honey Mustard, Raspberry Vinaigrette

**Henri's** - All Varieties

**Hy-Vee** -

Dressing (Bacon Ranch, Buttermilk Ranch, French, Italian, Lite Salad, Peppercorn Ranch, Ranch, Raspberry Vinaigrette, Salad, Thousand Island, Zesty Italian)

Light Dressing (Italian, Ranch, Thousand Island)

Light Salad Dressing (French, Italian, Ranch, Thousand Island)

Squeezable Salad Dressing

**Ken's Steak House** -

Chef's Reserve

Blue Cheese w/Gorgonzola

Creamy (Balsamic, Greek w/Fresh Oregano)

Farm House Ranch w/Buttermilk

French w/Applewood Smoke Bacon

Golden Vidalia Onion

Honey Dijon

Italian w/Garlic & Asiago Cheese

Ranch

Russian

Fat Free Dressings (Raspberry Pecan, Sun Dried Tomato)

Healthy Options

Balsamic Vinaigrette

Honey (Dijon, French)

Italian w/Romano & Red Pepper

Olive Oil & Vinegar

Parmesan & Peppercorn

Ranch

Raspberry Walnut

Sweet Vidalia Onion Vinaigrette

Lite Accents Vinaigrette (Balsamic, Honey Mustard, Italian, Raspberry Walnut)

Lite Dressings

  100 Calorie Reduced Sugar

  Balsamic & Basil

  Balsamic Vinaigrette

  Caesar

  Chunky Blue Cheese

  Country French w/Vermont Honey

  Creamy (Caesar, Cilantro, Parmesan w/Cracked Peppercorn)

  Honey Mustard

  Italian

  Northern Italian

  Olive Oil Vinaigrette

  Pineapple Coleslaw

  Ranch

  Raspberry (Pomegranate, Walnut)

  Red Wine Vinaigrette

  Sweet Vidalia Onion

  Sun Dried Tomato

Regular

  Balsamic & Basil

  Buttermilk Ranch

  Caesar

  Christo's Yasou Greek

  Chunky Blue Cheese

  Country French w/Vermont Honey

  Creamy (Caesar, French, Italian, Parmesan w/Cracked Peppercorn)

**S**

Greek

Honey Mustard

Italian (& Marinade, w/Aged Romano)

New & Improved Ranch

Ranch

Red Wine Vinegar & Olive Oil

Russian

Thousand Island

Three Cheese Italian

Sweet Vidalia Onion

Zesty Italian

**Kraft -**

Balsamic Vinaigrette

Catalina

Classic Caesar

Creamy (French, Italian, Poppyseed)

Dressing Made w/Extra Virgin Olive Oil (Basil & Parmesan Vinaigrette, Classic Balsamic Vinaigrette, Greek Vinaigrette, Italian Vinaigrette, Sun Dried Vinaigrette)

Free (Catalina, French, Italian, Thousand Island, Zesty Italian)

Greek Vinaigrette

Honey Dijon

Light (Balsamic Vinaigrette, Catalina, Creamy French Style, Italian House, Italian Zesty, Parmesan Asiago, Raspberry Vinaigrette, Sicilian Roasted Garlic Balsamic Vinaigrette, Thousand Island)

Ranch (Buttermilk, Cucumber, Light, Light Three Cheese, Peppercorn, Regular, w/Bacon)

Roasted Red Pepper Italian w/Parmesan

Roka Blue Cheese

Seven Seas (Green Goddess, Viva Italian)

Sun Dried Tomato Vinaigrette

Sweet Honey Catalina

Tangy Tomato Bacon
Thousand Island
Tuscan House Italian
Vidalia Onion Vinaigrette
Zesty Italian

**Laura Lynn** -
Buttermilk
California (French, Honey French)
Chunky Blue Cheese
Creamy (Cucumber, Italian)
French
Garlic Ranch
Italian (Fat Free, Regular)
Peppercorn Ranch
Poppyseed
Ranch (Fat Free, Lite, Regular)
Ranch Dressing Mix
Red Wine Vinegar & Oil
Salad Dressing
Thousand Island
Zesty Italian

**Lily's Gourmet Dressings** -
Balsamic Vinaigrette
Northern Italian
Poppyseed
Raspberry Walnut Vinaigrette

**Litehouse** -
Bacon Bleu Cheese
Balsamic Vinaigrette
Barbeque Ranch
Big Bleu

**S**

Bleu Cheese Vinaigrette

Buttermilk Ranch

Caesar

Chunky (Bleu Cheese, Garlic Caesar)

Coleslaw

Garden Veggie Ranch Dressing

Garlic Vinaigrette

Greek Feta

Harvest Cranberry Vinaigrette

Homestyle Ranch

Honey Mustard

Huckleberry Vinaigrette

Jalapeno Ranch

Lite (1000 Island, Bleu Cheese, Caesar, Coleslaw, Creamy Ranch, Greek, Honey Dijon Vinaigrette, Ranch)

Organic (Balsamic Vinaigrette, Caesar, Ranch, Raspberry Lime Vinaigrette)

Original Bleu Cheese

Pear Gorgonzola

Pomegranate Blueberry Vinaigrette

Poppyseed

Ranch

Raspberry Walnut Vinaigrette

Red Wine Olive Oil Vinaigrette

Reduced Sugar Caramel

Romano Caesar

Salsa Ranch

Spinach Salad

Sweet & Sour

Sweet French

Thousand Island

White Balsamic

Zesty Italian Vinaigrette

**Lowes Foods Brand** - Chunky Blue Cheese, Creamy Caesar, French, Italian (Fat Free, Regular), Ranch (Lite, Regular), Thousand Island

**Maple Grove Farms of Vermont** -

All Natural

Asiago & Garlic

Blueberry Pomegranate

Champagne Vinaigrette

Ginger Pear

Maple Fig

Strawberry Balsamic

Fat Free

Cranberry Balsamic

Greek

Honey Dijon

Lime Basil

Poppyseed

Vinaigrette (Balsamic, Raspberry)

Organic (Dijon, Italian Herb, Vinaigrette (Balsamic, Raspberry))

Regular & Lite

Balsamic Maple

Lite Caesar

Honey Mustard (Lite, Regular)

Sweet N' Sour

Sugar Free (Dijon, Italian Balsamic, Vinaigrette (Balsamic, Raspberry))

**Marcin** - Spoonable Salad Dressing

**Marzetti** -

Refrigerated Dressings

**S**

Asiago Peppercorn
Blue Cheese (Bistro, Chunky, Light Chunky, Organic, The Ultimate)
Caesar (Light Supreme, Organic, Supreme)
Honey Balsamic
Honey Dijon (Light, Regular)
Honey French (Light, Regular)
Organic Parmesan Ranch
Poppyseed
Ranch (Classic, Light Classic)
Slaw (Light, Regular)
Spinach Salad
Sweet Italian
Thousand Island
Ultimate Gorgonzola
Venice Italian
Vinaigrette (Balsamic, Light Balsamic, Light Caesar, Light Raspberry Cabernet, Roasted Garlic Italian, Strawberry Chardonnay, White Balsamic)
Shelf Stable
Asiago Peppercorn
Caesar (Creamy, Regular)
California French
Country French
Honey Balsamic
Honey Dijon (Fat Free, Mustard)
Italian (Creamy, Fat Free, House, Regular, w/Blue Cheese Crumbles)
Poppyseed
Potato Salad
Ranch (Aged Parmesan, Regular)
Slaw (Light, Low Fat, Original, Southern Recipe)

## salad dressing

**S**

    Sweet & Sour (Fat Free, Regular)
    Sweet Vidalia
    Thousand Island
    Venice Italian
    Vinaigrette (Balsamic, Light Balsamic, Organic Balsamic, Peppercorn, Strawberry)

**Midwest Country Fare -** French, Italian, Ranch, Thousand Island

**Miracle Whip -** Lite, Regular

**Nature's Promise -** Ranch

**Newman's Own -**

  Light
    Balsamic Vinaigrette
    Caesar
    Cranberry Walnut
    Honey Mustard
    Italian
    Lime Vinaigrette
    Raspberry Walnut
    Red Wine Vinegar & Olive Oil
    Roasted Garlic Balsamic
    Sun Dried Tomato Italian
  Organic (Light Balsamic Vinaigrette, Tuscan Italian)
  Refrigerated Dressings (Blue Cheese, Creamy Caesar, Ranch, Raspberry Balsamic)
  Regular
    Balsamic Vinaigrette
    Caesar
    Creamy (Caesar, Italian)
    Greek
    Olive Oil & Vinegar
    Parisienne Dijon Lime

**S**

    Parmesan & Roasted Garlic
    Ranch
    Red Wine Vinegar & Olive Oil
    Southwest
    Three Cheese Balsamic Vinaigrette
    Two Thousand Island
  Salad Mist (Balsamic, Italian)

**O Organics** - Light Balsamic, Ranch, Red Wine Vinegar, Thousand Island, Tuscan Italian

**Olde Cape Cod** - All Dressings

**Organicville** -

  Organic

    French
    Herbs De Provence
    Miso Ginger
    Non Dairy Ranch
    Olive Oil & Balsamic
    Orange Cranberry
    Pomegranate
    Sesame (Goddess, Tamari)
    Sundried Tomato & Garlic
    Tarragon Dijon

**Portmann's** - Spoonable Salad Dressing

**Pfeiffer** -

  Blue Cheese
  Caesar
  California French
  Cole Slaw
  French
  Garden Ranch
  Honey Dijon

## salad dressing

**S**

    Italian (Creamy, Fat Free, Light, Regular)
    Peppercorn Ranch
    Poppyseed
    Ranch (Fat Free, Light, Regular)
    Russian
    Sweet 'N Sour
    Thousand Island (Light, Regular)
    Tuscan Italian
    Vinaigrette (Balsamic, Red Wine, Roasted Garlic)
    Zesty Garlic Italian

**Publix** -
    Balsamic Vinaigrette
    California French
    Chunky Blue Cheese
    Creamy Parmesan
    Italian (Fat Free, Regular)
    Lite (Caesar, Honey Dijon, Ranch, Raspberry Walnut)
    Ranch
    Tangy Balsamic
    Thousand Island
    Zesty Italian

**Ring Bros Markets Dressings** - All Varieties *(Except Blue Cheese)*

**Safeway Brand** -
    1000 Island (Fat Free, Regular)
    California
    Creamy Italian
    Ranch (Light, Regular, w/Bacon)
    Zesty Italian (Light, Regular)

**Safeway Select** -
    Balsamic & Olive Oil Vinaigrette
    Basil Ranch

**S**

Blue Cheese

Garlic Caesar

Jalapeno Ranch

Parmesan & Herb

Raspberry Vinaigrette

Tuscan Basil Herb

**San-J** - Gluten Free Asian Dressing (Tamari Ginger●, Tamari Peanut●, Tamari Sesame●)

**Seeds of Change** - All Varieties

**Sharwood's** - Lemon Grass & Corriander, Sweet Chilli & Kaffir Lime

**Spartan Brand** - Blue Cheese, French, Italian (Light, Regular, Zesty), Thousand Island

**Spectrum** - Premium Organic Dressing (Prevencal Garlic Lover's, Rocky Mountain Ranch)

**Stop & Shop Brand** -

Balsamic Vinaigrette

Blue Cheese

Caesar

French (Creamy, Regular)

Italian (Creamy, Fat Free, Lite)

Ranch (Fat Free, Regular)

Raspberry Vinaigrette

Thousand Island

**Teresa's Select Recipes** -

Asiago Pepper Crème

Blackberry Poppyseed

Fat Free Honey Dijon

Raspberry White Balsamic

Strawberry Chardonnay

Vinaigrette (Balsamic, Roasted Garlic, Sun Dried Tomato)

## salad dressing

**S**

### Trader Joe's -

Dressings

Balsamic Vinaigrette (Fat Free, Organic, Regular)

Organic Red Wine and Olive Oil Vinaigrette

Raspberry Low Fat

Romano Caesar

Tuscan Italian w/Balsamic Vinegar

Refrigerated Dressings

Italian Vinaigrette

Low Fat Parmesan Ranch

Organic Red Wine & Olive Oil Vinaigrette

Pear Champagne Vinaigrette

### Walden Farms -

Single Serve Packets (Creamy Bacon, Honey Dijon, Italian, Ranch, Thousand Island)

Sugar Free No Carb

Asian

Bacon Ranch

Balsamic Vinaigrette

Blue Cheese

Caesar

Coleslaw

Creamy (Bacon, Italian)

French

Honey Dijon

Italian (Regular, w/Sun Dried Tomato)

Ranch

Raspberry Vinaigrette

Russian

Sweet Onion

Thousand Island

Zesty Italian

**S**

**Wegmans Brand** -

Balsamic w/Garlic Chunks

Basil Vinaigrette

Buttermilk Ranch

Casesar

Caramelized Onion & Bacon

Cracked Pepper Ranch Dressing

Creamy (Caesar, Curry & Roasted Red Pepper, Italian, Ranch)

Fat Free (Parmesan Italian, Red Wine Vinegar, Roasted Red Pepper)

Homestyle French

Honey French

Light (Garlic Italian, Golden Caesar, Italian, Parmesan Peppercorn Ranch, Ranch, Thousand Island)

Organic (Balsamic Vinaigrette, Creamy Caesar, Honey Mustard, Italian, Raspberry Vinaigrette, Sun Dried Tomato Vinaigrette)

Parmesan Italian

Roasted Sweet Red Bell Pepper & Garlic

Sun Dried Tomato Vinaigrette

Tarragon Vinaigrette

Thousand Island (Light, Regular)

Three Spice Garden French

Traditional Italian

Zesty Italian

**Wild Thymes** - Salad Refresher (Black Currant, Mango, Meyer Lemon, Morello Cherry, Passion Fruit, Pomegranate, Raspberry, Tangerine), Vinaigrette (Fig Walnut, Mandarin Orange Basil, Mediterranean Balsamic, Parmesan Walnut Caesar, Raspberry Pear Balsamic, Roasted Apple Shallot, Tahitian Lime Ginger, Tuscan Tomato Basil)

**Winn & Lovett** - Balsamic & Olive Oil, Blue Cheese Italian, Jalapeno Ranch, Manadarin Poppyseed, Parmesan Peppercorn Ranch, Sun-Dried Tomato Basil, Three Cheese Italian, Vadalia Onion

### Winn Dixie

Balsamic Vinaigrette

California French

Chunky Blue Cheese

Creamy (French, Ranch)

Fat Free (Italian, Ranch, Thousand Island)

Garden Ranch

Honey Dijon

Italian (Lite, Regular)

Robust Italian

Thousand Island

Zesty Italian

### Wish-Bone

Balsamic Oil & Herbs

Balsamic Vinaigrette

Blue Cheese (Chunky, Light)

Creamy Poppyseed

Deluxe French (Low Fat, Regular)

Italian (Fat Free, Light, Regular, Robusto)

Ranch (Light, Regular)

Raspberry Hazelnut Vinaigrette

Salad Spritzers Vinaigrette (Italian, Ranch)

Western

**Salami... see Sausage**

**Salmon... see Fish**... *All Fresh Fish Is Gluten-Free (Non-Marinated, Unseasoned)*

**Chicken Of The Sea** - All Salmon Products *(Except Salmon Steak In Mandarin Orange Glaze, Mandarin Orange Salmon Cups)*

**Crown Prince** - Pink (Fancy Alaskan)

**Crown Prince Natural** - Alaskan Pink, Alder Wood Smoked Alaskan Coho, Skinless & Boneless Pacific Pink

**S**    **Full Circle** - All Natural Alaskan Sockeye Salmon Fillets

**Great Value Brand (Wal-Mart)** - Canned (Alaskan Pink Salmon)

**Hannaford Brand** - Canned Pink Salmon

**Hy-Vee** - Frozen

**Kroger Brand** - Canned

**Morey's** - Wild Alaskan Salmon

**Publix** - Coho Salmon Fillets, Sockeye Salmon Fillets

**Trader Joe's** - Pink Salmon Skinless/Boneless, Premium Salmon Patties, Salmon Burger, Smoked Salmon

**Salsa**

**Albertsons** - Chunky (Medium, Mild)

**Amy's** - Organic (Black Bean & Corn, Fire Roasted Vegetable, Medium, Mild, Spicy Chipotle)

**Bone Suckin'** - Salsa

**Bravos** - Hot, Medium, Mild

**Chi-Chi's** - Con Queso, Fiesta, Garden, Natural, Original

**Dei Fratelli** - Black Bean 'N Corn Medium, Casera (Medium Hot, Mild), Chipotle Medium, Original (Medium, Mild)

**Drew's** - Organic (Black Bean Cilantro & Corn Medium, Chipotle Lime Medium, Double Fire Roasted Medium, Hot, Medium, Mild)

**Eat Smart** - Garden Style Sweet, Salsa Con Queso

**Emeril's** - Gaaahlic Lovers Medium, Kicked Up Chunky Hot, Original Recipe Medium, Southwest Style Medium

**Fischer & Wieser** - Das Peach Haus Peach, Salsa A La Charra, Salsa Verde Ranchera, Timpone's Organic Salsa Muy Rica

**Food Club Brand** - Hot, Medium, Mild

**Frontera** - Gourmet Mexican Salsa (Chipotle, Corn & Poblano, Double Roasted, Guajillo, Habanero, Jalapeno Cilantro, Mango Key Lime, Medium Chunky Tomato, Mild Chunky Tomato, Red Pepper & Garlic, Roasted Tomato, Spanish Olive, Tomatillo)

**Full Circle** - Organic (Black Bean & Corn, Hot, Medium, Mild)

**Grand Selections** - Black Bean & Corn (Medium, Mild)

**Green Mountain Gringo** - All Varieties

**Hannaford Brand -** Con Queso Medium Thick & Chunky (Hot, Medium, Mild), Southwestern (Medium, Mild)

**Herdez** - Salsa Casera

**Herr's** - Chunky (Medium, Mild)

**Hy-Vee -** Salsa Con Queso Medium, Thick & Chunky (Hot, Medium, Mild)

**Kroger Brand** - Picante Sauce (Hot, Medium, Mild), Thick & Chunky (Hot, Medium, Mild), Traditional (Hot, Medium, Mild)

**La Victoria -** Cilantro (Medium, Mild), Hot, Jalapena Extra Hot (Green, Red), Salsa Ranchera, Suprema (Medium, Mild), Thick 'N Chunky (Hot, Medium, Mild), Verde (Medium, Mild)

**Laura Lynn** - All Varieties

**Litehouse** - Medium

**Lowes Foods Brand** - Salsa Con Queso, Thick & Chunky (Medium, Mild)

**Meijer Brand -**
Original (Hot, Medium, Mild)
Restaurant Style (Hot, Medium, Mild)
Santa Fe Style (Medium, Mild)
Thick & Chunky (Hot, Medium, Mild)

**Miguel's** - Black Bean & Corn, Chipotle, Medium, Mild, Roasted Garlic

**Mrs. Renfro's -** Black Bean, Chipotle Corn, Garlic, Green, Mild, Peach, Raspberry Chipotle, Roasted

**Muir Glen -** Medium, Medium Black Bean & Corn, Medium Garlic Cilantro, Mild

**Nature's Promise** - Organic (Chipotle, Medium, Mild)

**Newman's Own** - Black Bean & Corn, Farmer's Garden, Hot, Mango, Medium, Mild, Organic (Cilantro, Medium), Peach, Pineapple, Roasted Garlic, Tequila

**O Organics** - Chipotle, Chunky Bell Pepper, Fire Roasted Tomato, Mild

**Old Dutch** - Restaurante Salsa (Medium, Mild)

**Old El Paso** - Cheese 'N Salsa (Medium, Mild), Salsa Thick N' Chunky (Hot, Medium, Mild)

**S**

**Organicville** - Medium, Mild, Pineapple

**Ortega -** Garden (Medium, Mild), Mexican Black Bean & Corn, Original (Medium, Mild), Picante (Hot, Medium, Mild), Roasted Garlic, Salsa Verde, Thick & Chunky (Medium, Mild)

**Publix -**

All Natural (Hot, Medium, Mild)

Con Queso Dip

Thick & Chunky (Hot, Medium, Mild)

**Publix GreenWise Market -** Organic (Medium, Mild)

**Safeway Select -** 3 Bean Medium, Chipotle Medium, Fiesta Fajita, Garlic Lovers, Peach Pineapple Medium, Roasted Tomato Medium, Southwest (Hot, Medium, Mild), Verde Medium

**Salpica -** Cabin Fever, Cilantro Green Olive, Fall Harvest, Garlic Chipotle, Habanero Lime, Mango Peach, Roasted Corn & Bean, Rustic Tomato, Salsa Con Queso, Spring Break, Summer Of Love, Tomato Jalapeno

**Santa Barbara -**

Fresh Salsa (3 Pepper, Black Bean & Corn, Deli Style, Garden Style, Grilled Pineapple Chipotle, Hot, Key Lime & Garlic, Mango & Peach, Medium, Mild, Pico De Gallo, Roasted (Chili, Garlic, Tomatillo), Salsa Taquera, Texas Style)

Shelf Stable Salsa (Artichoke, Black Bean & Corn, California Fiesta, Chipotle Pineapple, Fire Roasted Chili, Habanero Lime, Mango & Peach, Peach & Chipotle, Pepper Mash, Perfect Medium, Roasted (Garlic, Red Pepper Corn & Black Bean, Tomatillo), Salsa Tres Frijoles, Smoked Pasilla, Taco Stand)

**Stop & Shop Brand** - Hot, Medium, Mild, Simply Enjoy Salsa (Black Bean & Corn, Peach Mango, Pineapple Chipotle, Tequila Lime)

**TGI Fridays -** All Varieties

**Taco Bell -** Black Bean Con Queso, Chili Con Queso w/Beef, Thick 'n Chunky (Medium, Mild), Salsa Con Queso (Medium, Mild)

**Taste Of Inspirations -** Raspberry Lime & Corn & Chili

**Tostitos -**

All Natural

Hot Chunky

> Medium (Black Bean & Corn, Chunky, Picante, Pineapple &
>   Peach)
> Mild (Chunky, Picante)
> Salsa Con Queso

**Trader Joe's -**
> 3 Pepper
> Autentica
> Black Bean & Roasted Corn
> Chunky
> Corn & Chili Tomatoless
> Double Roasted
> Fire Roasted Tomato
> Fresh Salsa (All Varieties)
> Garlic Chipotle
> Hot & Smoky Chipotle
> Pineapple
> Spicy Smoky Peach
> Verde

**UTZ** - Mt. Misery Mike's Salsa Dip, Sweet Salsa Dip

**Ukrop's -** Pico De Gallo, Regular

**Wegmans Brand** - Hot, Medium, Mild, Organic (Hot, Mango,
  Medium, Mild), Roasted (Chipotle, Salsa Verde, Sweet Pepper,
  Tomato), Santa Fe Style

## Salt
**Albertsons -** Iodized, Regular

**Great Value Brand (Wal-Mart) -** Iodized, Plain

**Hannaford Brand -** Iodized, Regular

**Kroger Brand**

**Lawry's -** Seasoned

**Manischewitz**

**Meijer Brand -** Iodized, Plain

**S** **Morton** - Coarse Kosher Salt, Iodized Table Salt, Lite Salt Mixture, Plain Table Salt, Salt Substitute, Sea Salt (Coarse, Fine)

**No Salt** - Salt Substitute

**Odell's** - Popcorn Salt

**Publix**

**Safeway Brand** - Iodized, Plain

**Spartan Brand** - Garlic, Iodized, Plain

**Stop & Shop Brand** - Iodized Salt, Plain

**Wegmans Brand** - Iodized, Plain

Sandwich Meat... see Deli Meat

Sardines... *All Fresh Fish Is Gluten-Free (Non-Marinated, Unseasoned)*

**Bumble Bee** - Canned

**Chicken Of The Sea** - All Sardine Varieties

**Crown Prince** -

Crosspacked Brisling In Olive Oil

One Layer Brisling In (Mustard, Oil/No Salt Added, Soybean Oil, Tomato)

Two Layer Brisling In (Olive Oil, Soybean)

**Crown Prince Natural** - Skinless & Boneless In (Pure Olive Oil, Water)

**Kroger Brand** - Canned

**Ocean Prince** -

In (Louisiana Hot Sauce, Mustard, Spring Water, Tomato Sauce)

Lightly Smoked (In Oil, With Green Chilies)

Premium Skinless & Boneless In Oil

**Trader Joe's** - Skinless & Boneless Sardines in Olive Oil

Sauces... (includes Marinara, Pasta, Tomato, Misc.)

**A Taste Of Thai** - Curry Paste (Green, Panang, Red, Yellow), Fish Sauce, Garlic Chili Pepper Sauce, Pad Thai, Peanut Sauce Mix, Peanut Satay Sauce, Sweet Red Chili Sauce

**Ah So** - Sparerib Sauce

**Amy's** - Family Marinara, Garlic Mushroom, Low Sodium Marinara, Puttanesca, Roasted Garlic, Tomato Basil (Low Sodium, Regular)

**S**

**Baxters** - Mint Sauce

**Bertolli** -

Alfredo

Five Cheese

Marinara w/Burgundy Wine

Mushroom Alfredo

Tomato & Basil

Vidalia Onion w/Roasted Garlic

Vodka

**Black Horse** - Apricot Sauce, Chili Verde Sauce, Marionberry Pepper
Sauce, Raspberry Mustard Sauce, Savory Sauce, Spicy Sauce

**Bove's Of Vermont** - All Natural (Basil, Marinara, Mushroom & Wine,
Roasted Garlic, Sweet Red Pepper, Vodka)

**Butcher's Cut** - Jazz N Spicy Buffalo Wing Sauce

**Capa Di Roma** - Arrustica, Fresh Basil, Marinara, Roasted Garlic

**Classico** - Alfredo Sauce (All Varieties), Bruschetta (All Varieties),
Pesto (All Varieties), Red Sauce (All Varieties)

**Colameco's** - Bolognese (Beef, Turkey), Pomodoro Sauce

**Contadina** -

All Pizza Sauces

All Tomato Sauces *(Except Tomato Paste w/Italian Seasoning)*

Pasta Sauce (Glass Jar)

Pizza Squeeze

Sweet & Sour Sauce

**Daddy Sam's** - Bar B Que Sawce (Medium Ginger Jalapeno,
Original), Salmon Glaze

**Dave's Gourmet** - All Pasta Sauces

**Del Monte** - All Tomato Products *(Except Spaghetti Sauce Flavored
w/Meat)*

**Di Lusso** - Buffalo Wing Sauce, Sweet Onion Sauce

**Dorothy Lane Market** - Original Marinara

**S** **Eden Organic** - Apple Cherry Sauce, Spaghetti Sauce (No Salt Added, Regular)

**Emeril's** -

Pasta Sauce

Eggplant & Gaaahlic

Home Style Marinara

Italian Style Tomato & Basil

Kicked Up Tomato

Roasted (Gaahlic, Red Pepper)

Sicilian Gravy

Three Cheeses

Vodka

**Fischer & Wieser** -

Charred Pineapple Bourbon

Chipotle Sauce (Blackberry, Blueberry, Original Roasted Raspberry, Plum Chipotle BBQ, Pomegranate & Mango)

Granny's Peach 'N' Pepper Pourin'

Mango Ginger Habanero

Mom's (Artichoke Heart & Asiago Cheese, Caponata, Garlic & Basil Spaghetti, Martini, Puttanesca, Spicy Arrabbiata, Special Marinara)

Mom's Organic (Roasted Pepper, Traditional)

Papaya Lime Serrano

Steak & Grilling

Sweet & Savory Onion Glaze

Texas 1015 Onion Glaze

**Food Club** - 4 Cheese, All Natural Marinara, Mushroom, Mushroom & Green Pepper, Mushroom & Olive, Regular, Tomato Basil, Traditional (Meat, Mushroom, Original), w/Meat

**Frank's RedHot** - Buffalo Wing, Chile 'N Lime, Hot Buffalo Wing, Original, Sweet Heat BBQ Wing, Xtra Hot

**Frontera** -

Cocktail & Ceviche Sauce (Cilantro Lime, Tomato Chipotle)

## sauces

**S**

Cooking Sauce (Red Chile & Roasted Garlic, Roasted Garlic & Chipotle, Roasted Tomato & Cilantro)

Enchilada Sauce (Chipotle Garlic, Classic Red Chile)

Grilling Sauce (Chipotle Honey Mustard, Red Pepper Sesame)

Hot Sauce (Chipotle, Habanero, Jalapeno, Red Pepper)

Taco Sauce (Chipotle Garlic, Roasted Tomato)

**Full Circle -** Organic Pasta Sauce (Parmesan, Portabella Mushroom, Roasted Garlic, Tomato Basil), Organic Tomato Sauce

**Full Flavor Foods▲** - Sauce Mix (Alfredo●, Cheese●, Vegetarian Mushroom●)

**Great Value Brand (Wal-Mart)** -

Alfredo Sauce

Italian Garden Combination Chunky Pasta Sauce

Mushrooms & Green Peppers Spaghetti Sauce

Onion & Garlic Chunky Pasta Sauce

Pizza Sauce

Tomato Sauce

Traditional Spaghetti Sauce

**Hannaford Brand -** Four Cheese, Mushroom & Olive, Mushroom & Onion, Onion & Garlic, Roasted Garlic, Sweet Pepper & Onion, Tomato, Tomato & Basil, Tomato Onion & Garlic, Traditional

**Hargis House** - Steak

**Health Market -** Mushroom Onion, Organic Tomato Basil, Vegetable

**Home Harvest Brand** - Tomato Sauce

**House Of Blues -** Bayou Heat Hot Sauce

**Hunt's -**

Organic Pasta Sauce (Regular, w/Roasted Garlic)

Spaghetti Sauce (Garlic & Herb, Traditional)

Tomato Sauce (Basil Garlic & Oregano, No Salt Added, Regular, Roasted Garlic)

Tomatoes

**Hy-Vee** - Spaghetti Sauce (3 Cheese, Garden, Mushroom, Traditional, w/Meat), Tomato Onion Garlic Pasta Sauce

**S**    **Katy Sweet▲** - Saucy Stuff (Caramel●, Praline●)

**Kurtz** - Steak Sauce

**Las Palmas** - Red Chile, Red Enchilada

**Laura Lynn** - Chili, Elmer Ingle 1922

**Lee Kum Kee** -

    Choy Sun Oyster Flavored

    Duck

    Gold Label Plum

    Panda Brand Lo Mein Oyster Flavored

    Panda Oyster Flavored Sauce (5 Gal, 55 Gal)

    Plum Stir Fry & Dipping

    Satay

    Shrimp

    Sweet & Sour

**Lowes Foods Brand** - Spaghetti Sauce (Plain, w/Meat, w/Mushrooms), Tomato

**Manischewitz** - Original Marinara, Tomato, Tomato & Mushroom

**Mayacamas** - Gourmet Sauce (Hollandaise), Pasta Sauce Mix (Alfredo, Chicken Fettuccine, Creamy Clam, Creamy Pesto, Peppered Lemon, Pesto), Skillet Toss Mix (Black Olive Pesto, Dried Tomato, Garden Style Recipe, Green Olive Pesto, Mushroom Sauce, Seafood Pasta Recipe, Spicy Pasta Recipe)

**Meijer Brand** -

    Extra Chunky Spaghetti Sauce (3 Cheese, Garden Combo, Garlic & Cheese, Mushroom & Green Pepper)

    Pasta Sauce Select (Four Cheese, Marinara, Mushroom & Olive, Onion & Garlic, Original)

    Regular Spaghetti Sauce (Plain, w/Meat, w/Mushroom)

    Tomato Sauce (Organic, Regular)

**Midwest Country Fare** -

    Spaghetti Sauce

        All Natural Garlic & Onion

        Four Cheese

Garden Vegetable

Garlic & Herb

Meat Flavor

Mushroom

Roasted Garlic & Onion

Traditional

Tomato Sauce

**Moore's Marinade -** Buffalo Wing, Honey BBQ Wing, Original, Teriyaki

**Mr. Spice Organic -** Sauce & Marinade (Garlic Steak, Ginger Stir Fry, Honey BBQ, Honey Mustard, Hot Wing, Indian Curry, Sweet & Sour, Thai Peanut)

**Muir Glen -** Organic (Beef Bolognese, Cabernet Marinara, Chunky Tomato & Herb, Fire Roasted Tomato, Garden Vegetable, Garlic Roasted Garlic, Italian Herb, Italian Sausage w/Peppers, Portabello Mushroom), Tomato Sauce (Chunky, No Salt Added, Regular)

**Nature's Promise -** Organic Pasta Sauce (Garden Vegetable Parmesan, Plain)

**Newman's Own -**

Cabernet Marinara

Diavolo

Fire Roasted Tomato & Garlic

Five Cheese

Garlic & Peppers

Italian Sausage & Peppers

Marinara (Regular, w/Mushroom)

Organic (Marinara, Tomato Basil, Traditional Herb)

Pesto & Tomato

Sockarooni

Sweet Onion

Tomato (Basil, w/Roasted Garlic)

Vodka

**S** **O Organics** - Marinara, Mushroom, Roasted Garlic, Tomato, Tomato Basil

**Pastapali** - Pasta Sauce

**Patak's** - Sauces (Balti, Korma, Madras, Rogan Josh, Tikka Masala)

**Patsy's Pasta Sauce** - Marinara, Tomato Basil

**Prego -**

Chunky Garden (Combo, Mushroom & Green Pepper, Mushroom Supreme w/Baby Portobello, Tomato Onion & Garlic)

Flavored w/Meat

Fresh Mushroom

Heart Smart (Mushroom, Onion & Garlic, Ricotta Parmesan, Roasted Red Pepper & Garlic, Traditional)

Italian Sausage & Garlic

Marinara

Mushroom & Garlic

Organic (Mushroom, Tomato & Basil)

Roasted (Garlic & Herb, Garlic Parmesan)

Three Cheese

Tomato Basil Garlic

Traditional

**Publix -** Garden Style, Meat Flavored, Mushrooms, Parmesan & Romano, Premium (Basil & Tomato, Creamy Vodka, Six Cheese), Scampi Finishing Sauce, Tomato Sauce, Tomato & Garlic & Onion, Traditional

**Ragu -**

Chunky (Garden Combination, Mushroom & Green Pepper, Super Chunky Mushroom, Tomato Garlic & Onion)

Light Tomato & Basil

Old World Style (Flavored w/Meat, Mushroom, Traditional)

Organic (Garden Veggie, Traditional)

Robusto (7 Herb Tomato, Parmesan & Romano, Roasted Garlic, Sauteed Onion & Garlic, Sauteed Onion & Mushroom, Six Cheese, Sweet Italian Sausage & Cheese)

**S**

**Rao's** - Homemade (Arrabbiata, Cuore Di Pomodoro, Marinara, Puttanesca, Roasted Eggplant, Southern Italian Pepper & Mushroom, Vodka

**S &W** - All Canned Sauces

**Safeway Brand** - Sloppy Joe

**Safeway Select** -

    Chili Sauce

    Gourmet Dipping Sauces (Honey Mustard, Sweet & Sour)

    Pasta Sauce

        Arrabiatta

        Artichoke Pesto

        Chunky Vegetable

        Four Cheese

        Marinara

        Mushroom/Onion

        Roasted Garlic

        Spicy Red Bell Pepper

        Sun-Dried Tomatoes & Olives

        Vodka

    Taco Sauce Mild

**San-J** - Gluten Free (Asian BBQ●, Sweet & Tangy●, Szechuan●, Thai Peanut●, Teriyaki●)

**Sauces 'N Love** - Arrabbiata, Barely Bolognese, Cilantro Chimichurri, Fresh Marinara & Pizza Sauces, Mint Pesto, Parsley Chimichurri, Pesto, Pink Pesto, Pomodoro & Basilico, Puttanesca, Sugo Rosa, Tuscan Vodka

**Scarpetta** - Arrabbiata, Barely Bolognese, Bruschetta Toppings (Tomato & Artichoke, Tomato & Capers), Fresh Marinara & Pizza Sauces, Pesto, Pink Pesto, Puttanesca, Tomato & Arugula, Tuscan Vodka

**Seeds of Change** -

    Indian Simmer Sauce (Jalfrezi, Korma, Madras, Tikka Masala)

    Pasta Sauce

**S**

    Arrabiatta di Roma

    Marinara di Venezia

    Romagna Three Cheese

    Tomato Basil Genovese

    Tuscan Tomato & Garlic

    Vodka Americano

**Sharwood's -** Balti, Bhuna, Chicken Tikka, Chicken Korma, Dopiaza, Jalfrezi, Korma, Lime & Corriander, Madras, Oyster & Thai Basil Stir Fry Sauce, Plum Sauce, Rogan Josh, Saag Masala, Spicy Tikka Masala, Sweet Chilli & Lemongrass Stir Fry Sauce, Thai Mussaman Curry, Thai Yellow Curry, Tikka Masala

**Simply Boulder -** Culinary Sauce (Coconut Peanut●, Honey Dijon●, Lemon Pesto●, Pineapple Ginger●, Truly Teriyaki●)

**Simply Delicious -** Organic Balsamic & Mint Sauce

**Spartan Brand -** Chili, Pizza Sauce, Sloppy Joe, Spaghetti Sauce (Traditional, w/Meat, w/Mushroom), Tomato Sauce

**Stonewall Kitchen Sauce -** Classic Vodka, Roasted Garlic Basil, Traditional Marinara

**Stop & Shop Brand -**

    Simply Enjoy Sauce (Fra Diavolo, Marinara, Roasted Garlic, Sicilian Eggplant, Tomato Basil, Vodka)

    Tomato Sauce (No Added Salt, Regular)

**Taste Of Inspirations -** Green Olive Tapenade, Grilling Sauce (Carribbean Mango, Honey Bourbon, Red Apple), Pizza Sauce, Roasted Red Pepper & Tomato Bruschetta, Sun Dried Tomato Bruschetta

**Texas Pete -** Buffalo Wing, Garlic Hot Sauce, Hotter Hot Sauce, Original Hot Sauce, Pepper, Seafood

**Thai Kitchen -**

    Fish Sauce

    Less Sodium Fish Sauce

    Original Pad Thai

    Peanut Satay

    Premium Fish

**S**

Simmer Sauce (Green Curry, Panang Curry, Red Curry, Yellow Curry)

Spicy Thai Chili

Sweet Red Chili

**Trader Joe's -**

Organic

Marinara Sauce (No Salt Added, Regular)

Red Wine & Olive Oil Vinaigrette

Spaghetti Sauce

Tomato Basil Marinara

Vodka Sauce

Regular

Arrabiata

Bruschetta

Cacciatore Simmer

Chili Pepper

Curry Simmer

Italian Sausage

Korma Simmer

Marinara

Masala Simmer

Piccata Simmer

Pizza Fat Free

Punjab Spinach

Roasted Garlic Marinara

Rustico

Thai Curry (Red, Yellow)

Three Cheese

Tomato Basil (Marinara, Pasta Sauce)

Tuscano Marinara Low Fat

Whole Peeled Tomatoes w/Basil (All)

**S**

**Ukrop's** - Marinara, Pizza, Spaghetti w/Meat, Special

**Walden Farms** - Alfredo, Bruschetta, Marinara, Scampi

**Wegmans Brand** -

Bruschetta Topping (Artichoke Asiago, Roasted Red Pepper, Traditional Tomato)

Chunky (Marinara Pasta Sauce, Pizza Sauce)

Diavolo Sauce

Four Cheese

Horseradish Cream

Italian Classics (Arrabbiata, Bolognese Sauce, Marinara, Portabello Mushroom, Puttanesca, Seasoned Tomato)

Lemon Butter

Lemon & Caper Sauce

Mustard

Organic Pasta Sauce (Marinara, Roasted Garlic, Tomato Basil)

Prepared Horseradish

Remoulade

Roasted (Garlic Pasta Sauce, Sweet Red Pepper)

Smooth Marinara

Tomato (& Basil, Regular, Sauce, w/Italian Sausage)

Vodka Sauce

White Clam Sauce

**Wild Thymes** - Dipping Sauce (Indian Vindaloo, Moroccan Spicy Pepper, Thai Chili Roasted Garlic), Tropical Mango Lime Sauce

**Winn & Lovett** - Grilling Sauce (Apple Spice, Molasses Horseradish, Roasted Onion & Balsamic)

**Winn Dixie** - Classic (Fra Diavolo, Home Style, Marinara, Peppers & Onions, Tomato Basil), Classic Style (Double Garlic, Fat Free), Garden Vegetable Combination, Garlic & Onion, Meat, Mushroom, Parmesan & Romano, Pizza Sauce, Tomato Sauce, Traditional

**Woodstock Farms** - Tomato Sauce (Chunky, No Salt)

**S**

**Sauerkraut**
   Albertsons
   B&G
   Boar's Head
   Cortland Valley Organic
   Eden Organic - Organic
   Food Club Brand
   Flanagan
   Great Value Brand (Wal-Mart) - Canned
   Hannaford Brand
   Hy-Vee - Shredded Kraut
   Krrrrisp Kraut
   Laura Lynn
   Meijer Brand
   S&W - All Canned Vegetables
   Safeway Brand
   Silver Floss
   Spartan Brand
   Wegmans Brand
   Willie's
**Sausage**
   Abraham - Prusciutto
   Aidells -
      Apricot Ginger Breakfast Links
      Artichoke & Garlic
      Bier
      Burmese Curry
      Cajun Style Andouille
      Chicken & Apple Breakfast Links (Minis, Regular)
      Habanero & Green Chile
      Italian Style w/Mozzarella Cheese

**S**

Mango (Breakfast Links, Regular)

Maple & Smoked Bacon Breakfast Links

Organic (Andouille, Chicken & Apple, Spinach & Feta, Sun Dried Tomato, Sweet Basil & Roasted Garlic)

Pesto

Portobello

Roasted (Garlic & Gruyere Cheese, Pepper w/Corn)

Smoked Chorizo

Spinach & Feta

Sun Dried Tomato & Mozzarella

Whiskey Fennel

**Applegate Farms** -

Genoa Salami (Hot, Organic, Regular)

Joy Stick

Natural Uncured Hot Dogs (Beef, Big Apple, Chicken, Turkey)

Organic Sausages (Andouille, Chicken & Apple, Fire Roasted Red Pepper, Smoked Pork Andouille, Smoked Pork Bratwurst, Smoked Pork Kielbasa, Spinach & Feta, Sweet Italian)

Organic Uncured Hot Dogs (Beef, Chicken, Regular, Stadium Style, The Great Organic, Turkey)

Pancetta

Pepperoni

Sopressata (Hot, Regular)

The Greatest Little Organic Smokey Pork Cocktail Franks

Turkey Salami

**Boar's Head** - All Varieties

**Busseto** - Premium Genoa Salami

**Butcher's Cut** - Bratwurst, Italian Sausage (Mild, Regular), Jumbo Franks (Chicken, Pork, Turkey), Polska Kielbasa, Smoked Sausage

**Butterball** - Turkey Sausage (Fresh Bratwurst, Fresh Breakfast, Fresh Hot Italian, Fresh Sweet Italian, Polska Kielbasa Dinner, Smoked, Smoked Cheddar, Smoked Dinner, Smoked Hot)

## sausage

**S**

**Canino's** - Bratwurst●, Breakfast Sausage●, German Brand Sausage●, Hot Chorizo●, Hot Italian Sausage●, Mild Italian Sausage●, Polish Sausage●, Spicy Cajun Style Sausage●, Sweet Italian Sausage●

**Di Lusso** - Beef Summer

**Dietz & Watson** -

Beef Franks (New York Deli) *(Except Fat Free And Gourmet Lite)*

Black Forest Knockwurst

Bologna (Beef, German Brand, Regular, Ring)

Bratwurst

Capocolla (Hot, Sweet)

Cheddarwurst

Cooked Salami

Franks Regular *(Except Gourmet Lite)*

Honey Roll

Landjaeger On The Go

Lunch Roll

Mortadella (Regular, w/Pistachios)

Olive Loaf

P & P Loaf

Pancetta

Pepper (& Onion Sausage, Loaf)

Sopressata Friuli (Hot, Large)

Wieners

**Eckrich** -

Franks (Beef, Original)

Li'l Smokies

Polska Kielbasa

Smoked Grillers Smoked Sausage (Cheese, Original, Polish)

Smoked Sausage (Beef, Regular)

Smoky Breakfast Links (Beef, Cheese, Maple, Original)

**S** **Empire Kosher** - Roll (Turkey Bologna, Turkey Salami, White Turkey)
Turkey Franks

**Fairgrounds** - Hot Dogs (Jumbo, Regular)

**Farmer John** -

Breakfast Sausage Links & Patties (Firehouse Hot Roll, Firehouse
Hot Skinless Links, Old Fashioned Maple Skinless, Original Roll,
Original Skinless, Premium Original Chorizo, Premium PC
Links Lower Fat, Premium SC Links, Premium Sausage Patties
Lower Fat, Premium Spicy Hot Chorizo, Premium Traditional
Chorizo, Quick Serve Fully Cooked)

California Natural Chicken Sausage (Apple Chicken Smoked,
Asiago Chicken Smoked, Cajun Style Smoked, Chicken Brat
Smoked, Lemon Cracked Pepper Chicken Smoked, Mango &
Habanero Smoked)

Cotto Salami

Dinner Sausage (Hot Louisiana Smoked, Jalapeno Pepper
Premium Rope, Jalapeno Pepper Premium Smoked, Premium
Beef Rope, Premium Polish, Premium Pork Rope, Red Hots
Extra Hot Premium Smoked)

Franks & Wieners (Dodger Dogs, Premium Beef Franks, Premium
Jumbo Beef Franks, Premium Jumbo Meat Wieners, Premium
Meat Wieners, Premium Quarter Pounder Beef Franks)

**Farmington** - Mild Pork

**Five Star Brand** - Beef Franks Mild, Bratwurst, Cooked Salami, Garlic
Knockwurst, German Franks (Hot, Mild), Jumbo Beef Wieners,
Natural Casing Less Salt Kielbasa, SC Beef Wieners, SC Wieners
(Low Salt, Regular), Skinless Beef Kielbasa, Slovenian Franks

**Garrett County Farms** -

Andouille Sausage

Chorizo Sausage

Franks (4XL Big Beef, Chicken, Old Fashioned Beef, Original Deli,
Premium Beef, Turkey)

Kielbasa (Polska, Turkey)

Sliced Beef (Bologna, Salami)

Sliced Uncured Pepperoni

**S**

## Giant Eagle Brand -

Beef Franks

Breakfast Sausage (Brown & Serve, Hot Roll, Maple Links, Original Links, Original Patties, Regular Roll, Sage Roll)

Bun Size (Beef Franks, Franks)

Deli Beef Franks

Meat Franks (Lite, Regular)

Smoked Sausage (Beef, Pork)

Smoked Sausage Link (Cheese and Onion, Chili Cheese & Onion, Jalapeno and Cheese)

**Great Value Brand (Wal-Mart) -** Canned Vienna Sausage

**Hargis House -** Vienna

**Hebrew National -** Franks (Beef, Cocktail, Jumbo Beef)

**Hertel's -** All Original Fresh Sausages *(Except British Bangers)*

## Hillshire Farms -

Cheddar Wurst

Lit'l Beef Franks

Lit'l Polskas

Lit'l Smokies (Beef, Cheddar, Chipotle Hot, Regular)

Lit'l Wieners

Polska Beef Kielbasa

Smoked Bratwurst

Smoked Sausage (Beef, Lite, Original)

Turkey Smoked Sausage

## Honeysuckle White -

Hardwood Smoked Turkey Franks

Hickory Smoked Cooked Turkey Salami

Turkey Sausage Rolls (Breakfast, Mild Italian)

Turkey Sausage (Bratwurst, Breakfast Sausage (Links, Patties), Chipotle Smoked Links, Italian Sausage (Hot, Sweet), Original Smoked Links, Poblano Pepper Links, Tomato & Garlic Links)

**S**  Hormel -
Crumbled
Deli Sliced Cooked Pastrami
Hard Salami
Homeland Hard Salami
Little Sizzlers (Links, Patties)
Natural Choice (Hard Salami, Pepperoni)
Pepperoni
Smokies
Turkey Pepperoni

**Hy-Vee** - Beef, Beef Summer, Bratwurst, Cooked Salami, Little
Smokies (Beef, Regular), Pepperoni, Polish (Link, Rope), Smoked
w/Cheddar Cheese, Summer Sausage, Thin Sliced Pastrami

**Ian's** - Wheat Free Gluten Free Recipe Popcorn Turkey Corn Dogs

**Jennie-O Turkey Store** -
Breakfast Lover's Turkey Sausage
Extra Lean Smoked Turkey Sausage (Kielbasa, Regular)
Fresh
Breakfast Sausage (Maple Links, Mild Links, Mild Patties)
Dinner Sausage (Cheddar Turkey Bratwurst, Hot Italian, Lean
Turkey Bratwurst, Sweet Italian)
Lean Turkey Patties
Frozen
Fully Cooked Sausage (Links, Patties)
Italian Meatballs
Refrigerated (Dark Turkey Pastrami)
Turkey Franks

**Jimmy Dean** -
All Natural Pork Roll Sausage (Hot, Regular)
Fully Cooked Links (Original, Turkey)
Fully Cooked Patties (Hot, Original, Sandwich Size, Turkey)

Heat 'N Serve Sausage Links (Hot, Maple, Regular)

Hean 'N Serve Sausage Patties

Original (Links, Patties)

Premium Pork Roll Sausage (Bold Country, Bold Country Hot, Extra Mild Country, Hot, Italian, Light, Maple, Mild Country, Regular, Sage)

### Johnsonville -

Beddar w/Cheddar

Bratwurst (Butcher Shop Style Cooked, Cheddar, Hot 'N Spicy, Original, Smoked, Stadium Style)

Butcher Shop Style Cheddar Smoked

Butcher Shop Style Weiners

Chorizo

Hearty Beef Bologna

Irish O'Garlic

Italian (Hot, Mild, Sweet)

Italian Ground Sausage (Hot, Mild, Sweet)

New Orleans Brand Smoked

Original (Breakfast (Links, Patties), Ring Bologna)

Polish

Smoked Turkey

Stadium Style Beef Franks

Summer Sausage (Beef, Garlic, Old World Summer, Original)

Turkey w/Cheddar

Vermont Maple Syrup (Links, Patties)

### Jones Dairy Farm

All Natural

Hearty Pork Sausage Links●

Little Link Pork Sausage●

Light Pork Sausage and Rice Links●

Pork Sausage Patties●

**S**

Maple Sausage Patties●

Original Pork Roll Sausage●

All Natural Golden Brown Fully Cooked & Browned Sausage Patties (Maple●, Mild●)

All Natural Golden Brown Fully Cooked & Browned Turkey●

All Natural Golden Brown Light Fully Cooked & Browned Sausage & Rice Links●

All Natural Golden Fully Cooked & Browned Sausage Links (Made From Beef●, Maple●, Mild●, Pork & Uncured Bacon●, Spicy●)

**Lloyd's** - Original BBQ Sauce w/Cocktail Smokies

**Lou's Famous** - Chicken Sausage (Aged Provolone, Apple, Artichoke & Calamata, Buffalo Blue Cheese, Feta Cheese & Spinach, Peppers & Onion, Roasted Red Pepper & Garlic, Spicy Italian, Sundried Tomato)

**Maluma** - All Bison Sausage

**Members Mark** - Mushroom & Aged Swiss Chicken Sausage

**Mulay's** - Ground Sausage (Breakfast●, Mild Italian●, Original●, Original Italian●), Links (Breakfast●, Killer Hot●, Mild Italian●, Original●, Original Italian●)

**Nature's Promise** -

Italian Spicy Pork

Mild Italian Chicken

Red Pepper & Provolone Pork

Spiced Apple Chicken

Spinach & Feta Chicken

Sun Dried Tomato & Basil Chicken

**O Organics** - Spinach & Feta Sausage

**Old Wisconsin** - All Varieties *(Except Beef Jerky)*

**Organic Prairie** -

Frozen Organic (Beef Hot Dogs 10.5 oz., Bratwurst 12 oz., Breakfast Sausage 12 oz., Brown N Serve Breakfast Links 8 oz., Italian Sausage 12 oz.)

## sausage

Organic Pork Fresh (Classic Hot Dogs 12 oz., Sliced Pepperoni 5 oz.) **S**
Organic Poultry Fresh 12 oz. (Chicken Hot Dogs, Turkey Hot Dogs)

**Oscar Mayer -**

Beef Franks (Bun Length, Jumbo, Light, Regular)

Cheese Dogs

Little (Smokies, Wieners)

Mini Beef Hot Dogs

Premium Franks (Beef & Cheddar, Jalapeno & Cheddar)

Salami (Cotto, Del Think Beef, Hard)

Smokies (Beef, Sausage)

Summer Sausage (Beef, Regular)

Turkey Franks (Bun Length, Cheese Dogs, Regular)

Variety Pak (Bologna/Ham/Salami)

Wieners (98 % Fat Free, Bun Length, Jumbo, Light, Regular, Turkey Franks)

XXL Hot Dogs (Deli Style Beef, Hot & Spicy, Premium Beef, Smoked)

**Perdue -**

Deli Turkey (Bologna, Salami)

Turkey Sausage Seasoned Fresh Lean (Hot Italian, Sweet Italian)

**Primo Naturale -**

Chorizo (Sliced Dried, Stick Dried)

Chub Salami (Genoa, Original, w/Black Pepper, w/Herbs)

Pepperoni (Pillow Pack, Sliced Dried, Stick, Whole Large Diameter)

Sliced Salami (Hard, Original, Premium Genoa, w/Black Pepper, w/Herbs)

Sopressata (Regular, Sliced, Whole)

Whole Chorizo

Whole Salami (Black Pepper, Genoa, Herb & Wine, Hard, Original)

**Primo Taglio -** Pepperoni, Salami (Cervelat, Genoa, Peppered Coated w/Gelatin & Black Pepper), Sopressata

**S** **Publix** -

Bratwurst

Chorizo

Deli Pre Pack Sliced Hard Salami Reduced Fat

Franks (Beef, Meat)

Fresh Turkey Italian (Hot, Mild)

Hot Dogs (Beef, Meat)

Sausages Italian (Hot, Mild)

**Publix GreenWise Market** - Pork Sage Sausage

**Safeway Select** -

Beef Franks

Bratwurst

Italian (Hot, Mild, Pork)

Pepperoni

Polish

Regular Hot Dogs

**Shelton's** -

Bologna Uncured Turkey

Franks (Smoked Chicken, Smoked Turkey, Uncured Chicken, Uncured Turkey)

Turkey Sausage (Breakfast, Italian, Patties)

Turkey Sticks (Pepperoni, Regular)

**Smithfield** - Breakfast Sausage (Mild Pork Roll, Hot Pork Roll, Pork Links, Pork Patties), Smoked Sausage Links (Hot, Regular, w/Cheese), Smoked Sausage Loops (Hickory Smoke, Hickory Smoke Beef, Hickory Smoke Polska)

**SPAM** - Classic, Less Sodium, Lite, Oven Roasted Turkey, Smoke Flavored

**Spartan Brand** - Breakfast (Maple, Original), Mild, Hot

**Thrifty Maid** - Vienna Sausage (Chicken, Original)

**Thumann's** - All Varieties●

**Trader Joe's** - Prosciutto Di Italia, All Sausage, Uncured All Beef Hot Dogs

**Ukrop's** - Italian Sausage w/Peppers & Onions

**S**

## Wegmans Brand -

Beef Hot Dogs (Skinless)

Cocktail Hot Dogs (Skinless Frankfurters)

Pepperoni Italian Style (Regular, Sliced)

Red Hot Dogs Skinless (Lite, Regular)

Uncured Skinless (Beef Hot Dogs, Hot Dogs)

## Wellshire Farms -

Beef Franks Hot Dogs (4XL Big, The Old Fashioned, The Premium)

Cheese Franks

Cocktail Franks

Frozen

    Chicken Apple Sausage (Links, Patties)

    Country Sage Sausage (Links, Patties)

    Original Breakfast Sausage (Links, Patties)

    Sunrise Maple Sausage (Links, Patties)

    Turkey (Burgers, Maple Sausage (Links, Patties))

Liverwurst (Pork, Turkey)

Morning Maple Turkey Breakfast Link Sausage

Original Matt's Select Pepperoni Steaks ·

Polska Kielbasa

Pork Andouille Sausage

Pork Sausage (Chorizo, Linguica)

Sliced (Beef Pepperoni, Beef Salami)

Smoked Bratwurst

The Original Deli Franks

Turkey

    Andouille Sausage

    Dinner Link Sausage Mild Italian Style

    Franks

    Kielbasa

    Tom Toms (Hot & Spicy, Original)

**S**  **Wellshire Organic** - Organic (Andouille Sausage (Pork, Turkey), Franks (Beef, Chicken, Turkey), Kielbasa (Polska, Turkey))

**Winn Dixie** - Ground Mild Italian, Original Bratwurst, w/Green Onion

**Wranglers** - Franks

**Scalloped Potatoes**

**Dinty Moore** - Microwave Meals (Scalloped Potatoes & Ham)

**Scallops...** *All Fresh Seafood Is **Gluten-Free (Non-Marinated, Unseasoned)***

**Hy-Vee** - Frozen

**Publix** - Sea Scallops

**Whole Catch** - Sea Scallops

**Seafood Sauce... see also Cocktail Sauce**

**Food Club Brand** - Cocktail Sauce

**Frontera -** Cocktail & Ceviche Sauce (Cilantro Lime, Tomato Chipotle)

**Heinz -** Cocktail Sauce

**Laura Lynn** - Cocktail

**Mayacamas -** Seafood Pasta Skillet Toss Mix

**McCormick** - Cajun, Lemon Butter Dill (Fat Free, Regular), Lemon Herb, Mediterranean, Santa Fe Style, Scampi

**Safeway Brand** - Cocktail

**Spartan Brand**

**Stop & Shop Brand** - Seafood Cocktail Sauce

**Texas Pete -** Seafood Cocktail

**Trader Joe's** - Seafood Cocktail Sauce

**Ukrop's -** Cocktail Sauce

**Walden Farms**

**Seasoning Packets... see Seasonings**

**Seasonings**

**Accent** - Flavor Enhancer (All Varieties)

**Albertsons -** Bay Leaves, Chili Powder, Cinnamon, Black Pepper, Garlic Powder, Garlic Salt, Ginger, Nutmeg, Onion, Onion Powder, Paprika, Parsley Flakes, Seasoned Salt

**American Natural & Organic Spices** - *All The Following Products Are* **S**
*'Certified Gluten-Free'.*●

Adobo Seas Sf, All Purpose, Allspice Ground, Allspice Whole, Anise Ground, Anise Star Whole, Anise Whole, Annatto Ground, Annatto Seed, Apple Pie Spice, Arrowroot, Baharat Sf, Barbeque Sf, Basil, Beef Burger Sf, Bouquet Garni Sf, Cajun Seasoning, Caraway Seeds, Cardamom Decorticated, Cardamom Ground, Cardamom Pods Green, Cayenne Pepper, Celery Ground, Celery Salt, Celery Seeds, Chicken Kabob Sf, Chili Ancho Ground, Chili California Ground, Chili Chipotle Ground Chili Con Carne Sf, Chili Guajillo Ground, Chili Habanero Ground, Chili Jalapeno Ground, Chili New Mexico Ground, Chili Pepper Crushed, Chili Pepper Whole, Chili Powder, Chimichurri Seas Sf, Chinese Five Spice Sf, Chives, Cilantro Flakes, Cinnamon Ground, Cinnamon Sticks, Cloves Ground, Cloves Whole, Coriander Ground, Coriander Seeds, Cream Of Tartar, Cumin Ground, Cumin Seed Whole, Curry Powder, Curry Powder Hot, Curry Powder Salt Free, Curry Thai Red Salt Free, Dill Seed, Dill Weed, Dukka Seasoning, Epazote, Fajita Seasoning Sf, Fennel Ground, Fennel Seeds, Fenugreek (Ground, Seeds), Fines Herbes Sf, Fish Grill & Broil Sf, Flaxseed, French Four Spice Sf, Galangal, Garam Masala, Garlic (Bread, Granulates, Herbs, Minced, Pepper, Sliced, Toasted), Ginger Ground, Greek Seasoning Sf, Gumbo File, Harisa Sf, Herbs De Provence, Horseradish Powder, Italian Seasoning, Jerk Seasoning Sf, Juniper Berries, Lamb Seasoning Sf, Lavender, Lemon (Grass, Peel, Pepper), Mace Ground, Marjoram (Ground, Whole), Meatloaf Seasoning Sf, Mediterranean Seas Sf, Mexican Seasoning Sf, Mint (Peppermint, Spearmint), Mulling Spice Blend, Mustard (Ground, Seeds Brown, Seeds Yellow), Nigella Seed, Nutmeg (Ground, Whole), Onion Granulates, Orange Peel, Oregano (Ground, Mediterranean, Mexican), Ras El Hanout Sf, Rib Eye Steak Sf, Rice Seasoning Sf, Rosemary (Ground, Whole), Safflower, Saffron, Sage (Ground, Rubbed, Whole), Sambal Ulek Sf, Savory, Savory Ground, Sesame Seed (Black, White), Shawarma Seas Sf, Shish Kabob Sf, Shrimp/Crab Gr&Bl Sf, Sumac, Taco Seasoning Sf, Tandoori Masala Sf, Tarragon, Thai Spice Blend Sf, Thyme, Thyme

**S**

Ground, Tsatsiki (Greek Yogurt), Turmeric, Vanilla (Bean, Extract), Vegetable Seas Sf, Vindaloo Seasoning Sf, Wasabi Powder Sf, Zatar Sf

Organic (Allspice (Ground, Whole), Almond Extract, Anise Star Whole, Basil, Bay Leave Whole, Cajun Seasoning, Caraway Seeds, Cardamom (Green, Ground, Original), Cayenne Pepper, Celery Seeds, Chili (Ancho Ground, Chipotle Ground, Pepper Crush, Powder), Chinese Five Spice, Cinnamon (Ground, Sticks) Cloves (Ground, Whole), Coriander (Ground, Seeds), Cumin Ground, Cumin Seeds Whole, Curry (Powder, Thai Herb), Dill Weed, Fennel Seeds, Garam Masala, Garlic Granulates, Ginger Ground, Herbs De Provence, Italian Season, Juniper Berries, Lemon Extract, Marjoram Whole, Melange Pepper, Mexican Seasoning, Mustard (Ground, Seed Brown, Seed Yell), Nutmeg (Ground, Whole), Onion Granulates, Orange Extract, Oregano Mediterranean, Panch Phoron Sf, Paprika (Regular, Smoked), Parsley, Pasta Spaghetti Sf, Pepper Black Long, Pepper Ground (Black, White), Peppercorn (Black, Green, Melange, Melody, Pink, Szechuan, White), Pickling Seasoning, Pizza Spice Sf, Poppy Seeds, Pork Chop Sf, Poultry Seasoning, Pumpkin Pie Spice, Rosemary Whole, Saffron, Sage (Ground, Rubbed, Whole), Sesame (Seed Black, Seed White), Tarragon, Thyme, Turmeric, Vanilla Extract)

**Arora Creations** -

Organic Seasoning Packets (Bhindi Masala, Gobi, Punjabi Chole, Rajmah, Tandoori Chicken, Tikka Masala)

Regular Seasoning Packets (Bhindi Masala, Goan Shrimp Curry, Gobi, Punjabi Chole, Rajmah, Tandoori Chicken, Tikkam Masala)

**Bone Suckin'** - Seasoning & Rub

**Bragg** - Sea Kelp Delight, Sprinkle Seasoning

**Cali Fine Foods▲** - Gourmet Seasoning Packets (Dill Delight●, Garlic Gusto●, Herb Medley●, Spicy Fiesta●, Sweet & Spicy BBQ●)

**Chef Paul Prudhommes Magic** - All Seasoning Blends *(Except Breading Magic & Gravy Gumbo Magic)*

**Chi-Chi's** - Fiesta Restaurante Seasoning Mix

**Dorothy Lane Market** - Prime Rib Rub

## seasonings

**S**

**Durkee -** All Liquid Extracts, All Liquid Flavorings, All Food Coloring, Allspice, Alum, Anise Seed, Apple Pie Spice, Arrowroot, Basil, Bay Leaves, Buttermilk Ranch Dressing, Caraway Seed, Cardamom, Cayenne Pepper, Celery Flakes, Celery Seed, Chicken & Rib Rub, Chicken Seasoning, Chili Powder, Chives, Cilantro, Cinnamon, Cloves, Coriander, Crazy Dave's Lemon Pepper, Crazy Dave's Pepper & Spice, Crazy Dave's Salt & Spice, Cream of Tartar, Crushed Red Pepper, Cumin, Curry Powder, Dill Seed/Weed, Fennel, Garlic Minced, Garlic Pepper, Garlic Powder, Garlic Salt, Ginger, Hickory Smoke Salt, Italian Seasoning, Jamaican Jerk Seasoning, Lemon & Herb, Lemon Garlic Seasoning, Lemon Pepper, Lime Pepper, Mace, Marjoram, Meat Tenderizer, Mr. Pepper, Mint Leaves, MSG, Mustard, Nutmeg, Onion Minced, Orange Peel, Onion Powder, Onion Salt, Oregano, Oriental 5-Spice, Paprika, Parsley, Pepper Black/White (All), Pepper Green Bell, Pickling Spice, Pizza Seasoning, Poppy Seed, Poultry Seasoning, Pumpkin Pie Spice, Rosemary, Rosemary Garlic Seasoning, Sage, Salt Free Garden Seasoning, Salt Free Garlic & Herb, Salt Free Lemon Pepper, Salt Free Original All Purpose Seasoning, Salt Free Veg. Seasoning, Seasoned Pepper, Sesame Seed, Six Pepper Blend, Smokey Mesquite Seasoning, Spaghetti/Pasta Seasoning, Spicy Spaghetti Seasoning, Steak Seasoning, Tarragon, Thyme, Turmeric

**Durkee California Style Blends -** Garlic Powder, Garlic Salt, Onion Powder, Onion Salt

**Emeril's -**

Bam It Salad Seasoning

Essence (Bayou Blast, Garlic Parmesan For Bread, Italian, Original, Southwest)

Rubs (Chicken, Fish, Rib, Steak, Turkey)

**Food Club Brand -** Black Pepper, Chili Powder, Cinnamon, Garlic Powder, Garlic Salt, Iodized Salt, Minced Onion, Pure Vanilla Extract, Salt, Seasoned Salt

**Gayelord Hauser -** Spike Magic (5 Herb, Garlic, Hot N Spicy, Onion, Original, Salt Free, Vegit)

**S**

**Hannaford Brand** - Basil Leaves, Bay Leaves, Celery Salt, Chili Powder, Crushed Red Pepper, Garlic Powder, Garlic Salt, Ground Black Pepper, Ground Cinnamon, Ground Ginger, Ground Mustard, Ground Nutmeg, Minced Onion, Oregano Leaves, Paprika, Taco Seasoning Mix

**Home Harvest Brand** - Basil, Chili Powder, Cinnamon, Crushed Red Peppers, Garlic Powder, Garlic Salt, Ground Black Pepper, Minced Onion, Onion Powder, Oregano, Oregano Flakes, Seasoned Salt

**Hy-Vee** - Basil Leaf, Bay Leaves, Black Pepper, Chicken Grill Seasoning, Chili Powder, Chopped Onion, Dill Weed, Garlic Powder, Garlic Salt, Grinders (Black Peppercorn, Peppercorn Melange, Sea Salt), Ground Cinnamon, Ground Cloves, Ground Mustard, Iodized Salt, Italian Seasoning, Lemon Pepper, Meat Tenderizer, Oregano Leaf, Paprika, Parsley Flakes, Plain Salt, Red Crushed Pepper, Rosemary, Salt & Pepper Shaker, Seasoned Salt, Steak Grilling Seasoning, Thyme

**Jack's Grill Rubs** - Beef & Burger, Chicken & Poultry, Fish & Seafood, Pork

**Konriko -** Chipotle All Purpose Seasoning, Creole Seasoning

**Laura Lynn** - Black Pepper, Steak Seasoning

**Lawry's -**

Black Pepper Seasoned Salt, Garlic Pepper, Garlic Powder w/Parsley, Garlic Salt, Lemon Pepper, Salt Free 17, Seasoned Pepper, Seasoned Salt

Seasoning Mixes (Chicken Fajitas, Chicken Taco, Extra Thick & Rich Spaghetti Sauce, Fajitas, Guacamole, Original Style Spaghetti Sauce, Sloppy Joes, Tenderizing Beef Marinade Mix)

**Litehouse** - Dried (Basil, Chives, Cilantro, Dill, Garlic, Italian Herb Blend, Oregano, Parsley, Poultry Herb Blend, Red Onion, Salad Herb Blend)

**Lowes Foods Brand** - Black Pepper, Chili Powder, Cinnamon Ground, Garlic Powder, Paprika, Salt & Pepper Shaker Set, Steak Seasoning

**Marcum Spices** - Black Pepper, Canadian Steak Seasoning, Chili Powder, Crushed Oregano, Crushed Red Pepper, Coarse Ground Black Pepper, Fried Chicken Seasoning, Garlic Powder, Garlic Salt,

## seasonings

**S**

Ground Cinnamon, Italian Seasoning, Lemon Pepper, Minced Onion, Onion Powder, Onion Salt, Paprika, Parsley Flakes, Rubbed Sage, Seasoned Meat Tenderizer, Soul Seasoning, Vanilla

**Marsh Brand** - Oregano Leaves, Paprika, Seasoned Salt

**Mayacamas** - Chicken BBQ, Curry Blend, Salad Delight, Savory Salt

**McCormick** -

Grill Mates Dry Rub (Chicken, Pork, Seafood, Steak, Sweet Smoky)

Grill Mates Grinders Seasoning (Montreal Chicken, Montreal Steak)

Grill Mates Seasoning Blends (25% Less Sodium Montreal (Chicken, Steak), Barbecue, Mesquite)

Roasting Rub (Cracked Peppercorn Herb, French Herb, Savory Herb)

Seasoning Packets (Creamy Garlic Alfredo Sauce, Enchilada, Fajitas, Guacamole, Italian Style Spaghetti, Salsa, Taco (30% Less Sodium, Chicken, Hot, Mild, Original), Tex Mex Chili)

Spices (Alum, Anise Seed, Apple Pie Spice, Basil Leaves, Bay Leaves, Caraway Seed, Celery Flakes, Celery Seed, Chili Powder, Chives, Cilantro Leaves, Cinnamon Sticks, Cinnamon Sugar, Cream of Tartar, Cumin Seed, Curry Powder, Dill Seed, Dill Weed, Fennel Seed, Ground Allspice, Ground Cinnamon, Ground Cloves, Ground Cumin, Ground Ginger, Ground Mace, Ground Marjoram, Ground Mustard, Ground Nutmeg, Ground Oregano, Ground Sage, Ground Thyme, Ground Turmeric, Hot Mexican Style, Italian Seasoning, Marjoram Leaves, Mixed Pickling Spice, Mustard Seed, Oregano (Oregano Entero), Oregano Leaves, Paprika, Parsley Flakes, Poppy Seed, Poultry Seasoning, Pumpkin Pie Spice, Rosemary Leaves, Rubbed Sage, Sage Leaves, Sesame Seed, Tarragon Leaves, Texas Style Chili Powder, Whole Allspice, Whole Cloves, Whole Mexican)

**Meijer Brand** - Black Pepper, Chili Powder, Cinnamon, Garlic Powder, Garlic Salt, Mild Taco Seasoning Packet, Minced Onion, Onion Salt, Oregano Leaves, Paprika, Parsley Flakes, Seasoned Salt, Spaghetti Mix, Taco Seasoning Packet

**Midwest Country Fare** - Chili Powder, Chopped Onion, Cinnamon, Garlic Powder, Garlic Salt, Ground Black Pepper, Onion Powder, Parsley Flakes, Pure Ground Black Pepper, Season Salt

**S**   Morton

Canning & Pickling Salt

Garlic Salt

Hot Salt

Lite Salt Mixture

Nature's Seasons Seasoning Blend

Popcorn Salt

Salt & Pepper Shakers

Sausage & Meat Loaf Seasoning

Seasoned Salt

Smoke Flavored Sugar Cure

Sugar Cure

Tender Quick

**Mrs. Dash** - Caribbean Citrus, Extra Spicy, Fiesta Lime, Garlic & Herb, Grilling Blends, Lemon Pepper, Low Pepper/No Garlic, Onion & Herb, Original Blend, Southwest Chipotle, Table Blend, Tomato Basil Garlic

**Nantucket Off-Shore** - Rub (Bayou, Dragon, Holiday Turkey, Mt. Olympus, Nantucket, Prairie, Pueblo, Raj, Rasta, Renaissance, St. Remy), Shellfish Boil

**Nielsen-Massey** - Madagascar Bourbon Pure Vanilla Powder●

**O Organics** - Basil Leaves, Bay Leaves, Cayenne Peppers, Chili Powder, Ground Cinnamon, Ground Cloves, Ground Cumin, Ground Nutmeg, Paprika

**Old Bay** - 30% Less Sodium, Blackened Seasoning, Garlic & Herb, Lemon & Herb, Original, Rub, Seafood Steamer

**Ortega** - Chipotle Mix, Guacamole Mix, Jalapeno & Onion Mix, Taco 40% Less Sodium Mix, Taco Meat Mix

**Polaner** - Ready To Use Wet Spices (Basil, Garlic, Jalapenos)

**Publix Brand** - Adobo Seasoning w/Pepper, Adobo Seasoning w/o Pepper, Ajo En Polvo Garlic Powder, Basil, Bay Leaves, Black Pepper, Chili Powder, Cinnamon, Comino Molido Ground Cumin, Condimento Completo Seasoning, Garlic Powder, Garlic

**S**

Powder w/Parsley, Garlic Salt, Ground Cumin, Ground Ginger, Ground Mustard, Ground Nutmeg, Ground Red Pepper, Italian Seasonings, Minced Onion, Onion Powder, Oregano, Paprika, Parsley Flakes, Salt, Seasoned Salt, Taco Seasoning Mix, Whole Black Pepper

**Safeway Brand** - Fajita Seasoning Mix

**Sharwood's** - Curry Powder (Hot, Medium, Mild)

**Spartan Brand** - Black Pepper, Brine Salt (Black Sleeve), Chili Powder, Cinnamon, Garlic Powder, Garlic Salt, Ground Nutmeg, Imitation Vanilla, Iodized Salt, Iodized Salt Crystals, Minced Onion, Oregano Leaves, Paprika, Parsley Flakes, Salt, Vanilla Extract

**Spice Islands** - All Liquid Extracts, All Liquid Flavorings, All Food Coloring, Allspice, Alum, Anise Seed, Apple Pie Spice, Arrowroot, Basil, Bay Leaves, Buttermilk Ranch Dressing, Caraway Seed, Cardamom, Cayenne Pepper, Celery Flakes, Celery Seed, Chicken & Rib Rub, Chicken Seasoning, Chili Powder, Chives, Cilantro, Cinnamon, Cloves, Coriander, Crazy Dave's Lemon Pepper, Crazy Dave's Pepper & Spice, Crazy Dave's Salt & Spice, Cream of Tartar, Crushed Red Pepper, Cumin, Curry Powder, Dill Seed/Weed, Fennel, Garlic Minced, Garlic Pepper, Garlic Powder, Garlic Salt, Ginger, Hickory Smoke Salt, Italian Seasoning, Jamaican Jerk Seasoning, Lemon & Herb, Lemon Garlic Seasoning, Lemon Pepper, Lime Pepper, Mace, Marjoram, Meat Tenderizer, Mr. Pepper, Mint Leaves, MSG, Mustard, Nutmeg, Onion Minced, Orange Peel, Onion Powder, Onion Salt, Oregano, Oriental 5-Spice, Paprika, Parsley, Pepper Black/White (All), Pepper Green Bell, Pickling Spice, Pizza Seasoning, Poppy Seed, Poultry Seasoning, Pumpkin Pie Spice, Rosemary, Rosemary Garlic Seasoning, Sage, Salt Free Garden Seasoning, Salt Free Garlic & Herb, Salt Free Lemon Pepper, Salt Free Original All-Purpose Seasoning, Salt Free Veg. Seasoning, Seasoned Pepper, Sesame Seed, Six Pepper Blend, Smokey Mesquite Seasoning, Spaghetti/Pasta Seasoning, Spicy Spaghetti Seasoning, Steak Seasoning, Tarragon, Thyme, Turmeric

**Spice Islands Grilling Gourmet & World Flavors** - All Varieties

**S**

**Spice Islands Salt-Free** - All Varieties

**Spice Islands Specialty** - Beau Monde, Chili Powder, Crystallized Ginger, Garlic Pepper Seasoning, Fine Herbs, Italian Herb Seasoning, Old Hickory Smoked Salt, Saffron, Summer Savory, Vanilla Bean

**Thai Kitchen** - Beef & Broccoli Seasoning Mixes

**Tones** - All Liquid Extracts, All Liquid Flavorings, All Food Coloring, Allspice, Alum, Anise Seed, Apple Pie Spice, Arrowroot, Basil, Bay Leaves, Buttermilk Ranch Dressing, Caraway Seed, Cardamom, Cayenne Pepper, Celery Flakes, Celery Seed, Chicken & Rib Rub, Chicken Seasoning, Chili Powder, Chives, Cilantro, Cinnamon, Cloves, Coriander, Crazy Dave's Lemon Pepper, Crazy Dave's Pepper & Spice, Crazy Dave's Salt & Spice, Cream of Tartar, Crushed Red Pepper, Cumin, Curry Powder, Dill Seed/Weed, Fennel, Garlic Minced, Garlic Pepper, Garlic Powder, Garlic Salt, Ginger, Hickory Smoke Salt, Italian Seasoning, Jamaican Jerk Seasoning, Lemon & Herb, Lemon Garlic Seasoning, Lemon Pepper, Lime Pepper, Mace, Marjoram, Meat Tenderizer, Mr. Pepper, Mint Leaves, MSG, Mustard, Nutmeg, Onion Minced, Orange Peel, Onion Powder, Onion Salt, Oregano, Oriental 5-Spice, Paprika, Parsley, Pepper Black/White (All), Pepper Green Bell, Pickling Spice, Pizza Seasoning, Poppy Seed, Poultry Seasoning, Pumpkin Pie Spice, Rosemary, Rosemary Garlic Seasoning, Sage, Salt Free Garden Seasoning, Salt Free Garlic & Herb, Salt Free Lemon Pepper, Salt Free Original All-Purpose Seasoning, Salt Free Veg. Seasoning, Seasoned Pepper, Sesame Seed, Six Pepper Blend, Smokey Mesquite Seasoning, Spaghetti/Pasta Seasoning, Spicy Spaghetti Seasoning, Steak Seasoning, Tarragon, Thyme, Turmeric

**Trader Joe's** - All Spices

**Tropical Sun Spices** - Caribbean Garlic Lemon Herb, Caribbean Guava Delite, Caribbean Seasoning Salt, Caribbean Tangerine Pepper, Citrus Delite Spice, Creole Spice, Cuban Rum Spice, Fisherman's Seasoning, Jamaican Black Pepper, Key Lime Jerk Seasoning, Mesquite Grilling Spice, Pizza Pasta Rice, Salsa Seasoning Spice, Sexy Spice, Spanish Sazon Completa, Southwest Santa Fe Spice, Strawberry Spice Rub, Sweet Orange Habanero Spice

**Watkins** - Organic Beef Seasoning

**Weber Grill Creations -**

  Club Pack Seasoning (Gourmet Burger, Smokey Mesquite)

  Grinders (Chicago Steak, Gourmet Burger, Kick 'N Chicken, N'Orleans Cajun, Smokey Mesquite, Veggie Grill, Zesty Lemon Seasoning)

  Rub (Burgundy Beef, Classic BBQ)

  Seasoning (Chicago Steak, Gourmet Burger, Kick 'N Chicken, Mango Lime, N'Orleans Cajun, Roasted Garlic & Herb, Seasoning Salt, Smokey Mesquite, Veggie Grill)

**Wegmans Brand -** Baby Leaves, Black Pepper, Cinnamon, Cloves, Cracked Pepper Blend, Cream of Tartar, Fleur De Sel (Sea Salt), Garlic Powder, Garlic Salt, Herbes De Provence, Lemon Pepper Seasoning, Minced Onions, Nutmeg, Onion Powder, Oregano, Paprika, Parsley Flakes, Pepper Black, Poultry Seasoning, Sage (Ground & Rubbed)

## Seaweed -

  **Eden Organic** - Agar Agar Bars, Agar Agar Flakes

  **Nagai's** - Sushi Nori Roasted Seaweed

  **Yaki** - Sushi Nori Roasted Seaweed

  **Yamamotoyama -** Sushi Party Toasted Seaweed, Toasted Seaweed Nori

## Seeds

  **Arrowhead Mills** - Flax, Golden Flax, Mechanically Hulled Sesame, Sunflower, Unhulled Sesame

  **Durkee** - Anise, Celery, Dill, Poppy, Sesame

  **Eden** - Organic Pumpkin (Dry Roasted & Salted, Spicy Dry Roasted w/Tamari)

  **Food Club Brand** - Dry Roasted Sunflower Kernels

  **Frito Lay** - Flamin' Hot Flavored Sunflower Seeds, Ranch Sunflower Seeds, Sunflower Seed Kernels, Sunflower Seeds

  **Goraw** - Seeds (Sprouted Pumpkin●, Sprouted Sunflower●), Seed Mix (Simple●, Spicy●)

  **Hy-Vee** - Dry Roasted Sunflower Kernels

**S** **Laura Lynn** - Sunflower

**Meijer Brand** - Sunflower (Plain, Salted In Shell)

**Publix** - Sunflower Seeds

**Shiloh Farms** - Black Sesame Seeds

**Spartan Brand** - Sunflower Kernels

**Spice Island** - Anise, Caraway, Celery, Dill, Poppy, Sesame

**Tones** - Anise, Caraway, Celery, Dill, Poppy, Sesame

**Trader Joe's** - Pumpkin Seeds & Pepitas, Sunflower

**Woodstock Farms** -

> Non Organic Seeds (Pumpkin (Regular, Roasted Salted), Sunflower Hulled (Regular, Roasted No Salt, Roasted Salted))

> Organic Seeds (Flax, Pumpkin (Regular, Roasted & Salted), Hulled Sesame, Sunflower (Hulled, Hulled Roasted No Salt, Roasted & Salted, Tamari), Tamari Pumpkin, White Quinoa)

**Sesame Oil... see Oil**

**Sesame Seeds... see Seeds**

**Shakes**

**Amazake** -

> Almond
>
> Amazing Mango
>
> Banana Appeal
>
> Chocolate (Almond, Chimp)
>
> Cool Coconut
>
> Go (Go Green, Hazelnuts)
>
> Oh So Original
>
> Rice Nog
>
> Tiger Chai
>
> Vanilla (Gorilla, Pecan Pie)

**Gatorade** - Nutrition Shakes (All Varieties)

**Glucerna** - Butter Pecan, Chocolate, Homemade Vanilla, Strawberries 'N Cream

**Kashi** - GoLean Shake (Chocolate, Vanilla)

**Nasoya** - Silken Creations Non Dairy Starter For Smoothies & Desserts

**Nesquik** - Milk Shake

**Odwalla** - All Drinks *(Except Super Protein Vanilla Al Mondo & Superfood)*

**Safeway Brand** - Nutritional Shake/Drink (Including Plus) (All Flavors), Weight Loss Shake (Chocolate Royale, Milk Chocolate, Vanilla)

**Worldwide Pure Protein** - Banana Crèam, Chocolate, Strawberry Cream, Vanilla

Shortening

**Albertsons**

**Crisco** - Butter Flavor, Regular

**Earth Balance** - Vegetable Shortening

**Food Club Brand**

**Great Value Brand (Wal-Mart)** - All Vegetable Shortening

**Home Harvest Brand** - Pre Creamed

**Hy-Vee** - Vegetable (Butter Flavor Shortening, Oil Shortening)

**Laura Lynn** - #3 Vegetable, 42 oz. Shortening

**Lowes Foods Brand** - Shortening

**Meijer Brand**

**Midwest Country Fare** - Pre Creamed Shortening

**Publix** - Vegetable Shortening

**Spartan Brand** - All Vegetable, Butter Flavored Vegetable Shortening

**Stop & Shop Brand** - Meat Fat/Vegetable Shortening, Vegetable

**Wegmans Brand** - Vegetable

Shrimp... *All Fresh Seafood Is **Gluten-Free** (Non-Marinated, Unseasoned)*

**Captain's Choice** - Cooked Tail On Shrimp

**Chicken Of The Sea** - All Shrimp Products

**Crown Prince** - Shrimp (Broken, Tiny)

**Great Value Brand (Wal-Mart)** - Canned Tiny Shrimp

**Hy-Vee** - Frozen Cooked, Platter

**Publix** - Cooked (All Sizes), Fresh (All Sizes)

**S**  **Publix GreenWise Market** - All Sizes (Cooked, Fresh)

**Starfish** - Just Grilled Shrimp●

**Trader Joe's** - Quinoa Pilaf w/Shrimp & Vegetables, Roasted Poblano Peppers w/Shrimp Rice & Cheese, Shrimp Stir Fry

**Ukrop's**

**Wegmans** - Shrimp From Beliza Uncooked

**Whole Catch** - Cooked, Raw, Wild Key West Pink (Shell On, Tail Off)

**Shrimp Sauce... see Cocktail Sauce**

**Sloppy Joe/Sloppy Joe Sauce**

   **Food Club Brand**

   **Hannaford Brand**

   **Heinz**

   **Hormel** - Not So Sloppy Joe

   **Hy-Vee**

   **Laura Lynn**

   **Meijer Brand** - Sloppy Joe Mix, Sloppy Joe Sauce

   **Safeway**

   **Spartan Brand**

**Smoke**

   **Colgin** - All Varieties

   **Stop & Shop Brand** - Hickory Smoke, Original

   **Wright's** - Liquid Smoke (Hickory, Mesquite)

**Smoked Sausage... see Sausage**

**Smoked Turkey... see Turkey**

**Smoothies**

   **Cascade Fresh** - Cascaders (Acai, Peach, Raspberry, Strawberry)

   **Ella's Kitchen** - Smoothie Fruits (The Red One, The Yellow One)

   **Hansen's Smoothie Nectar** - Energy Island Blast, Guava Strawberry, Mango Pineapple, Peach Berry, Pineapple Coconut, Strawberry Banana

   **Lucerne** - All Varieties

   **Silk Live! Smoothies** - All Varieties

## snacks

**S**

**Stonyfield Farms** - Banana Berry●, Peach●, Raspberry●, Strawberry●, Vanilla●, Wild Berry●

**Tillamook** - All Yogurt Smoothies

**Tropicana Fruit Smoothies** - Mixed Berry, Strawberry Banana, Tropical Fruit

**V8 Splash -** Strawberry Banana, Tropical Colada

**Whole Soy & Co.** - All Varieties

**Zola -** Antioxidant, Energy, Immunity

### Snacks

**Annie's** - Organic Bunny Fruit Snacks (Berry Patch, Tropical Treat)

**Baffles** - Snack Clusters (Caramel Crunch, Cheddar Cheese, Chocolate, Cinnamon Crisp, Trail Mix)

**Baked! Cheetos** - Crunchy Cheese Flavored Snacks, Flamin' Hot Cheese Flavored Snacks

**Baken-Ets -** Cracklins Hot 'N Spicy, Pork Skins (BBQ, Fried, Hot 'N Spicy)

**Betty Lou's** - Krispy Bites, Nut Butter Balls (Almond, Cashew Pecan, Chocolate Walnut, Coconut Macadamia, Peanut, Spirulina Ginseng)

**Carole's** - Soycrunch (Coconut, Cinnamon Raisin, Original, Sesame, Toffee)

**Caroline's Desserts** - Krispette/Mmmmini (Amaretto Bianco●, Boo-Boo Bar●, Caramel Apple●, Cocoa-Jo●, EggNog●, Mint Everest●, Myrtle's Turtles●, Not So Plain-Jayne●, Oh Joy!●, Peanut Casanova●, Peppermint Spark●, Roca Crunch●, Sonoma Sunshine●, Sweet Cherrity●, Sweet Joe●, The Great Almondo●, Tiki Bar●, Triple Chocolate Nirvana)

**CheeCha -** Potato Puffs (Luscious Lime, Mediterranean Ginger, Original, Sea Salt & Spiced Pepper, Sea Salt & Vinegar)

**Cheetos -**

Flavored Snacks

    Cheddar Jalapeno Cheese

    Chile Limon

    Crunchy Cheese

**S**

Crunchy Salsa Roja Cheese

Crunchy Wild White Cheddar Cheese

Fantastix Flavored Baked Corn/Potato (Chili Cheese, Flamin' Hot)

Flamin' Hot (Cheese, Limon Cheese)

Giant Puffs (Cheese, Flamin' Hot Cheese)

Jumbo Puffs (Cheese, Flamin' Hot Cheese)

Natural White Cheddar Puffs Cheese

Puffs Cheese

Twisted Cheese

Xxtra Flamin' Hot

**Chester's -**

Butter Flavored Puffcorn

Cheddar Cheese Flavored Popcorn

Cheese Flavored Puffcorn

Flamin' Hot Flavored Fries

**Chi-Chi's -** Nacho Cheese Snackers

**Corn Nuts -** Barbeque, Chile Picante, Nacho Cheese, Original, Ranch

**Cracker Jack -** Original Caramel Coated Popcorn & Peanuts

**Cupoladua Oven -** Cupola Clouds (Parmesan Pink Peppercorn●, Smoked Gouda●)

**Deep River Snacks -** All Varieties

**Eat Smart -** Cheddairs (Apple Cinnamon, Regular, Zesty Cheddar), Soy Crisps (Parmesan Garlic & Olive Oil, Tomato Romano & Olive Oil), Veggie Crisps (Creamy Cucumber & Dill, Regular, Sun Dried Tomato & Pesto)

**Eden Organic -** All Mixed Up (Regular, Too), Wild Berry Mix

**Food Club Brand -** Cheese Balls, Cheese Puffs, Potato Sticks

**Funyuns -** Onion Flavored Rings (Flamin' Hot, Regular)

**Gladcorn -** Bar BQ, Gourmet Cheddar, Original

**Glenny's -** Brown Rice Marshmallow Treat (Chocolate●, Peanut Caramel●, Raspberry Jubilee●, Vanilla●)

**Glutano▲** - Snacks

**Goraw** - Flax Snax (Pizza●, Simple●, Spicy●, Sunflower●), Ginger Snaps●, Granola (Apple Cinnamon●, Live●, Live Chocolate●, Simple●), Seed Mix (Simple●, Spicy●), Seeds (Sprouted Pumpkin●, Sprouted Sunflower●), Super Chips (Pumpkin●, Spirulina●)

**Herr's** -

Cheese Curls (Honey, Hot, Regular)

Crunchy Cheese Sticks

Pork Rinds (BBQ Flavored, Original)

Potato Sticks

**Home Harvest Brand** - Cheese (Curls, Puffs)

**Hy-Vee** -

Cheese Balls

Cheeze Eze

Corn Chips (Regular, Scoop)

Fruit Snacks (Build A Bear, Curious George, Dinosaurs, Mayor & Miguel, Peanuts, Sharks, Variety Pack)

Nut Trail Mix (Chocolate, Raisin)

Strawberry Fruit Rolls

Tropical Fruit Mix

**Katy Sweet▲** -

Chewy Pralines (Coconut Pecan●, Maple Walnut●, Peanut Pie●, Pecan●)

Cookie Cutters (Bayou Bites●, Enchantments●, Fleur-De-Lis●, Lone Stars●, Longhorns●, Razorbacks●, Sooners●)

Creamy Pralines (Fudge Pecan●, Maple Walnut,● Original Pecan●, Original Walnut●)

No Sugar Added Chewy Pralines (Almond●, Mixed●, Pecan●, Walnut●)

Organic Chewy Pralines (Maple Walnut●, Original Pecan●)

Organic Creamy Pralines (Fudge Pecan●, Maple Walnut●, Original Pecan●, Original Walnut●)

**S** **Krinkle Sticks -** Sea Salt, Sour Cream & Onion

**Laura Lynn -**

Baked Cheese Curls

Cheese Krunchy

Fruit Snacks (Aliens, Animal, Creapy, Dinosaur)

**Little Bear -** Cheddar Puffs Lite

**Lowes Foods Brand -** Cheese Crunchy, Cheese Puffs, Pork Rinds (BBQ, Hot, Regular)

**Manischewitz -** Viennese Crunch

**Mareblu Naturals -**

Crunch (Almond Coconut, Almond, Cashew Coconut, Cashew, CranMango Cashew, Dark Chocolate Cashew, Pecan Cinnamon, Pistachio, Pistachio Pumpkin Seed)

Trail Mix Crunch (Blueberry Pomegranate, Cranberry Pomegranate, Cranblueberry, Cranstrawberry, Pecan, Pistachio, Regular)

**Meijer Brand -**

Fruit Rolls

Justice League Galactic Berry

Rescue Heroes

Strawberry (Garfield, Regular)

Wildberry Rush

Fruit Snacks

African Safari

Curious George

Dinosaurs

Jungle Adventure

Justice League (Big Box, Regular)

Mixed Fruit

Peanuts

Rescue Heroes Big Box

Sharks

Underwater World

Variety Pack (Big Boy, Regular)

Veggie Tales

Snacks

Caramel Corn

Cheese (Popcorn, Pops, Puffs)

Cheezy Treats

Chicago Style Popcorn

Potato Sticks

Purple Cow Butter Popcorn

White Cheddar (Popcorn, Puffs)

Xtreme Snack Bars

**Michael Season's -**

Baked Cheddar Cheese Puffs (Cheddar)

Baked Cheese Curl (Cheddar, Hot Chili Pepper)

Baked Cheese Pops (White Cheddar Pops)

Ultimate (Cheddar Cheese Curls, Cheddar Cheese Puffs, White Cheddar Cheese Puffs)

**Mrs. May's Naturals** - Crunch (Almond●, Black Sesame●, Cashew●, Coconut Almond●, Cran Blueberry●, Cran Tropical●, Pom-Raspberry●, Pumpkin●, Strawberry Pineapple●, Sunflower●, Ultimate●, Walnut●, White Sesame●)

**Munchos** - Regular Potato Crisps

**Nu-World Foods -**

Mini Ridges (Cheddar●, Rosemary Basil●, Sun Dried Tomato●)

Snackers (BBQ Sweet Sassy●, Chili Lime●, French Onion●)

**O Organics** - Baked Cheese Curls

**Old Dutch** - Bac'N Puffs, Cheese Pleesers, Hawkins, Nacho Crunchys, Popcorn Twists

**Original Tings -** Crunchy Corn Sticks

**Oskri Organics -** Almond Honey Crunch, Cashew Honey Crunch w/Cranberries, Pecan Honey Crunch w/Cinnamon

**S**  **Pirate's Booty** - Aged White Cheddar, Barbeque, Bermuda Onion, Carmel, Sea Salt & Vinegar, Veggie

**Publix** - Crunchy Cheese Curls, Crunchy Cheese Puffs, Deli Snacks (Crunchy Cheese Curls, Jumbo Cheese Puffs, Popcorn), Fruit Snacks (Curious George, Dinosaurs, Sharks, Snoopy, Veggie-Tales), Mini Rice Cakes (Caramel Fat Free, Cheddar, Ranch)

**Smart Puffs** - Real Wisconsin Cheddar

**Smartfood** - White Cheddar Cheese Flavored (Reduced Fat, Regular)

**Snyder's Of Hanover** - Butter Flavored Popcorn, Cheese Twists, Multigrain Puffs (Aged Cheddar, White Cheddar)

**Spartan Brand** - Cheese Puffs, Curious George, Dinosaurs, Fruit Rolls (Strawberry, Wild Berry), Justice League, Rescue Heroes, Sharks

**Stop & Shop Brand** -

Corn Cakes (Apple Cinnamon, Caramel)

Fruit Snacks (Curious George, Dinosaur, Justice League, Peanuts, Sharks, Tom & Jerry, Underwater World Fruit, Variety Pack, Veggie Tales)

Snacks (Build A Bear Fruit Snacks, Circus Peanuts, Crunchy Cheese Corn Snacks, Puff Cheese Corn Snacks, Simply Enjoy Fruit Medley)

**Trader Joe's** -

Buccaneer Joes White Cheddar Corn Puffs

Corn Tortilla Strips (White, Yellow)

Cranberry Nut Clusters Popcorn

Crunchy Curls

Green Bean Snacks

Reduced Fat Cheese Crunchies

Sea Salt & Pepper Rice Crisps

Sour Cream & Onion Rice Crisps

Soy Crisps BBQ

Thai Rice Sweet Sesame Snacks

**UTZ** - Baked Cheese Balls, Cheese Curls (Baked, Crunchy, White), Puff'N Corn (Caramel, Cheese, Plain), Popcorn (Butter, Cheese, White Cheddar)

**S**

**Wegmans Brand -** Cheese Puffs

**Wise -**

Cheez Doodles (Crunchy, Puffed, White Cheddar Puffed)

Doodle O's

Nacho Twisters

Popcorn (Butter Flavored, Hot Cheese, Reduced Fat Butter Flavored, Reduced Fat White Cheddar, White Cheddar Cheese)

Onion Flavored Rings

**Woodstock Farms -** Organic Snack Mixes (California Supreme, Campfire, Cape Cod Cranberry, Cascade, Chocolate Cherry Munch, Chocolate Cranberry Crunch, Cranberry (Cove, Walnut Cashew), Enchanted Trail, Goji Berry Bliss, Goji Berry Power, Gourmet Trail, In The Raw, Mocha Madness, On The Trail, Organic, Sunglow, Tamari Delight, Tropical Delight, Tropical Fruit)

## Snaps

**Edward & Sons -** Brown Rice Snaps (Black Sesame, Cheddar, Onion Garlic, Plain (Unsalted), Salsa, Sesame (Tamari, Unsalted), Tamari Seaweed, Toasted Onion, Vegetable)

## Soda Pop/Carbonated Beverages

**7up -** All Varieties

**A&W -** Root Beer

**Aquafina -** FlavorSplash (Citrus Blend, Raspberry, Wild Berry)

**Barq's Root Beer -** Caffeine Free, Diet, Diet Red Crème Soda, French Vanilla Crème, Regular

**Boylan's -** Soda

**Canada Dry -**

Club Soda (All Varieties)

Gingerale (Diet, Regular)

Tonic Water (All Varieties)

**Coca-Cola -**

Cherry Coke (Diet, Regular, Zero)

Classic Coke (Caffeine Free, Regular, w/Lime, Zero)

Diet Coke (Caffeine Free, Plus, Regular, w/Lime, w/Splenda)

**S**
    Minute Maid Light Lemonade
    Vanilla Coke (Regular, Zero)

**Cott** - All Varieties

**Crush** - All Varieties

**Dasani** - Essence, Lemon, Plus Cleanse & Restore, Plus Refresh & Revive, Regular

**Diet Rite** - All Varieties

**Dr. Pepper** - All Varieties

**Enviga** - Sparkling Green Tea (Berry, Green)

**Fanta** - Grape, Orange (Regular, Zero)

**Fiesta Mirinda** - Mango, Pina, Stawberry

**Fresca**

**Full Throttle**

**Hansen's** - All Sodas

**Hires** - Root Beer

**Hy-Vee** Soda -
    Black Cherry (Diet, Regular)
    Cherry Cola
    Club Soda
    Cola (Diet, Regular)
    Cream Soda
    Diet Tonic
    Dr. Hy-Vee
    Fruit Punch (Coolers, Regular)
    Gingerale
    Grape
    Hee Haw (Diet, Regular)
    Lemon Lime
    Orange (Diet, Regular)
    Root Beer (Diet, Regular)
    Sour

## soda pop/carbonated beverages

Strawberry

Tonic Water

Water Cooler (Black Cherry, Key Lime, Kiwi Strawberry, Mixed Berry, Peach, Peach Melba, Raspberry, Strawberry, White Grape)

**I.B.C.** - Root Beer

**Kas Mas**

**Kroger Brand** - Big K Soft Drinks

**Lowes Foods Brand** -

Club Soda

Cola (Diet, Regular)

Dr. Sparkle

Fruit Punch

Ginger Ale

Grape

Kiwi Strawberry

Lemonade

Mountain Breeze

Orange

Root Beer

Seltzer (Lemon Lime, Mandarin Orange, Original, Raspberry Lime)

Sparkle Up

Tonic Water (Diet, Regular)

**Manzanita Sol**

**Mello Yello** - All Varieties

**Minute Maid** - All Varieties

**Mountain Dew** -

Baja Blast

Caffeine Free

Caffeine Free Diet

Code Red (Diet, Regular)

Diet (Regular, Ultraviolet)

**S**     Game Fuel (Citrus Cherry, Wild Fruit)

Live Wire

Regular

Throwback

Voltage

**Mr. Pibb**

**Mug** - Root Beer (Diet, Regular), Cream Soda (Diet, Regular)

**O Organics** - Italian Soda (Blood Orange, Lemon, Orange Blueberry, Pomegranate)

**Orangina** - Sparkling Citrus Beverage

**Patio** - Gingerale, Quinine Tonic

**Pepsi** -

Caffeine Free Pepsi (Diet, Regular)

Jazz (Black Cherry French Vanilla, Caramel Cream)

Lemon (Diet, Regular)

Lime (Diet, Regular)

Max

Natural

One

Pepsi (Diet, Regular)

Throwback

Vanilla (Diet, Regular)

Wild Cherry (Diet, Regular)

**Publix** -

Black Cherry Soda

Cherry Cola

Club Soda

Cola (Caffeine Free, Regular)

Cream Soda

Diet (Cola, Ginger Ale, Tonic Water)

Dr. Publix

## soda pop/carbonated beverages

**S**

Fruit Punch

Ginger Ale

Grape Soda

Lemon Lime Seltzer

Lemon Lime Soda (Diet, Regular)

Orange Soda

Raspberry Seltzer

Root Beer (Diet, Regular)

Seltzer

Tonic Water

**RC Cola** - All Varieties

**Reed's** - Ginger Brew (Cherry, Extra, Original, Premium, Raspberry, Spiced)

**Safeway Brand -** Blackberry, Cherry Go2 Soda, Cream Soda, Ditto (Diet, Regular), Dr. Skipper, Ginger Ale, Grape, Go2 Cola (Diet, Regular), Grapefruit, Mountain Breeze, Orange (Diet, Regular), Punch, Root Beer (Diet, Regular), Strawberry

**Safeway Select** - Clear Sparkling Water (Cranberry Raspberry, Grapefruit Tangerine, Key Lime, Raspberry Black Cherry, Strawberry Kiwi, Strawberry Watermelon, Tangerine Lime, Wild Cherry), Sodas (All Varieties)

**Schweppes** - All Varieties

**Sierra Mist -** Cranberry Splash (Diet, Regular), Free, Regular, Ruby Splash (Diet, Regular)

**Slice -** Grape, Orange (Diet, Regular), Peach, Strawberry

**Spartan Brand -** Cola, Ginger Ale, Grape, Lemon Lime, Mountain Blast, Orange, Red, Root Beer

**Sprite** - Diet, Regular, Zero

**Squirt** - All Varieties

**Stewarts** - All Varieties

**Sun Drop -** Diet, Regular

**Sunkist** - Diet, Regular

**S**  **Tab** - All Varieties

**Trader Joe's -**

    French Market Sparkling Beverages

    Organic Sparkling Beverages (Lemon, Grapefruit)

    Refreshers (Blueberry, Pomegranate, Tangerine)

    Sparkling Juice Beverages (Apple Cider, Blueberry, Cranberry, Pomegranate)

    Sparkling Water (All Flavors)

**Tropicana Twister Soda** - Grape, Orange (Diet, Regular), Strawberry

**Tubz** - Diet Root Beer

**Vernors** - Diet, Regular

**Villa Italia** - Soda (Lemon, Orange)

**Virgil's** - Root Beer

**Wegmans Brand** -

    Aqua Mineral Water

        Lemon

        Lemongrass

        Lime

        Mixed Berry

    Frizzante European Soda

        Blood Orange

        Blueberry Lemon

        Sicilian Lemon

        Sour Cherry Lemon

    Soda

        Black Cherry

        Cherry (Regular, Wedge Diet)

        Club Soda

        Cola (Caffeine Free, Caffeine Free Diet, Diet, Lime, Regular)

        Cranberry Raspberry Sparkling Soda

        Cream Soda

## soda pop/carbonated beverages

**S**

    Diet (Lime, Orange, W Up)

    Dr. W (Diet, Regular)

    Fountain Root Beer (Diet, Regular)

    Ginger Ale (Diet, Regular)

    Grape Soda

    Green Apple Sparkling Soda (Diet, Regular)

    Mango

    Mountain Citrus

    Mt. W

    Orange (Diet, Regular)

    Tonic (Diet, Regular)

    W UP (Diet, Regular)

    Wedge Diet (Cherry Grapefruit, Grapefruit, Peach Grapefruit, W)

Sparkling Beverage

    Black Cherry

    Cranberry Raspberry (Diet, Regular)

    Key Lime (Diet, Regular)

    Kiwi Strawberry (Diet, Regular)

    Lemonade

    Mineral Water

    Mixed Berry (Diet, Regular)

    Peach (Diet, Diet Wedge, Grapefruit (Diet, Regular), Regular)

Sparkling Beverage w/Sweeteners (Black Cherry, Key Lime, Tangerine Lime, White Grape)

Sparkling Juices (Cranberry Blend, Grape Pink, Grape Red, Grape White)

**Welch's** - All Varieties

**Winn Dixie** -

    Black Cherry Soda

    Club Soda

    Cola (Caffeine Free, Cherry, Diet Vanilla, Regular, Vanilla)

**S**

Cream Soda

Diet (Chek, Kountry Mist Soda, Lemon Lime, Orange Soda, Root Beer, Strawberry Soda, Vanilla Cola)

Ginger Ale

Grape Soda

Green Apple Soda

Kountry Mist Soda

Lemonade

Lemon Lime Soda

Orange Soda

Orange Pineapple Soda

Peach Soda

Premium Draft Style Root Beer

Punch

Red (Alerts Soda, Cream Soda)

Root Beer

Seltzer Water

Sparkling Water (Country Strawberry, Green Apple, Key Lime, Mandarin Orange, Mellow Peach, White Grape, Wild Cherry, Zesty Raspberry)

Strawberry Soda

### Sorghum

**Shiloh Farms** - Sorghum Grain

### Soup

**A Taste Of Thai** - Coconut Ginger Soup Mix

**Amy's** -

Black Bean Vegetable

Chunky Tomato Bisque (Light In Sodium)

Chunky Vegetable

Cream of Tomato (Light Sodium, Regular)

Fire Roasted Southwestern Vegetable

Lentil (Curried, Light Sodium, Regular)

Lentil Vegetable (Light Sodium, Regular)

Split Pea (Light In Sodium, Regular)

Summer Corn & Vegetable

Thai Coconut

Tuscan Bean & Rice

**Baxters** -

Deli Inspired Roast Tomato & Parmesan w/Smoked Garlic

Favourites

Chicken Broth

Cock A Leekie

French Onion

Lentil & Bacon

Pea & Ham

Potato & Leek

Scotch Broth

Scotch Vegetable

Healthy Choice

Chicken & Vegetable

Chunky (Carrot Bean & Quinoa, Chicken & Vegetable Casserole, Country Vegetable, Smoked Bacon & Three Bean)

Puy Lentil & Tomato

Spicy Tomato & Rice w/Sweetcorn

Tomato & Brown Lentil

Luxury (Consomme (Beef, Chicken), Lobster Bisque)

Soup Bowl (Medley of Country Vegetables Soup, Smoked Bacon & Mixed Bean Soup)

Vegetarian (Carrot & Butterbean, Country Garden, Mediterranean Tomato, Tomato & Butterbean)

**Caskey's** - Chicken w/Rice Soup

**Dinty Moore** - Stew (Beef, Chicken)

**S**

**Dr. McDougall's** - Black Bean & Lime, Light Sodium Split Pea, Pad Thai Noodle, Tamale w/Baked Chips, Tortilla w/Baked Chips

**Edward & Sons** - Miso Cup (Golden, Japanese Restaurant Style, Organic Traditional w/Tofu, Reduced Sodium, Savory Seaweed)

**El Peto▲** - Onion, Tomato, Tomato Vegetable, Vegetable

**Ener-G ▲** - Cream Of Mushroom

**Fantastic World Foods** -

Simmer Soups (Blarney Stone Creamy Potato)

Soup

Baja Black Bean Chipotle

Buckaroo Bean Chili

Creamy Potato Leek

Great Lakes Cheddar Broccoli

Split Pea Soup

**Fischer & Wieser** - Mom's Limited Edition Tomato Basil

**Food Club Brand** - Beef Stew Seasoning Mix

**Full Flavor Foods▲ -** Soup Mix (Beef●, Chicken●, Cream●, Vegetarian Mushroom●)

**Fungus Among Us** - Organic Soup Mix (Moroccan Porcini & Green Lentil, Smoked Oyster Mushroom Chowder, Spicy Shiitake & Vegetable)

**Glutino▲ -** Soup Base (Chicken, Soup)

**Health Valley** -

Fat Free (5 Bean Vegetable, 14 Garden Vegetable, Black Bean & Vegetable, Corn & Vegetable, Lentil & Carrots, Split Pea & Carrots, Tomato Vegetable)

Organic (Cream of Celery, Cream of Chicken, Cream of Mushroom, Lentil, Potato Leek, Split Pea)

Organic No Salt Added (Black Bean, Lentil, Potato Leek, Split Pea, Tomato, Vegetable)

**Heinz** - Cream Of Tomato, Potato & Leek Soup

**Home Harvest Brand** - Onion Soup Mix

**Hormel** - Microwave (Bean & Ham, Chicken w/ Vegetable & Rice)

**Imagine** -
  Organic Creamy
    Acorn Squash & Mango
    Broccoli
    Butternut Squash
    Portobello Mushroom
    Potato Leek
    Sweet (Corn, Pea)
    Tomato (Basil, Regular)

**Kaskey's** - Chicken w/Rice Soup

**Kettle Cuisine** - Organic (Carrot & Coriander, Mushroom & Potato), Roasted Vegetable, Tomato & Garden Vegetable

**Laura Lynn** - Chicken And Rice Soup, Soup Mix (Beefy Onion, Onion)

**Lipton** - Recipe Secrets Onion Soup & Dip Mix

**Lowes Foods Brand** - Chicken & Wild Rice, New England Style Clam Chowder

**Manischewitz** - Borscht, Chicken, Clear Chicken Consomme, Condensed Clear Chicken, Hearty Bean Cello Mix, Schav, Split Pea w/Seasoning Cello Mix

**Mayacamas** - Dark Mushroom, French Onion, Lentil, Potato Leek, Tomato

**Meijer Brand** - Condensed Chicken w/Rice, Homestyle Chicken w/Rice

**Mixes From The Heartland▲** - Beer Cheese●, Broccoli N' Cheese●, Cajun Bean●, Cajun Pastalaya●, Cheeseburger Chowder●, Cheesy Chowder●, Chicken Veggie●, Corn Chowder●, Cowboy●, Crab Bisque●, Cream Of (Asparagus●, Broccoli●, Celery●, Mushroom●), Green Chili Hamburger●, Green Chili Potato●, Green Chili Stew●, Hamburger Pasta●, Harvest Chicken N' Rice●, Italian Bean●, Minestrone●, Navy Bean●, Pasta Veggie●, Potato●, Southwest Chicken Stew●, Spicy Corn Chowder●, Spicy Potato●, Texas Sausage N' Bean●, Tex Mex Pasta●, Tortilla Pasta●, Wild Rice N Mushroom●

**Organ▲** - Garden Vegetable, Sweet Corn, Tomato

**S**    Pacific Natural Foods -

- Buttery Sweet Corn
- Cashew Carrot Ginger
- Creamy Roasted Carrot
- Curried Red Lentil
- Organic (Creamy Butternut Squash, Creamy Tomato, French Onion, Roasted Red Pepper & Tomato, Tomato)
- Organic Light Sodium (Creamy Butternut Squash, Creamy Tomato, Roasted Red Pepper & Tomato)
- Organic Savory (Chicken & Wild Rice, White Bean w/Smoked Bacon)
- Organic Spicy (Black Bean w/Chicken Sausage, Chicken Fajita)
- Organic Split Pea w/Ham & Swiss Cheese

**Progresso**

- 45% Less Sodium Chicken & Wild Rice
- Light Homestyle Vegetable & Rice
- Microwaveable Bowl Chicken & Wild Rice Soup
- Rich & Hearty
  - Chicken Corn Chowder
  - New England Clam Chowder (Chunky Style)
- Traditional
  - Chicken & Wild Rice
  - Chicken Rice w/Vegetables
  - Green Split Pea w/Ham *(Vegetable Classics Style Is NOT Gluten-Free)*
  - New England Clam Chowder
  - Potato Broccoli & Cheese Chowder
  - Southwestern Style Chicken
- Vegetable Classics
  - Creamy Mushroom
  - French Onion
  - Garden Vegetable

Hearty Black Bean w/Bacon

Lentil

**Safeway Brand** - Condensed (Chicken w/Rice, Homestyle Chicken w/Wild Rice), Onion Soup Mix

**Safeway Select** -

Chicken w/Rice

Signature Soups

Autumn Harvest Butternut Squash

Baked Potato Soup

Fajita Chicken & Toasted Corn Chowder

Fiesta Chicken Tortilla

Rosemary Chicken & White Bean

**Shari** - Organic (Italian White Bean, Split Pea, Tomato w/Roasted Garlic)

**Shelton's** - Black Bean & Chicken, Chicken Corn Chowder, Chicken Rice, Chicken Tortilla

**Simply Asia** - Rice Noodle Soup Bowl (Garlic Sesame, Sesame Chicken, Spring Vegetable)

**Spartan Brand** - 16 Bean Chili, 16 Bean w/Ham, Chicken & 16 Bean, Onion Soup & Dip

**Stop & Shop Brand** - Condensed Chicken w/Rice Soup, Ready To Serve Chunky Vegetable Soup

**Thai Kitchen** -

Instant Rice Noodle Soup (Bangkok Curry, Garlic & Vegetable, Lemongrass & Chili, Spring Onion, Thai Ginger)

Rice Noodle Soup Bowls (Lemongrass & Chili, Mushroom, Roasted Garlic, Spring Onion, Thai Ginger)

Soup Cans (Coconut Ginger, Hot & Sour)

**Trader Joe's** -

Organic Soup

Black Bean

Creamy Corn & Roasted Red Pepper (Low Sodium, Regular)

Creamy Tomato

**S**

Split Pea

Sweet Potato Bisque

Tomato & Roasted Red Pepper

Tomato Bisque

Regular Soup

Butternut Squash

Carrot Ginger

Creamy (Corn & Roasted Red Pepper, Corn Chowder Potbelly, Vegetable Medley Bisque)

Garden Patch Veggie

Instant Rice Noodle Soup (Mushroom, Roasted Garlic, Spring Onion)

Latin Black Bean

Lentil Soup w/Vegetables (All)

Miso Soup (4 Pack)

Sweet Potato Bisque

**Wegmans Brand** - Broccoli & Vermont White Cheddar, Chili Soup Vegetarian, Gazpacho, Lobster Bisque, Moroccan Lentil w/Chick Pea, Spicy Red Lentil Chili

**Sour Cream**

**Albertsons** - Fat Free, Regular

**Cabot** - Lite, Regular

**Cascade Fresh**

**Daisy Brand** - Fat Free, Light, Regular

**Friendship** - All Natural, Fresh Salsa, Light, Nonfat

**Great Value Brand (Wal-Mart)**

**Hood** - All Varieties

**Horizon Organic** - All Varieties

**Hy-Vee** - Light, Regular

**Kemps** - All Varieties

**Kroger Brand**

**Laura Lynn** - Regular

**Lowes Foods Brand** - Lite, Nonfat, Regular

**Lucerne** - Low Fat, Nonfat, Regular

**Nancy's** - All Cultured Products

**Organic Valley** - Low Fat, Regular

**Prairie Farms** - Fat Free, Light, Regular

**Publix** - Fat Free, Light, Regular

**Shamrock Farms** - Light, Regular, Squeeze

**Spartan Brand** - Nonfat, Regular

**Stop & Shop Brand** - Light, Nonfat

**Tillamook** - All Varieties

**Trader Joe's** - All Varieties

**Wegmans Brand** - Fat Free, Light, Regular

**Winn Dixie** - Fat Free, Light, Regular

## Soy Beverage/Soy Milk

**365 Organic Every Day Value** - Organic Soymilk (Chocolate, Original, Unsweetened, Vanilla)

**Eden Organic** - EdenBlend, Edensoy (Unsweetened)

**Full Circle** - All Natural Chocolate Soymilk, Organic Soymilk (Chocolate, Regular, Vanilla)

**Hy-Vee** -
    Refrigerated Soy Milk (Chocolate, Original, Vanilla)
    Soy Milk (Chocolate, Original, Vanilla)

**Kroger Brand** - Soy Drink (Plain, Vanilla)

**Laura Lynn** - Soy Milk

**Lucerne** - Soy Beverage (Low Fat Vanilla, Regular)

**Nature's Promise** -
    Chocolate Soymilk
    Organic (1%, 2%, Chocolate Soymilk, Fat Free, Soymilk, Vanilla Soymilk, Whole)

**O Organics** - Soy Beverage Vanilla

**Organic Valley** - Chocolate, Original, Unsweetened, Vanilla

**Pacific Natural Foods** - All Varieties

**S**   **Publix GreenWise Market** - Soy Milk Regular (Chocolate, Plain, Vanilla), Light (Chocolate, Plain, Vanilla)

**San Sui** - All Varieties

**Silk Soymilk** - All Varieties

**Soy Dream** -

    Refrigerated Non Dairy Soymilk (Classic Original, Enriched (Original, Vanilla))

    Shelf Stable Non Dairy Soymilk (Classic Vanilla, Enriched (Chocolate, Original, Vanilla))

**Sunrise** - Soya Beverage (Sweetened, Unsweetened)

**Trader Joe's** - All Refrigerated Soy Milks, All Soy Beverages

**Vitasoy** - Soymilk (Holly Nog, Peppermint Chocolate)

**Wegmans Brand** - Organic (Chocolate, Original, Vanilla)

**Westsoy** -

    Organic Soymilk (Original)

    Organic Unsweetened Soymilk (Almond, Chocolate, Original, Vanilla)

    Soymilk Lite (Plain, Vanilla)

    Soymilk Non Fat (Plain, Vanilla)

    Soymilk Plus (Plain, Vanilla)

**Wild Wood Organic** - All Varieties

**ZenSoy** - All Varieties

**Soy Burgers... see Burgers**

**Soy Chips... see Chips**

**Soy Crisps... see Crisps**

**Soy Flour... see Flour**

**Soy Sauce**

    **Eden Organic** - Organic Tamari Soy Sauce (Brewed in U.S.)

    **Food Club**

    **Great Value Brand (Wal-Mart)**

    **Hannaford Brand**

    **Hy-Vee**

**S**

Jade Dragon

Kurtz

**La Choy** - Lite, Regular

**Panda** - Kari Out Packets

**San-J** - Organic Tamari Wheat Free Soy Sauce (Reduced Sodium●, Regular●)

**Spartan Brand** - Original

Soy Yogurt... see Yogurt

Soybeans... see Beans and/or Edamame... *All **Fresh** Fruits & Vegetables Are **Gluten-Free***

Soymilk... see Soy Beverage/Soy Milk

Spaghetti... see Pasta

Spaghetti Sauce... see Sauces

Spices... see Seasonings

Spinach... *All **Fresh** Fruits & Vegetables Are **Gluten-Free***

**Birds Eye** - All Plain Frozen Vegetables *(Except With Sauce)*

**C & W** - All Plain Frozen Vegetables

**Cascadian Farm** - Chopped, Organic Frozen Cut Spinach

**Del Monte** - All Canned Vegetables

**Food Club Brand** - Canned Cut Leaf

**Freshlike** - Frozen Plain Vegetables *(Except Pasta Combos & Seasoned Blends)*

**Great Value Brand (Wal-Mart)** - Canned (Whole Leaf Spinach), Chopped, Frozen (Cut Leaf Spinach)

**Green Giant** - Frozen Vegetables (Creamed Spinach w/Artificial Cream Flavor)

**Hannaford Brand -** Whole Leaf

**Hy-Vee -** Canned, Frozen (Chopped, Leaf)

**Laura Lynn** - Canned

**Lowes Foods Brand** - Frozen (Chopped, Leaf)

**Meijer Brand** - Canned (Cut Leaf, No Salt, Regular), Frozen Spinach (Chopped, Leaf)

**S**

O Organics - Chopped, Frozen

Pictsweet - All Plain Vegetables (Frozen)

Publix -

Canned Spinach

Frozen (Chopped, Cut Leaf, Leaf)

Publix GreenWise Market - Organic (Baby Spinach Blend, Baby Spinach Salad, Spinach)

S&W - All Canned Vegetables

Safeway Brand - Canned Leaf, Frozen Chopped

Spartan Brand - Canned, Frozen (Chopped, Cut, Leaf)

Stop & Shop Brand - Chopped, Cut, Leaf, No Salt Added, Regular

Tasty Bite - Kashmir Spinach, Spinach Dal

Trader Joe's - All Plain Vegetables (Frozen)

Wegmans Brand - Chopped Spinach (Frozen), Cut Leaf (Frozen), Spinach in Cream Sauce (Frozen), Whole Leaf

Winn Dixie - Canned (No Salt Added, Regular), Frozen (Chopped, Cut Leaf)

Woodstock Farms - Organic Frozen Cut Spinach

**Sports Drinks**

Gatorade - All Varieties (Be Tough X-Factor, Bring It Fierce, Elite Series Endurance Formula, Elite Series Gatorade Performance Series, Focus Gatorade Tiger, G2, Gatorade, No Excuses Rain, Powder, Shine On Gatorade AM)

Laura Lynn - Sports Drink

Meijer Brand - Drink Thirst Quencher (Fruit Punch, Lemon Lime, Orange)

Powerade - Grape, Ion 4, Mountain Blast

Spartan Brand - Dr. Quencher, Isotonic Sport Drink

Wegmans Brand -

MVP Sport Drink (Blue Freeze, Fruit Punch, Grape, Green Apple, Lemon Lime, Orange, Raspberry Lemonade)

Velocity Fitness Water (Berry, Black Cherry, Grape, Kiwi Strawberry, Lemon)

## Spread

**S**

**Benecol** - Light, Regular

**Bett's** - Cheddar Cheese & Horseradish Spread

**Bionaturae** - Fruit Spread (All Varieties)

**Canoleo** - 100% Canola Margarine

**Cantare** - Olive Tapenade (Original, w/Goat Cheese Feta)

**Country Crock** - All Spreads

**Di Lusso** - Sandwich Spread

**Dietz & Watson** - Sandwich Spread

**Dorothy Lane Market -** Asiago Roasted Garlic, Balsamic Parmesan, BLT, Cheddar Pimento, Danish Gouda And Nut, Emerald Pub, Scallion Cream Cheese, Smoked Salmon

**Earth Balance -**

  Natural Buttery Spread

    Olive Oil

    Original

    Soy Free

    Soy Garden

  Natural Shortening

  Organic Buttery Spread (Original Whipped)

  Vegan Buttery Sticks

**Eden Organic** - Butter (Apple, Cherry)

**Fleischmann's** - All Varieties

**Food Club Brand** - Margarine (No Ifs Ands or Butter, Spread)

**Home Harvest Brand -** 52% Quarters, Spread (48% Crock, Regular)

**Hy-Vee -**

  100% Corn Oil Margarine

  Soft Margarine (Regular, Rich & Creamy)

  Soft Spread

  Vegetable Margarine Quarters

**Ian's -** Soy Butter 4 ME

**S** **I Can't Believe It's Not Butter** - All Varieties

**Kraft** - Cheez Whiz, Old English, Pimento

**Kroger Brand** - Margarine, Vegetable Spreads

**Land-O-Lakes** - Butter w/Olive Oil, Fresh Buttery Taste, Garlic Butter, Honey Butter, Margarine, Salted Butter, Spreadable Butter w/Canola Oil, Unsalted Butter, Whipped Unsalted Butter, Whipped Salted Butter

**Laura Lynn** - Margarine Spread (Light, Quarters, Squeezeable, Taste Like Butter)

**Lowes Foods Brand** - Patties, Quarters, Soft 1lb., Spread, Squeeze

**Lucerne** -

Butterliscious

Country Style 48%

Sandwich Spread

**Manischewitz** - Apple Butter Spread

**Maple Grove Farms of Vermont** - Blended Maple, Honey Maple, Pure Maple

**Marsh Brand** - Sandwich Spread

**Meijer Brand** -

Margarine Corn Oil Quarters

Margarine Soft (Sleeve, Tub)

Spread (48% Crock, 70% Quarters, No Ifs Ands Or Butter)

**Odell's** - Clarified Butter

**Publix** -

Corn Oil Margarine Quarters

Homestyle Spread (39% Vegetable Oil)

Homestyle Squeeze Spread (60% Vegetable Oil)

It Tastes Just Like Butter Spread (65% Vegetable Oil)

Original Spread Quarters (65% Vegetable Oil)

**Shedd's Spread Country Crock** - All Spreads

**Smart Balance** - All Varieties

**Spartan Brand** - 52% Crock, Butter, Is It Butter (70% Crock, 70% Spread Tub), Margarine (Corn Oil Quarters, Quarters, Soft Sleeve, Soft Tub), Spread (70% Quarters, Regular), Unsalted

**Stop & Shop Brand** - Simply Enjoy Smoked Salmon Dill Sandwich Spread

**Trader Joe's** - Artichoke Red Pepper Tapenade, Eggplant Garlic Spread, Olive Green Tapenade, Red Pepper Spread w/Garlic & Eggplant, Wild Maine Blueberry Fruit Sauce

**Ukrop's** - Charleston Shrimp, Cream Cheese & Olive, Hawaiian Pineapple Nut, Pimento Cheese

**Underwood Spreads** - Deviled Ham

**Walden Farms** - Spreads (Apple Butter, Apricot, Blueberry, Grape, Orange Marmalade, Raspberry, Strawberry)

**Wegmans Brand** - Margarine Sticks

**Sprinkles... see Baking Decorations & Frostings**

**Squash...** *All Fresh Fruits & Vegetables Are Gluten-Free*

   **Albertsons** - Frozen

   **C & W** - All Plain Frozen Vegetables

   **Cascadian Farm** - Organic Frozen (Winter Squash)

   **Meijer Brand** - Frozen Squash (Cooked)

   **Pictsweet** - All Plain Vegetables (Frozen)

   **Publix** - Frozen (Cooked Squash, Yellow Sliced)

   **Spartan Brand** - Frozen Yellow

   **Stop & Shop Brand**

   **Trader Joe's** - All Plain Vegetables (Frozen)

   **Winn Dixie** - Frozen Yellow

**Starch**

   **AgVantage Naturals▲** - Tapioca

   **Argo** - Corn

   **Authentic Foods▲** - Potato

   **Bob's Red Mill▲** - Arrowroot, Corn, Potato

   **Clabber Girl** - Corn

**S**   El Peto▲ - Arrowroot, Corn, Potato, Tapioca
    Ener-G ▲ Potato
    Expandex▲ - Modified Tapioca Starch●
    Food Club Brand - Corn
    Great Value Brand (Wal-Mart)
    Hearth Club - Corn
    Hodgson Mill▲ - Pure
    Hy-Vee - Corn
    Kingsford - Corn
    Kinnikinnick▲ - Corn, Potato, Tapioca
    Kroger Brand - Corn
    Laura Lynn - Corn
    Manischewitz - Potato
    Meijer Brand - Corn
    Rumford - Corn
    Safeway Brand - Corn
    Spartan Brand - Corn

Steak ... *All **Fresh** Cut Meat Is **Gluten-Free (Non-Marinated, Unseasoned)***

Steak Sauce
    A-1
    Fischer & Wieser - Jethro's Heapin' Helping, Steak & Grilling Sauce
    Great Value Brand (Wal-Mart) - Regular, Thick & Zesty
    Hannaford Brand
    Hargis House
    Heinz -Traditional
    Home Harvest Brand - Regular
    Jack Daniel's - Original, Smokey
    Kurtz
    Laura Lynn
    Lea & Perrins - Traditional
    Meijer Brand

**S**

**Mr. Spice Organic** - Garlic Steak
**Publix**
**Safeway Select -** Bold, Original
**Spartan Brand** - Original
**Wegmans Brand -** Bold, Regular
**Winn & Lovett**

## Stew

**Dinty Moore** - Beef, Chicken Stew, Microwave Meals Beef Stew

## Stir Fry Sauce

**Lee Kum Kee** - Plum Stir Fry & Dipping Sauce
**Mr. Spice Organic** - Ginger Stir Fry Sauce & Marinade

## Stir Fry Vegetables

**Albertsons** - Stir Fry Vegetables
**Amy's** - Asian Noodle, Thai
**Cascadian Farm** - Organic Frozen (Chinese Style, Thai Style)
**Lowes Foods Brand** - Peking Stir Fry
**Meijer Brand** - Frozen Vegetable Stir Fry
**Stop & Shop Brand** - Japanese Stir Fry Blend
**Trader Joe's** - Shrimp Stir Fry
**Wegmans Brand** - Asian, Cleaned & Cut Stir Fry Vegetables, Far East, Hong Kong

## Stock

**Emeril's** - Beef, Vegetable
**Full Flavor Foods ▲ -** Soup Stock Mix (Beef●, Chicken●)
**Kitchen Basics** - Beef, Chicken, Clam, Ham, Pork, Seafood, Turkey, Unsalted (Beef, Chicken), Vegetable
**Massel** - Advantage Stock Powder (Beef Style, Chicken Style), Dietary Stock Powder (Beef Style, Chicken Style, Vegetarian Style), Gourmet Plus Light Stock (Chicken Style, Vegetable), Perfect Stock Powder (Beef Style, Chicken Style, Vegetable Style), Beef Stock Powder (Beef, Chicken, Vegetable)

**S**   Swanson - Beef (Carton), Chicken (Carton)

   **Wegmans Brand** - Culinary Stock (Beef Flavored, Chicken, Thai, Vegetable)

Strawberries... *All **Fresh** Fruits & Vegetables Are **Gluten-Free***

   **Albertsons** - Frozen (Sliced w/Sugar, Whole)

   **Cascadian Farm** - Organic Frozen Strawberries

   **Food Club Brand** - Frozen

   **Full Circle -** Organic Whole Strawberries

   **Great Value Brand (Wal-Mart)** - Frozen (Sliced, Sliced w/Sugar, Whole)

   **Hy-Vee** - Frozen (Sliced, w/Sugar, Whole)

   **Kroger Brand -** Plain Frozen Fruit

   **Meijer Brand** - Frozen (Organic, Sliced), Whole Individually Quick Frozen

   **Publix** - Frozen (Sliced, Sweetened, Whole)

   **Safeway Brand -** Frozen (Sliced w/Sugar, Sliced w/Sweetener, Whole)

   **Spartan Brand** - Sliced, Whole

   **Stop & Shop Brand** - Sliced Strawberries (In Sugar, Regular, w/Artificial Sweetener), Strawberries

   **Trader Joe's -** Frozen

   **Wegmans Brand** - Frozen Sliced w/Sugar

   **Winn Dixie** - Frozen (Sugar Whole, Sweetener, Whole)

   **Woodstock Farms** - Organic Frozen Whole Strawberries

Stuffing

   **Aleia's ▲-** Plain●, Savory●

   **Andrea's Fine Foods▲** - Stuffing Croutons

   **El Peto▲** - Stuffing

   **Gluten-Free Pantry▲** - GF Stuffing

   **Whole Foods Market Gluten Free Bakehouse ▲-** Stuffing Cubes

Succotash

   **Publix** - Frozen Vegetable Blend

   **Spartan Brand** - Frozen

   **Winn Dixie -** Frozen Yellow

# Sugar

**S**

**Diamond Falls** - Brown, Granulated, Powdered

**Dixie Crystals** - All Varieties

**Domino** - Brown, Brownulated, Confectioners, Cubes, Demerara Washed Raw Cane, Granulated, Organic, Pure D'Lite, Sugar 'N Cinnamon, Superfine, Tablets

**Food Club Brand** - Granulated, Light Brown, Powdered

**Full Circle** - Organic Cane Sugar

**Great Value Brand (Wal-Mart)** - Confectioners Powdered, Extra Fine Granulated, Light Brown, Pure Cane

**Hannaford Brand** - Dark Brown, Granulated, Light Brown, Powdered

**Home Harvest Brand** - Confectioners Powdered, Dark Brown, Granulated, Light Brown

**Hy-Vee** - Confectioners Powdered, Dark Brown, Light Brown, Pure Cane

**Imperial Sugar** - All Varieties

**Kroger Brand** - Dark Brown, Granulated, Light Brown, Powdered

**Laura Lynn** - Brown, Confectioner, White

**Lowes Foods Brand** - Granulated, Light Brown, Powdered

**Meijer Brand** - Confectioners, Dark Brown, Granulated, Light Brown

**Midwest Country Fare** - Granulated, Light Browned, Powered

**Nielsen-Massey** - Madagascar Bourbon Pure Vanilla Sugar●

**O Organics**

**Publix** - Granulated, Light Brown, Dark Brown, Powdered

**Rapunzel** - Powdered

**Safeway Brand** - Brown (Dark, Light), Granulated, Powdered

**Spartan Brand** - Confectioners Powdered, Dark Brown, Granulated, Light Brown

**Stop & Shop Brand** - Granulated

**Tops** - Light Brown

**Trader Joe's** - All Varieties

**United Sugar Products** - Crystal Sugar Products

**S**

 **Wegmans Brand** - Cocktail Sugar (Cosmopolitan, Lemon, Mandarin), Dark Brown, Granulated White, Light Brown

 **Wholesome Sweeteners** - All Varieties *(Except Organic Light Corn Syrup)*

 **Winn Dixie** - Granulated, Light Brown, Powdered

 **Woodstock Farms** - Organic Sugar (Brown, Pure Cane, Powdered, Turbinado)

**Sugar Substitute/Sweetener**

 **Albertsons** - Aspartame, Saccharin

 **Equal**

 **Food Club Brand** - Asparatame, Sugar Substitute

 **Great Value Brand (Wal-Mart)** - Calorie Free Sweetener

 **Hannaford Brand** - Sweetener (Aspartame, Sweet Choice)

 **Hy-Vee** - Aspartame Sweetener

 **Kroger Brand**

 **Lowes Foods Brand** - Sucralose Sweetener

 **NutraSweet**

 **Spartan Brand**

 **Splenda** - Brown Sugar Blend, Café Sticks, Flavor Accents (Lemon, Raspberry), Flavors For Coffee (Caramel, Cinnamon Spice, French Vanilla, Hazelnut, Mocha), No Calorie Sweetener (Granulated, w/Fiber), Sugar Blend

 **Sweet And Low**

 **Sweet Fiber** - All Natural Sweetener●

 **Wegmans Brand** - Sugar Substitute w/Saccharin

 **Wholesome Sweeteners** - All Varieties *(Except Organic Light Corn Syrup)*

**Sunflower Seeds... see Seeds**

**Sweet & Sour Sauce**

 **Contadina**

 **La Choy** - Regular, Sweet & Sour Duck Sauce

 **Lee Kum Kee**

**Mr. Spice Organic** - Sweet & Sour Sauce & Marinade

**San-J** - Gluten Free Sweet & Tangy●

**Wegmans Brand** - Sweet & Sour

**Sweet Potatoes**

**Meijer Brand** - Cut (Light Syrup)

**Sweetener... see Sugar Substitute/Sweetener**

**Swiss Chard...** *All Fresh Fruits & Vegetables Are Gluten-Free*

**Swordfish...see also Fish...** *All Fresh Fish Is Gluten-Free (Non-Marinated, Unseasoned)*

**Full Circle** - All Natural Swordfish Steaks

**Wegmans** - Swordfish

**Whole Catch** - Fillet

**Syrup**

**365 Organic Every Day Value** - Maple Syrup (Grade A (Dark, Light, Medium), Grade B)

**Albertsons** - Chocolate, Strawberry Pancake (Buttery, Light, Original)

**Black Horse** - Marionberry, Raspberry

**Beehive** - Corn Syrup

**Brer Rabbit** - Syrup (Full, Light)

**Cabot** - Vermont Pure Maple Syrup

**Crown** - Corn Syrup

**Food Club Brand** - Butter, Light Corn, Original

**Full Circle** - Organic Maple

**Golden Griddle** - Pancake Syrup

**Grand Selections** - 100% Pure Maple

**Great Value Brand (Wal-Mart)** - Butter Flavored, Pancake & Waffle (Light, Microwaveable, Regular)

**Hannaford Brand** - Pancake (2% Maple, Butter Flavored, Lite)

**Hershey's** - Chocolate (Lite, Regular)

**Hy-Vee** - Butter Flavor, Chocolate, Lite, Pancake & Waffle, Strawberry

**Karo** - All Varieties

**S**

**Laura Lynn** - Pancake & Waffle (Butter, Lite, Regular)

**Lily White** - Corn Syrup

**Log Cabin** - Butter Flavored, Country Kitchen, Lite, Original

**Lowes Foods Brand** - 2% Maple (Lite, Regular), Butter Flavored, Chocolate, Light Corn Syrup

**Lundberg▲** - Sweet Dreams Brown Rice Syrup (Eco Farmed, Organic)

**Maple Grove Farms of Vermont** -

Flavored Syrups (Apricot, Blueberry, Boysenberry, Raspberry, Strawberry)

Pure & Organic Maple Syrup

Sugar Free Syrup (Butter Flavor, Maple Flavor, Vermont)

**Maple Ridge** - Buttery, White Corn

**Meijer Brand** - Butter, Chocolate, Lite Butter, Lite Corn, Lite, Regular

**Midwest Country Fare** - Pancake & Waffle (Butter, Original)

**Mrs. Renfro's** - Cane, Country

**Nescafe** - Ice Java Coffee Syrup (All Flavors)

**Nestle** - Nesquik Syrup (All Flavors)

**O Organics** - 100% Pure Maple

**Old Colony** - All Varieties

**Old Tyme** - All Varieties

**Organic Nectars** - Chocagave, Vanillagave

**Promenade** - Chocolate Syrup

**Publix** - Butter Maple (Lite, Regular), Chocolate (Regular, Sugar Free), Pancake (Lite, Regular)

**Safeway Brand** - Butter Light, Chocolate, Light, Old Fashioned

**Smucker's** - All Fruit Syrup, Sugar Free Breakfast Syrup

**Spartan Brand** - 2% Real Maple, Artificial Butter, Corn Syrup, Reduced Calorie (Butter, Lite)

**Taste Of Inspirations** - Blueberry, Red Raspberry, Strawberry

**Trader Joe's** - Maple Syrup (All)

**Uncle Luke's** - 100% Pure Maple Syrup

**Vermont Maid** - All Varieties

**S**

**T**

**Walden Farms -**
  Fruit Syrups (Blueberry, Strawberry)
  Single Serve Packets (Chocolate, Pancake)
  Syrup (Chocolate, Pancake)
**Wegmans Brand -**
  Buttery Flavor (Light, Syrup)
  Regular
    Chocolate (Milk, Triple Chocolate)
    Creamy Caramel
    Maraschino Cherry Flavored
    Pancake (Light, Made w/ 2% Real Maple, Regular)
    Pure Maple (Organic Dark Amber, Regular)
    Sugar Free
**Winn & Lovett -** Maple Syrup (All Varieties)
**Winn Dixie -** Butter Flavor, Chocolate, Lite, Regular, Strawberry


# T

**Taco Sauce**
  **Chi-Chi's -** Taco Sauce
  **Del Pino's**
  **Food Club Brand -** Mild
  **Frontera -** Taco Sauce (Chipotle Garlic, Roasted Tomato)
  **Hy-Vee -** Medium, Mild
  **La Victoria -** Green (Medium, Mild), Red (Medium, Mild)
  **Laura Lynn -** Regular
  **Lowes Foods Brand -** Mild
  **Old El Paso -** Hot, Medium, Mild
  **Ortega -** Hot, Medium, Mild
  **Safeway Brand**

**T**    Spartan Brand - Fat Free (Medium, Mild)

Taco Bell - Restaurant Sauce (Hot, Medium, Mild)

**Taco Seasoning... see also Seasonings**

Albertsons - Taco Seasoning Mix

Chi-Chi's - Fiesta Restaurante Seasoning Mix

Hy-Vee

Meijer Brand - Taco Seasoning

Old El Paso - Taco Seasoning Mix (40% Less Sodium, Hot & Spicy, Mild, Original)

Ortega - Chipotle Mix, Jalapeno & Onion Mix, Taco 40% Less Sodium Mix, Taco Meat Mix

**Taco Shells**

Food Club Brand - Taco Shells

Hy-Vee - Taco Dinner, Taco Shells, White Corn Tortilla

Lowes Foods Brand - Taco Dinner Kit, Taco Shells

Meijer Brand - Taco Shells

Old El Paso -

Stand 'N Stuff Yellow Corn Taco Shells

Taco Shells (Super Stuffer, White Corn, Yellow Corn)

Tostada Shells

Ortega - Hard Shells (Yellow, White), Tostada Shells, Whole Grain

Safeway Brand - Taco Shells (Jumbo, White Corn)

Taco Bell - Taco Shells (12 ct, 18 ct)

**Tahini**

Arrowhead Mills - Organic Sesame Tahini

Lee Kum Kee - Sesame Seed Paste

MaraNatha - Natural w/Salt (Raw, Roasted)

**Tamales**

Amy's - Black Bean Verde, Cheese Verde, Roasted Vegetable

Delimex - Beef (6 ct., 12 ct.), Chicken & Cheese (12 ct.), Costco Beef (15 ct., 20 ct.), Sam's Club 20 ct.

**Hargis House**

**Hormel** - Beef

**Trader Joe's** - Beef, Cheese, Chicken, Handmade Green Chili & Cheese

Tangerines... *All **Fresh** Fruits & Vegetables Are **Gluten-Free***

Tapioca

**Let's Do...Organic** - Organic (Granules, Pearls, Starch)

Taquitos

**Delimex** -

Taquitos

3 Cheese (25 ct.)

Beef (12 ct., 25 ct., 36 ct., 60 ct., Costco 66 ct., Sam's Club 60 ct.)

Chicken (12 ct., 25 ct., 36 ct., Costco 66 ct.)

**El Monterey** - Taquitos Corn Tortillas (Beef, Chicken, Shredded Steak)

**Trader Joe's** - Black Bean, Chicken

Tartar Sauce

**Best Foods**

**Food Club Brand**

**Heinz**

**Hellmann's**

**Laura Lynn** - Squeeze Tartar

**McCormick** - Fat Free, Original

**Old Bay**

**Simply Delicious** - Organic Tartar Sauce

**Spartan Brand**

**Wegmans Brand**

Tarts

**Crave Bakery▲** - Lemon, Pumpkin

**El Peto▲** - Butter, Pecan, Lemon, Raspberry

**Tater Tots... see Potatoes**

**T** Tea

**365 Organic Every Day Value** - Berry Black, Green w/Lemon & Ginger, Lemon Black, Mint Green, White Jasmine, White Peach

**Arizona** - All Varieties

**Authentic Food Artisan** - Organic Rishi Tea (Jasmine Pearl, Silver Needle, Wild Tou Cha Pu-erth)

**Bigelow Tea** -

American Classical Tea

Darjeeling

Decaffeinated

Constant Comment

Earl Grey

English Teatime

French Vanilla

Green Tea

Green Tea w/Lemon

Lemon Lift

Spiced Chai

English Breakfast

English Teatime

Flavored Tea

Cherry Vanilla

Cinnamon Stick

Constant Comment

Earl Grey

French Vanilla

Lemon Lift

Plantation Mint

Pumpkin Spice

Raspberry Royale

Spiced Chai

Vanilla (Almond, Caramel, Hazelnut)

Vanilla Chai

Green Tea

Constant Comment Green

Earl Grey Green

Green Tea w/ (Chai, Chinese Oolong, Jasmine, Lemon, Mango, Mint, Peach, Pomegranate, Tangerine)

Regular

Herbal Tea

Apple Cider

Berri Good

Chamomile Lemon

Chamomile Mint

Cinnamon Apple

Cozy Chamomile

Cranberry Apple

Fruit & Almond

Ginger Snappish

Hibiscus & Rose Hips

I Love Lemon (Regular, w/Vitamin C)

Mint Medley

Orange & Spice

Peppermint

Perfect Peach

Pomegranate Pizzazz

Red Raspberry

Sweet Dreams

Sweetheart Cinnamon

Taste Of The Tropics

Tasty Tangerine

**T**

Iced Tea
  Perfect Peach
  Red Raspberry
Loose Tea
  Constant Comment
  Earl Grey
  English Breakfast
  Green
Novus (All Varieties)
Organic (All Varieties)
Premium
  Black
  Blend
  Decaf
  Iced
  Green
Ready To Drink
  Mocha Chai Latte
  Vanilla Chai Latte
Tea In No Time
  Green Mandarine & Mango
  Green Lemon w/Honey
  Original
  Peach
  Raspberry
**Celestial Seasonings -**
  Black Teas
    Decaf Devonshire English Breakfast
    Fast Lane
    Golden Honey Darjeeling
    Mango Darjeeling Organic

  Morning Thunder
  Organic Black
  Tuscany Orange Spice
  Victorian Earl Grey Regular
Chai
  Chocolate Caramel Enchantment
  Decaf India Spice
  Honey Vanilla White
  India Spice
  Vanilla Ginger Green Tea
Cool Brew Iced Tea
  Blueberry Ice
  Lemon Ice
  Peach Ice
  Raspberry Ice
Green Tea
  Antioxidant
  Blueberry Breeze
  Decaf (Green, Honey Chamomile, Lemon Myrtle Organic, Mandarin Orchard, Mint Green)
  Goji Berry Pomegranate
  Green Tea Sampler
  Honey Lemon Ginseng
  Lemon Zinger
  Organic Green
  Raspberry Gardens
  Tropical Acai Berry
Herbal Tea
  Acai Mango Zinger
  Bengal Spice
  Black Cherry Berry

**T**

Caffeine Free
Chamomile
Cinnamon Apple Spice
Country Peach Passion
Cranberry Apple Zinger
Fruit Tea Sampler
Herb Tea Sampler
Honey Vanilla Chamomile
Lemon Zinger
Mandarin Orange Spice
Mint Magic
Peppermint
Raspberry Zinger
Red Zinger
Sleepytime
Sweet (Apple Chamomile, Clementine Chamomile Organic)
Tangerine Orange Zinger
Tension Tamer
Tropic Of Strawberry
True Blueberry
Wild Berry Zinger

Holiday Tea
Candy Cane Lane
Nutcracker Sweet

Rooibos Tea
African Orange
Madagascar Vanilla Red
Mango African
Moroccan Pomegranate Red
Peach Apricot Honeybush
Red Safari Spice

**T**

Wellness Tea
    Diet Partner
    Echinacea Complete Care *(Echinacea Regular Wellness Tea Contains Gluten)*
    Honey Peach Ginger
    Sleepytime Extra
    Tension Tamer Extra
    Throat Soothers
    Tummy Mint
White Tea
    Decaf China Pearl
    Imperial White Peach
    Perfectly Pear
    Powerfully Plum
    Vanilla Apple Organic

**Food Club Brand** - Green Tea (Decaf, Regular), Instant Tea, Southern Sweet Tea

**Full Circle -** Organic Tea (Chai, Chamomile, Earl Gray, English Breakfast, Green, Peppermint, Night Time Blend)

**Gloria Jean's -** All Varieties

**Gold Peak -** Iced Tea (Diet, Green Sweetened, Lemon, Sweetened, Unsweetened)

**Great Value Brand (Wal-Mart)** - Tea 100% Natural (Decaf, Regular), Refrigerated (Green, Sweet Tea, Sugarfree Sweet Tea)

**Green Mountain -** All Varieties

**Hansen's -** All Varieties

**Higgins & Burke -** All Varieties

**Home Harvest Brand -** Tea Bags (Apple Cinnamon, Bagless, Chamomile, Earl Gray, English Breakfast, Exotic Fruit Green, Green, Green Peach), Iced Tea w/Lemon & Sugar

**Honest Tea** - Assam Black, Black Forest Berry, Community Green, Green Dragon, Honey Green, Jasmine Green Energy, Just Black, Just Green, Lemon Black, Lori's Lemon, Mango Acai, Mango

**T**

Green, Moroccan Mint Green, Peach Oolalong, Peach White, Pearfect White, Pomegranate Red, Pomegranate White

**Hy-Vee** - Decaf (Green, Tea Bags), Chai Black, Chamomile Herbal, Cinnamon Apple Herbal, Dream Easy Herbal, Earl Gray Black, English Breakfast Black, Family Size Tea Bags, Green Tea, Green Tea Bags, Green Tea w/Pomegrante, Honey Lemon Ginseng, Instant, Jasmine Green, Peppermint Herbal, Orange & Spice Specialty

**Inko's White Tea** - Apricot, Blueberry, Cherry Vanilla, Energy, Honeydew, Lemon, Lychee, Original, Unsweetened Hint O'Mint, Unsweetened Honeysuckle, Unsweetened Original, White Peach

**Kettle Brewed** - Unsweetened Green & White Tea

**Kroger Brand** - Tea (Bagged, Instant)

**Laura Lynn** - Cold Brew, Decaf, Family, Family Decaf, Green, Tagless, Tea Bags

**Lipton** -

Diet Ice Tea Mix (Lemon (Decaf, Regular), Peach, Raspberry, Tea & Lemonade)

Regular

Calorie Free Ice Tea Mix (Lemon)

Green Tea Bags (Jasmine, Regular)

Instant Ice Tea (100% Instant & Decaf)

Soothing Moments

Flavored Tea Bags (Blackberry Regular & Decaf, Mint, Orange & Spice Regular & Decaf, Raspberry)

Herbal Tea Bags (Cinnamon Apple, Country Cranberry, Gentle Orange, Ginger Twist, Moonlight Mint, Peppermint, Quietly Chamomile)

**Lowes Foods Brand** - Green (Decaf, Regular), Tea Bags (Decaf, Regular)

**Meijer Brand** - Iced Tea Mix, Instant, Tea Bags (Decaf, Green, Green Decaf, Regular)

**Midwest Country Fare** - Tea Bags 100 Count

**Mother Parkers** - All Tea (Black, Flavored, Green, Herbal)

**Nature's Promise** - Organic Fair Trade Green Tea (Decaf, Lemon, Regular)

**Nestea** - All Flavors

**Newman's Own** - Lemonade Iced Tea

**Numi** - All Varieties

**O Organics** - Bags (Earl Grey), Bottled (Black Tea w/Lemon, Oolong Tea w/Peach, White Tea w/Pomegranate, White Tea w/Spearmint)

**Oregon Chai** - All Varieties

**Orient Emporium** - All Varieties

**Pacific Natural Foods** - Organic Iced Tea (Green, Lemon, Peach, Raspberry, Sweetened Black)

**Prairie Farms** - Sweetened Iced Tea

**Publix** -
Iced Tea (Sweetened, Unsweetened)
Instant (Lemon, Regular)
Tea Bags (All Varieties)

**Red Rose** - All Varieties

**Republic Of Tea** - All Varieties●

**Rishi Tea** - All Varieties

**Safeway Brand** - Iced Tea Mix (All Flavors), Tea Bags (Decaffeinated)

**Safeway Select** - Chai Tea, Earl Gray, Herbal Tea (Chamomile, Evening Delight, Lemon, Peppermint), Quiet Morning, Specialty Tea, Tea (Black, Green, Orange Spice)

**Salada Tea** - Decaffeinated & Regular (Green, White)

**Snapple** - All Varieties

**SoBe** - Black, Green, Oolang

**Somerset** - Iced Tea Mix, Instant Tea

**Spartan Brand** - Iced Tea w/Lemon & Sugar, Orange Pekoe (Decaf, Regular), Tea Bags (Black, Decaffeinated, Green, Instant)

**Stash Tea** - All Varieties

**Tazo Tea** - All Varieties *(Except Green Ginger, Tazo Honeybush, Lemon Ginger, Tea Lemonade)*

**Tejava** - Unsweetened Tea

**Trader Joe's** - All Tea, Green Tea Unsweetened

**T**   **Twinings Tea** - All Varieties

**Wegmans Brand** -

Black Tea

Decaf (Black Tea, Green Tea)

Earl Grey (Black, Black Decaf, Green, Supreme, Supreme Decaf)

English Breakfast (Black, Organic)

Green Tea

Ice Tea Mix (Decaf, Regular, w/Natural Lemon Flavor & Sugar (Decaf, Regular))

Iced Tea (Diet, Lemon, Regular)

Organic (Chai, Chamomile, Earl Grey, English Breakfast, Jasmine Green, Peppermint, Rooibos Strawberry Cream)

Regular Bags

Sencha Pure Japanese Green

**Winn Dixie** -

Organic Sweet Tea (Black w/Lemon, Green, Red w/Mango & Mandarin Orange, White w/Raspberry)

Organic Unsweetened Tea (Green, Red w/Pomegranate)

Regular & Family (Decaffeinated, Tea Bags)

**Teff**

**Bob's Red Mill▲** - Flour, Whole Grain Teff

**La Tortilla Factory** - Gluten Free Teff Wraps (Dark●, Ivory●)

**Shiloh Farms** - Brown, Ivory

**Tempeh**

**Lightlife** - Flax, Garden Veggie, Organic Soy, Wild Rice

**White Wave** - Original Soy, Soy Rice

**Tequila...** *All **Distilled** Alcohol is **Gluten-Free*** [2]

**Teriyaki Sauce**

**La Choy** - Teriyaki Marinade & Sauce

**Moore's Marinade** - Teriyaki

**Organicville** - Organic (Island Teriyaki, Sesame Teriyaki)

**Premier Japan** - Wheat Free

**San-J** - Gluten Free Teriyaki Stir Fry & Marinade●

**Simply Boulder** - Truly Teriyaki Culinary Sauce●

Tikka

    **Amy's** - Indian Paneer Tikka

    **Sharwood's** - Chicken Tikka

    **Stop & Shop** - Simply Enjoy (Tikka Masala)

Tilapia... see Fish... *All Fresh Fish Is Gluten-Free (Non-Marinated, Unseasoned)*

Tofu

    **Amy's** - Indian Mattar Tofu

    **Lightlife** - Tofu Pups

    **Mori-Nu** - All Silken Tofu

    **Nasoya Foods** - Cubed, Extra Firm, Firm, Lite Firm, Lite Silken, Silken, Soft

    **Stop & Shop Brand** - Tofu (Extra Firm, Firm)

    **Trader Joe's** - Tofu Organic (Extra Firm, Firm)

    **Wegmans Brand** - Asian Classic, Firm, Organic X Firm

    **White Wave** -

        Extra Firm Tofu

        Fat Reduced Tofu

        Organic Tofu (Extra Firm Vacuumed Pack, Firm Water Pack, Soft Water Pack)

    **Woodstock Farms** - Organic Tofu (Extra Firm, Firm)

Tomatillos... *All Fresh Fruits & Vegetables Are Gluten-Free*

    **Las Palmas** - Crushed Tomatillos

Tomato Juice... see Drinks/Juice

Tomato Paste

    **365 Everday Value** - Organic Tomato

    **Albertsons** - Regular

    **Contadina** - All Varieties *(Except Tomato Paste w/Italian Seasonings)*

    **Del Monte** - All Tomato Products *(Except Spaghetti Sauce Flavored w/Meat)*

**T**

Food Club Brand
Full Circle - Organic
Great Value Brand (Wal-Mart)
Hannaford Brand
Home Harvest Brand - Regular
Hy-Vee - Regular Tomato
Lowes Foods Brand - Tomato
Meijer Brand - Domestic, Organic
Muir Glen
Publix
S&W - All Canned Vegetables
Spartan Brand - 26% Tomato
Wegmans Brand - Tomato
Winn Dixie

Tomato Puree
Contadina
Dei Fratelli
Full Circle - Organic
Hunt's
Meijer Brand
Muir Glen
S&W - All Canned Vegetables
Wegmans Brand
Winn Dixie

Tomato Sauce... see Sauces

Tomatoes... *All **Fresh** Fruits & Vegetables Are **Gluten-Free***
365 Every Day Value - Diced, Peeled Whole
365 Organic Every Day Value - Organic (Diced, Diced No Salt
  Added, Diced w/Basil, Italian Cherry Tomato w/Basil, Whole Peeled)
Albertsons - Canned, Celery & Bell Peppers, Diced Tomatoes &
  Green Chilies, Diced w/Jalapenos, Stewed (Italian, w/Onions),
  Whole (No Salt, Regular)

**T**

**Cara Mia** - Sun Dried

**Contadina -** All Crushed, All Diced, All Stewed, Whole

**Dei Fratelli -**

Canned

Chili Ready Diced

Chopped (Italian, Mexican, w/Onion & Garlic)

Crushed (Regular, w/Basil & Herbs)

Diced (& Green Chilies, In Hearty Sauce, Low Sodium, Seasoned)

No Salt Whole

Petite Diced (Regular, w/Onion & Celery & Pepper)

Stewed

Whole (In Puree, Regular)

**Del Monte** - All Tomato Products *(Except Spaghetti Sauce Flavored w/Meat)*

**Diane's Garden** - Canned

**Eden Organic** - Crushed (Regular, w/Basil, w/Onion & Garlic), Diced (Regular, w/Basil, w/Chilies, w/Green Chilies, w/Roasted Onion), Whole Tomatoes (w/Basil, Regular)

**Food Club Brand** - Tomatoes (Crushed, Diced, Diced Chili Style, Diced w/Garlic & Onion Original Stewed, Italian Style Stewed, Mexican Style Stewed, Petite Diced, Puree, Whole Peeled)

**Full Circle -** Organic (Crushed Tomatoes w/Basil, Diced)

**Great Value Brand (Wal-Mart) -**

Chili Ready Tomatoes

Concentrated Crushed Tomatoes

Diced Tomatoes in Tomato Juice

Italian Tomatoes w/Basil Garlic & Oregano (Diced, Stewed)

No Salt Added Diced Tomatoes

Petite Diced Tomatoes

Sliced Stewed In Tomato Sauce

Sliced Stewed Tomatoes

Vegetable Pear Tomato Strips w/Basil

**T**

Whole Peeled Pear Tomatoes w/Basil

Whole Tomatoes In Tomato Juice

**Hannaford Brand -**

Diced (Crushed, Kitchen Ready Crushed In Heavy Puree, Italian, No Salt, Puree, Regular, w/Green Chilies, w/Roasted Garlic & Onion, Whole Peeled)

Stewed (Italian, Mexican, No Salt, Regular)

**Home Harvest Brand** - Diced, Peeled Whole, Stewed

**Hunt's -**

Crushed

Diced (Basil Garlic & Oregano, Fire Roasted, Fire Roasted w/Garlic, Regular, w/Balsamic Vinegar Basil & Oil, w/Basil Garlic & Oregano, w/Green Pepper Celery & Onions, w/Roasted Garlic, w/Sweet Onions)

Organic (Crushed, Diced, Diced w/Basil Garlic & Oregano)

Petite Diced (Regular, w/Mild Green Chilies, w/Mushrooms)

Paste (Basil Garlic & Oregano, No Salt Added, Regular)

Puree

Stewed (No Salt Added, Regular)

Whole (No Salt Added, Regular)

**Hy-Vee** - Diced (Chili Ready, Regular, w/Chilies, w/Garlic & Onion), Italian Style (Diced, Stewed), Original Diced & Green Chilies, Petite Diced (Regular, w/Garlic & Olive Oil, w/Sweet Onion), Petite Diced, Stewed, Tomato Paste, Whole Peeled

**Laura Lynn** - Tomato Products

**Lowes Foods Brand** - Crushed, Diced, Diced No Salt, Diced Petite, Diced w/Green Chilies, Italian, Paste, Sauce, Stewed, Whole

**Meijer Brand** - Crushed In Puree, Diced (Chili Ready, Green Chilies, In Italian, In Juice, Organic, Petite), Stewed (Italian, Mexican, Regular), Whole (Organic, Peeled, Peeled No Salt, w/Basil Organic)

**Midwest Country Fair** - Diced, Stewed, Whole Peeled

**Muir Glen** - Crushed (Fire Roasted, w/Basil), Diced (Fire Roasted w/Green Chilies, No Salt Added, w/Basil & Garlic, w/Garlic &

Onion, w/Italian Herbs), Stewed, Whole (Fire Roasted, Peeled, Peeled Plum, Peeled w/Basil)

**O Organics -** Diced (No Salt Added, Regular, w/Basil Garlic & Oregano), Whole Peeled

**Pictsweet** - All Plain Vegetables (Frozen)

**Publix -** Crushed, Diced, Diced No Salt, Diced w/Green Chilies, Diced w/Roasted Garlic & Onion, Paste, Peeled Whole, Pureed, Sauce, Sliced & Stewed

**Publix GreenWise Market -** Organic (Crushed, Diced, Diced w/Basil Garlic & Oregano, Fancy Sliced, Fancy Sliced Italian, Paste, Pureed, Sauce)

**S&W** - All Canned Vegetables

**Safeway Brand -** Crushed, Diced (Fire Roasted, Peeled, Peeled No Salt, Petite), Italian Style Stewed, Mexican Style Stewed, Whole Peeled

**Spartan Brand -** Diced (For Chili, Italian, Mexican, Regular, w/Green Chilies, w/Roasted Garlic & Onions), Italian Stewed, Specialty Crushed, Stewed, Whole

**Stop & Shop Brand** -

Crushed (Italian Seasonings, No Added Salt, Regular)

Diced (Italian Seasonings, No Added Salt, Regular)

Stewed (Italian Seasonings, Mexican Style, No Added Salt, Regular)

Whole Peeled (No Added Salt, Regular)

**Trader Joe's** - All Sun Dried Tomatoes, All Whole Peeled Tomatoes w/Basil

**Wegmans Brand** -

Crushed

Diced (Chili Style, Italian Style, Petite, Regular, Roasted Garlic & Onion)

Coarse Ground

IC (Crushed w/Herb)

Italian Classics San Marzano Tomatoes Whole Peeled

Italian Style (Diced Tomatoes, Stewed, Whole w/Basil)

**T**

Kitchen Cut w/Basil

Organic (Diced, Diced In Juice)

Peeled Whole

Petite Diced Tomatoes w/Garlic Olive Oil & Seasoning

Puree

Stewed

Whole Peeled

**Winn Dixie** - Canned (Crushed, Diced, Diced w/Chilies, Italian Style (Diced, Stewed), Paste, Petite Diced, Petite Diced w/Onion Celery Green Peppers, Puree, Sauce, Stewed, Whole Peeled)

**Woodstock Farms** - Crushed (Basil, Original), Diced (Basil & Garlic, Italian Herbs), Organic Canned Tomatoes (Diced No Salt, Diced Original, Paste, Sauce Original, Whole Peeled), Whole Peeled

**Tonic...** see Soda Pop/Carbonated Beverages

**Toppings...** see Baking Decorations & Frostings

**Tortilla Chips...** see Chips

**Tortilla Soup...** see Soup

**Tortillas**

**Don Pancho** - Gluten Free Flour Tortillas

**Food For Life** - Brown Rice, Sprouted Organic Corn

**French Meadow Bakery** - Gluten Free Tortillas●

**La Tortilla Factory** - Gluten Free Teff Wraps (Dark●, Ivory●)

**Laura Lynn** - Ole Corn Tortillas

**Manny's** - Corn Tortillas

**Mission** - Corn Tortillas (Extra Thin, Super Size White, Super Size Yellow, White, Yellow)

**Que Pasa** - Corn Tortillas

**San Carlos** - Masa Lista

**Trader Joe's** - Corn Tortillas (Handmade, Original)

**Trail Mix...** see also Nuts

**Baffles** - Snack Clusters Trail Mix

**Eden Organic** - All Mixed Up, All Mixed Up Too

**T**

**Enjoy Life▲** - Not Nuts! (Beach Bash●, Mountain Mambo●)

**Frito Lay** - Original

**Hy-Vee** - Berry, Chocolate & Nut, Dark Chocolate & Cranberry, Fruit & Nut Medley, Island Medley, Mountain, Raisin & Nut, Tropical

**Mareblu Naturals** -

Crunch (Almond, Almond Coconut, Cashew, Cashew Coconut, CranMango Cashew, Dark Chocolate Cashew, Pecan Cinnamon, Pistachio, Pistachio Pumpkin Seed)

Trail Mix Crunch (Blueberry Pomegranate, Cranberry Pomegranate, Cranblueberry Trail, Cranstrawberry Trail, Pecan Trail, Pistachio Trail, Regular)

**Nonuttin' Foods▲** - Trail Mix (Energy Explosion, Hiker's Delight)

**Oskri Organics** - Almond Honey Crunch, Cashew Honey Crunch w/Cranberries, Pecan Honey Crunch w/Cinnamon

**Safeway Brand** - Trail Mix w/Candy Pieces

**Trader Joe's** -

Almonds Cranberries Pistachio & Cherry Mix

Go Raw Trek Mix

Nutty American Trek Mix

Organic Trek Mix w/Chocolate Chips Peanuts Berries & Almonds

Pumpkin Seeds And Pepitas

Rainbows End Trail Mix

Simply Almonds Cashews & Cranberries Trek Mix

Simply The Best Trek Mix

Sweet Savory & Tart Trek Mix

Tempting Trail Mix

**Trek Mix... see Trail Mix**

**Tuna... see also Fish...** *All Fresh Fish Is Gluten-Free (Non-Marinated, Unseasoned)*

**Albertsons** - Canned Tuna (Albacore, Chunk Light)

**Bumble Bee** - All Varieties *(Except Crackers In Ready-to-Eat Salads & Crackers)*

**T**

**Chicken Of The Sea** - All Products *(Except Ahi Tuna Steak In Grilled Herb Marinade, Ahi Tuna Steak In Teriyaki Sauce, Teriyaki Tuna Cups, Tuna Salad Kits w/Crackers)*

**Crown Prince Natural** - Solid White Albacore Tuna (No Salt Added Packed In Spring Water, Packed in Spring Water)

**Food Club Brand** - Tuna In Water

**Full Circle -** All Natural Yellowfin Tuna Steaks

**Grand Selections** - Solid White Albacore Tuna

**Great Value Brand (Wal-Mart)** -

Premium Chunk Light Tuna In Water

Solid White Albacore Tuna In Water

**Hy-Vee** - Chunk Light Tuna In (Oil, Water)

**Kroger Brand** - Canned, Pouch

**Laura Lynn** - Chunk, Solid White Albacore

**Lowes Foods Brand** - Chunk Lite

**Member's Mark -** Highest Quality Solid White Albacore Tuna In Water

**Midwest Country Fare** - Chunk Light Tuna Packed In Water

**Portside** - Chunk Light In Water

**Publix -** Tuna Fillets

**Safeway Brand** - Chunk Light

**Safeway Select -** Solid White Albacore

**Spartan Brand** - Chunk Light, Solid White Albacore

**Starkist** -

Starkist Select (All)

Starkist Tuna (All) *(Except Crackers In Starkist Lunch To-Go)*

Starkist Tuna Creations (All) *(Except Herb & Garlic, Tomato Pesto Albacore Variety)*

Starkist Tuna Fillets (Pouch) (All) *(Except Light Meat Teriyaki Variety)*

**Trader Joe's** - Canned Tuna (All), Marinated Ahi Tuna Steaks

**Ukrop's -** Tuna Kabob

**Wegmans Brand** - Albacore In Water, Yellowfin Light In Water

**Turkey... see also Deli Meat ...** *All Fresh Meat Is Gluten-Free (Non-Marinated, Unseasoned)*

**Applegate Farms -**

Organic (Herb Turkey Breast, Smoked Turkey Breast)

Organic Turkey Burgers

Organic Uncured Turkey Hot Dogs

Natural (Herb Turkey, Honey & Maple Turkey Breast, Roasted Turkey, Smoked Turkey Breast, Turkey Bologna, Turkey Salami)

Natural Uncured Turkey Hot Dogs

The Greatest Little Organic Smokey Pork Cocktail Franks

Turkey Salami

**Boar's Head -** All Varieties

**Butcher's Cut -** Ground Turkey, Jumbo Turkey Franks, Oven Roasted Turkey Breast (98% Fat Free, Regular)

**Butterball -**

All Natural Turkey (Cutlets, Filets, Strips, Tenders)

Fresh Li'l Butterball Turkey *(Except Gravy Packet w/Wheat Flour)*

Fresh Whole Turkey *(Except Gravy Packet w/Wheat Flour)*

Frozen Fully Cooked Li'l Butterball Baked Turkey *(Except Gravy Packet w/Wheat Flour)*

Frozen Fully Cooked Turkey (Baked, Smoked) *(Except Gravy Packet w/Wheat Flour)*

Frozen Li'l Butterball *(Except Gravy Packet w/Wheat Flour)*

Frozen Whole Turkey *(Except Stuffed Turkeys & Gravy Packet w/Wheat Flour)*

Ground Turkey (Italian Style, Regular, Seasoned, White)

Lunch Meat

Extra Thin Sliced Deep Fried Turkey Breast (Buttery Herb, Cajun Style, Original,Thanksgiving Style)

Extra Thin Turkey Breast (Honey Roasted, Oven Roasted, Smoked)

**T**

Lean Family Size (Honey Roasted Turkey Breast, Oven Roasted Turkey Breast, Smoked Turkey Breast, Turkey Bologna, Turkey Ham)

Thick Sliced (Honey Roasted, Oven Roasted, Smoked)

Thick Sliced Deep Fried Turkey Breast (Cajun Style, Original, Thanksgiving Style)

Thin Sliced (Honey Roasted, Oven Roasted, Smoked)

Oven Roasted Turkey Breast Strips

Turkey Bacon (Lower Sodium, Regular, Thin & Crispy)

Turkey Breasts (Fresh, Frozen)

Turkey Burgers (All Natural, Seasoned)

Turkey Drumsticks

Turkey Mignons

Turkey Sausage (Fresh Bratwurst, Fresh Breakfast, Fresh Hot Italian, Fresh Sweet Italian, Polska Kielbasa Dinner, Smoked, Smoked Cheddar, Smoked Dinner, Smoked Hot)

Turkey Thighs

Turkey Wings

**Castle Wood Reserve** - Thinly Sliced Oven Roasted Turkey

**Dietz & Watson** -

Bacon Lover's Turkey

Banquet Breast of Turkey

Black Forest Turkey

Classic Homestyle Turkey

Fire Roasted Breast of Turkey

Glazed Honey Cured Turkey Breast

Golden Brown Turkey Breast Original

Gourmet Lite Turkey Breast

Homestyle Black Pepper Turkey

Italian Turkey

London Broil Turkey

Maple & Honey Cured Turkey Breast

## turkey

**T**

Mesquite Turkey Breast
No Salt Turkey
Oven Classic Turkey Breast
Pepper & Garlic Turkey
Santa Fe Turkey
Smoked Peppercorn Turkey Breast

**Empire Kosher** -
Fresh Chill Pack Turkey
Fully Cooked Barbecue Turkey (Fresh, Frozen)
Ground Turkey (Fresh, Frozen)
Honey Smoked Turkey Breast (Skinless)
Premiere Signature Edition
    All Natural Turkey Breast (Skinless, w/Skin)
    Smoked Turkey Breast (Skinless)
    Turkey (Breast Pastrami Skinless, Pastrami Skinless)
Roll (Turkey Bologna, Turkey Salami, White Turkey)
Signature Edition Turkey Breast (Oven Prepared, Smoked)
Slices (Smoked Turkey Breast, Turkey Bologna, Turkey Breast, Turkey Pastrami)
Turkey Franks
Whole Turkey & Turkey Breasts (Frozen)

**Farmer John** - Lunch Meat Premium Oven Roasted Turkey Breast

**Garrett County Farms** -
Frozen Turkey Maple Breakfast Links
Turkey Andouille
Turkey Breast (Pan Roasted, Sliced (Roasted, Smoked, Turkey Ham, Turkey Ham Steak), Smoked)
Turkey Franks
Turkey Kielbasa
Turkey Tom Tom Snack Sticks

**T**

**Hillshire Farms -**

Deli Select Thin Sliced Turkey Breast (Honey Roasted, Oven Roasted, Smoked)

Deli Select Ultra Thin Turkey Breast (Honey Roasted, Oven Roasted)

**Honeysuckle White -**

Estate Recipe Turkey Deli Meat

Buffalo Style

Canadian Brand Maple

Dry Roasted

Hickory Smoked (Honey Pepper, Original, Sun Dried Tomato)

Honey Smoked

Mesquite Smoked

Fresh

Breast (Bone In, Cutlets, Roast, Strips, Tenderloins, Thin Cut Slices)

Drumsticks

Neck Pieces

Split Breast

Thighs

Wing (Drumettes, Portions)

Wings

Frozen (Boneless Turkey w/Gravy, Turkey Burgers, Zesty Rotisserie Flavor Boneless Turkey Breast)

Fully Cooked Hickory Smoked Bone In Turkey Breast

Ground Turkey

All (85/15, 93/7, 97% Fat Free, 99% Fat Free, Italian Style Seasoned, Roll, Patties, Taco Seasoned, Value Pack)

Hardwood Smoked (Bacon, Franks)

Hickory Smoked (Cooked Turkey Salami, Turkey Ham, Turkey Pastrami)

Lunch Meat Deli Sliced
  Hickory Smoked Honey Turkey Breast
  Hickory Smoked Turkey Breast
  Oven Roasted Turkey Breast
  Turkey Pastrami
Marinated Turkey Selections
  Creamy Dijon Mustard Breast Tenderloins
  Homestyle Breast Tenderloins
  Italian Herb Rotisserie Boneless Breast Roast
  Lemon Garlic Breast Tenderloins
  Original Style Rotisserie Boneless Breast Roast
  Rotisserie Breast Tenderloins
  Zesty Italian Herb Breast Tenderloins
Original Rotisserie Turkey Ham
Sausage
  Bratwurst
  Links (Breakfast, Chipotle Smoked, Hot Italian, Original
    Smoked, Poblano Pepper, Sweet Italian, Tomato & Garlic)
  Patties
  Roll (Breakfast, Mild Italian)
Simply Done
  Split Turkey Breast (Lemon Garlic, Mesquite, Rotisserie)
  Whole Young (Turkey, Turkey Breast)
Turkey Bologna
Turkey Breast Deli Meats
  Cajun Style Hickory Smoked
  Golden Roasted
  Hickory Smoked (Regular, Peppered)
  Honey Mesquite Smoked
  Oil Browned

**T**

    Original Rotisserie

    Oven Prepared

  Whole Young Turkeys

    All Natural

    Cajun Style

    Fresh

    Frozen

    Fully Cooked (Hickory Smoked, Oven Roasted)

    Honey Roasted

**Hormel** -

  Deli Sliced (Oven Roasted, Smoked)

  Chunk Meats Turkey

  Julienne Turkey

  Natural Choice Deli (Honey, Oven Roasted, Smoked)

  Turkey Pepperoni

  Turkey Stroganoff Fully Cooked Entrée

**Hy-Vee** -

  Deli Thin Slices Turkey Breast (Honey Roasted, Oven Roasted)

  Thin Sliced (Honey Turkey, Turkey)

**Isaly's** - All Deli Meat

**Jennie-O Turkey Store** -

  Breakfast Lover's Turkey Sausage

  Extra Lean Smoked Turkey Sausage (Kielbasa, Regular)

  Festive Tender Cured Turkey

  Flavored Tenderloins (Applewood Smoked, Balsamic Herb & Olive Oil, Lemon Garlic, Roast Flavor, Seasoned Pepper, Smoky SW Style, Tequila Lime, Tomato Basil)

  Fresh

    Breakfast Sausage (Maple Links, Mild Links, Mild Patties)

    Dinner Sausage (Cheddar Turkey Bratwurst, Hot Italian, Lean Turkey Bratwurst, Sweet Italian)

**T**

Ground Turkey (Extra Lean, Italian, Lean, Taco Seasoned)

Lean Turkey Patties

Tray (Breast Slices, Breast Strips, Tenderloins)

Frozen

Fully Cooked Sausage (Links, Patties)

Ground Turkey (Regular, Seasoned)

Italian Meatballs

Turkey Burgers

Grand Champion Turkey Breast (Hickory Smoked, Homestyle Pan Roasted, Honey Cured, Mesquite Smoked, Oven Roasted, Tender Browned)

Hickory Smoked Turkey Breast (Cracked Pepper, Garlic Pesto, Honey Cured, Sun Dried Tomato)

Natural Choice Turkey Breast (Oven Roasted, Peppered, Tender Browned)

Oven Ready Turkey (Garlic & Herb, Homestyle)

Oven Ready Turkey Breast *(Except Gravy Packet)*

Oven Roasted Turkey Breast

Pan Roasts w/Gravy (White, White/Dark Combo)

Prime Young Turkey (Fresh or Frozen) *(Except Gravy Packet)*

Refrigerated (Dark Turkey Pastrami, Honey Cured Turkey Ham, Turkey Ham)

Refrigerated Quarter Turkey Breasts (Cajun Style, Cracked Pepper, Hickory Smoked, Honey Cured, Oven Roasted, Sun Dried Tomato)

Smoked Turkey Breast (Hickory, Honey Cured, Mesquite)

Smoked Turkey Wings & Drumsticks

So Easy Slow Roasted Turkey Breast

Turkey Breast

Apple Cinnamon

Garlic Peppered

Honey (Maple, Mesquite)

**T**

    Hot Red Peppered
    Italian Style
    Maple Spiced
    Mesquite Smoked
    Oven Roasted
    Peppered
    Smoked (Peppered, Regular)
    Tender Browned
    Tomato Basil
  Turkey Franks

**Kayem** - Turkey Breast (Honey Smoked, Regular)

**Kroger Brand** - Fresh & Frozen Plain Turkey (Breast, Thighs)

**Manor House** - Frozen Enhanced Turkey

**Meijer Brand** -
  Gold Turkey (Hen, Tom)
  Hen Turkey
  Frozen (Breast Tenders, Duckling, Split Breast, Young)
  Regular Turkey Breast
  Sliced Chipped Meat
  Tom Turkey
  Turkey Basted w/Timer
  Turkey Breast (Fresh, Fresh Natural, Hickory Smoked, Honey
    Roasted, Zipper 97% Fat Free)

**Nature's Basket** - Golden Roasted, Rustic Herb, Slow Smoked

**Northwestern** - Deli Turkey (Hickory Smoked, Oven Roasted, Turkey
  Pastrami)

**Organic Prairie**
  Fresh Organic
    Hardwood Smoked Turkey Bacon 8 oz.
    Sliced Roast Turkey Breast 6 oz.
    Sliced Smoked Turkey Breast 6 oz.
    Turkey Hot Dogs 12 oz.

Frozen Organic

    Ground Turkey 12 oz.

    Hardwood Smoked Turkey Bacon 8 oz.

    Whole Young Turkey (10-14 lbs., 14-18 lbs.)

**Oscar Mayer** -

Deli Fresh Meats (Oven Roasted (98% Fat Free Turkey, Turkey Breast), Smoked Turkey Breast)

Shaved Deli Fresh Meats (Cracked Black Peppered Turkey Breast, Honey Smoked Turkey Breast, Mesquite Turkey Breast, Oven Roasted Turkey Breast, Smoked Turkey Breast)

Thin Sliced Deli Fresh (Honey Smoked Turkey Breast, Mesquite Turkey Breast, Oven Roasted Turkey Breast, Smoked Turkey Breast)

**Perdue** -

Carving Classics Pan Roasted Turkey Breast (Cracked Pepper, Honey Smoked, Original)

Carving Turkey (Ham Honey Smoked, Whole)

Carving Turkey Breast (Hickory Smoked, Honey Smoked, Mesquite Smoked, Oven Roasted)

Deli Dark Turkey Pastrami Hickory Smoked

Deli Pick Ups Sliced Turkey (Golden Browned, Honey Smoked, Mesquite Smoked, Oven Roasted, Smoked)

Deli Pick Ups Sliced Turkey Ham Honey Smoked

Deli Turkey (Bologna, Breast Oil Browned, Ham Hickory Smoked, Salami)

Ground Turkey (Burgers, Fresh Breast, Fresh Lean)

Healthsense Turkey Breast Oven Roasted (Fat Free, Reduced Sodium)

Rotisserie Turkey Breast

Short Cuts Carved Turkey Breast Oven Roasted

Slicing Turkey Ham

Tender & Tasty Products

**T**

Turkey Sausage Seasoned Fresh Lean (Hot Italian, Sweet Italian)

Whole Turkey Seasoned w/Broth

**Primo Taglio -** Turkey Breast (Dinner Roast, Honey Maple, Mesquite Smoked, Natural Hickory Smoked, Natural Hickory Smoked Peppered, Pan Roasted, Salsa Seasoned)

**Publix -**

Deli Fully Cooked Turkey (Breast, Whole)

Deli Pre-Pack Lunch Meats (Extra Thin Sliced Oven Roasted Turkey Breast, Extra Thin Sliced Smoked Turkey Breast, Smoked Turkey, Turkey Breast)

Fresh Young Turkey (Breast, Whole)

Fully Cooked Smoked Turkey (Breast, Whole)

Ground Turkey (Breast, Regular)

**Shelton's -** Free Range Ground Turkey (#1 Chub Pack, #3 Chub Pack), Free Range Ground White Turkey (#1 Chub Pack), Free Range Whole Turkey (8-15 lbs, 16-26 lbs), Organic (Large, Whole Small), Turkey Burgers

**SPAM -** Classic, Less Sodium, Lite, Oven Roasted Turkey, Smoked Flavored

**Stop & Shop Brand -** Turkey Breast (Oven Roasted Fat Free, Smoked)

**Thumann's -** All Varieties●

**Trader Joe's -** Mesquite Smoked Turkey Breast Sliced

**Ukrop's -** Oven Roasted Turkey Breast

**Valley Fresh -** All Varieties

**Wegmans Brand -**

Lean Ground Turkey (94%, 99%)

Organic Turkey Breast (Honey Roasted, Oven Roasted)

Sliced Turkey Breast (Hickory Smoked, Oven Browned)

Split Turkey Breast

Thin Sliced Turkey Breast Cutlets

Turkey (Breast Tenders, Drumsticks, London Broil, Thighs, Wings)

**Wellshire Farms** -

 All Natural Turkey Breast (Pan Roasted, Smoked)

 Morning Maple Turkey Breakfast Link Sausage

 Sliced (Oven Roasted Turkey Breast, Smoked Turkey Breast, Turkey Bologna, Turkey Ham)

 Turkey (Andouille Sausage, Franks, Kielbasa, Liverwurst)

 Turkey Dinner Link Sausage Mild Italian Style

 Turkey Ham (Ham Steak, Nuggets, Whole)

 Turkey Tom Toms (Hot & Spicy, Original)

**Wellshire Organic -** Organic Turkey (Andouille, Bacon, Franks, Kielbasa)

**Turkey Bacon... see Bacon**

**Turkey Breast... see Turkey**

**Turkey Burgers... see Burgers... see Turkey**

**Turkey Ham... see also Ham... see also Turkey**

 **Honeysuckle White -** Hickory Smoked Turkey Ham

 **Jennie-O** - Refrigerated Honey Cured Turkey Ham, Refrigerated Turkey Ham

 **Perdue** - Deli Turkey Ham Hickory Smoked

**Turkey Jerky... see Jerky/Beef Sticks**

**Turkey Lunch Meat... see Deli Meat**

**Turkey Sticks... see Jerky/Beef Sticks**

**Turnips...** *All **Fresh** Fruits & Vegetables Are **Gluten-Free***

 **C & W** - All Plain Frozen Vegetables

 **Laura Lynn -** Canned Turnip Greens w/Diced Turnips

 **Lowes Foods Brand** - Diced

 **Pictsweet** - All Plain Vegetables (Frozen)

 **Safeway Brand -** Frozen Chopped

 **Winn Dixie** - Frozen (Chopped, w/Turnips)

# U U
# V V

Vanilla Extract... see Extract

Vanilla Powder

  Authentic Foods▲

Vegenaise

  **Follow Your Heart** - Expeller Pressed, Grapeseed Oil, Organic, Original, Reduced Fat

Vegetable Juice... see Juice/Drinks

Vegetable Oil... see Oil

Vinegar

  **Albertsons** - Apple Cider, Red Wine, White Distilled

  **Authentic Food Artisan (AFA)** - Lorenzi Balsamic

  **Bakers & Chefs** - White Distilled

  **Bionaturae** - Balsamic

  **Bragg** - Apple Cider

  **Di Lusso** - Red Wine

  **Eden Organic** - Organic (Apple Cider, Brown Rice, Red Wine, Ume Plum)

  **Food Club Brand** - Cider, White

  **Full Circle** - Organic Balsamic Vinegar

  **Grand Selections** - Balsamic of Modena, Red Wine, White Wine

  **Great Value Brand (Wal-Mart)** - Apple Cider, Balsamic, Distilled White, Premium (Garlic Flavored Red Wine, Red Wine)

  **Hannaford Brand** - Red Wine, White Apple Cider

  **Heinz** - Apple Cider (Flavored, Regular), Distilled White, Garlic Wine, Red Wine

  **Holland House** - All Vinegars *(Except Malt Vinegar)*

  **Home Harvest Brand** - White

  **Hy-Vee** - Apple Cider Flavored Distilled, White Distilled

  **Kurtz** - Apple Cider, White

**V**

**W**

**Lowes Foods Brand** - Cider, White

**Meijer Brand** - Balsamic Aged (4 Yr, 12 Yr), Cider, Red Wine, White Distilled, White Wine

**Musselman's** - Apple Cider, White Distilled

**Newman's Own Organics** - Balsamic

**O Organics** - Balsamic

**Publix -** Apple Cider, Balsamic, Red Wine, White Distilled

**Regina** - All Varieties

**Safeway Select -** Apple Cider, Distilled, Red Wine, Rice, White Wine

**Spartan Brand** - Cider, White

**Spectrum** - Balsamic, Organic (Balsamic, Brown Rice, Distilled White, Filtered Apple Cider, Golden Balsamic, Red Wine, Seasoned Brown Rice, Unfiltered Apple Cider, White Wine)

**Star** - Balsamic, Garlic Wine, Natural Rice, Red Wine, Seasoned Rice, White Wine

**Stop & Shop Brand** - Cider, Simply Enjoy (Balsamic Of Modena, White Balsamic), White, Wine

**Trader Joe's** - Orange Muscat Champagne

**Wegmans Brand** - Apple Cider, Asian Classic Rice Vinegar, Balsamic, Chianti Red Wine, Red Wine, Tuscan White Wine, White Distilled

**Westcott** - Apple Cider, White

**Winn & Lovett -** Apple Pear Balsamic, Apricot Chardonay, Pomegranate Zinfandel, Raspberry Champagne

**Winn Dixie -** Apple Cider, White

Vitamins... see Gluten-Free OTC Pharmacy Section

Vodka... *All **Distilled** Alcohol is **Gluten-Free** [2]*

# W

Wafers... see Cookies

Waffles/Waffle Mix... see Pancakes/Pancake Mix

**W** Walnuts... see Nuts

**Wasabi**

    **Dietz & Watson** - Wasabi Mustard

    **Eden** - Wasabi Powder

    **Hime** - Powdered Sushi Wasabi

    **S & B** - Prepared Wasabi In Tube

    **Spectrum** - Organic Wasabi Mayonnaise

    **Sushi Sonic** - Real Wasabi

    **Trader Joe's** - Wasabi Mayo

**Water**

    **Aquafina** -

        Flavor Splash (Grape, Lemon, Peach Mango, Raspberry, Strawberry Kiwi, Wild Berry)

        Purified Drinking Water

        Sparkling (Berry Burst, Citrus Twist)

    **Crystal Geyser** - Alpine Spring

    **Dasani** - Essence (Black Cherry, Lime, Strawberry Kiwi), Grape, Lemon, Raspberry, Strawberry, Regular

    **Deja Blue** - Purified Drinking Water

    **Evian**

    **Fiji** - Natural Artesian

    **Food Club Brand** - Distilled, Drinking, Spring

    **Hannaford Brand** - Sparkling (Black Cherry, Key Lime, Kiwi Strawberry, Peach, Tropical Punch, Raspberry, White Grape)

    **Hy-Vee** - 10 oz. Fun Pack (Flavored, Regular), Mother's Choice Infant Water w/Fluoride, Natural Spring, Premium Distilled, Purified, Spring, Tonic

    **Ice Mountain**

    **Kroger Brand** - Crystal Clear Flavored Waters

    **Lowes Foods Brand** - Distilled, Drinking, Spring

    **Meijer Brand** - Calcium, Distilled, Natural Calcium, Spring

    **Poland Spring** - Sparkling Spring

## whipping cream

**Publix** - Spring Water

**Safeway Brand -** Drinking, Purified Drinking, Spring

**San Pellegrino** - Sparkling Water

**Smartwater (Glaceau)**

**Snapple** - All Varieties

**Spartan Brand** - Water (Distilled, Drinking, Natural Spring, Spring)

**Sweet Bay -** Distilled, Drinking Water w/Minerals, Natural Spring Water Sodium Free

**Trader Joe's -** All Sparkling

**Vitaminwater (Glaceau)** - All Varieties

**WaterPlus**

**Wegmans Brand** -

Aqua Mineral Water (Italian, Lemon Italian, Lemongrass, w/Lemon, w/Lime)

Aqua V Vitamin Infused Lemonade

Sparkling Water (Berry, FYFGA Natural, Lemon, Lime, Mandarin Orange, Mineral, Mixed Berry, Orange, Raspberry, Tangerine Lime)

Spring (Regular, w/Fluoride)

**Winn Dixie -** Distilled, Drinking, Purified, Sparkling Water (Country Strawberry, Green Apple, Key Lime, Mandarin Orange, Mellow Peach, White Grape, Wild Cherry, Zesty Raspberry), Spring

## Water Chestnuts

**Reese** - Sliced, Whole

**Spartan Brand** - Canned

## Watermelon... *All **Fresh** Fruits & Vegetables Are **Gluten-Free**

## Whipping Cream

**Albertsons** - Aerosol (Extra Creamy, Original), Frozen (Fat Free, Light, Regular), Whipping Toppings

**Cabot -** Whipped Cream Aerosol

**Food Club Brand** -

Aerosol Whipped Topping (Extra Creamy, Original)

Frozen Whipped Topping (Fat Free, Light, Original)

**Garelick Farms -** Ultra Pasteurized Heavy Whipping Cream

**Great Value Brand (Wal-Mart) -** Heavy Whipping Cream, Sweetened Whipped Cream Ultra-Pasteurized Aerosol (Extra Creamy, Regular)

**Home Harvest Brand -** Frozen Whipped Toppings

**Hood -** Instant Whipped Cream, Sugar Free Light Whipped Cream

**Horizon Organic -** All Varieties

**Hy-Vee -** Aerosol (Extra Creamy, Light), Frozen Lite Whipped, Frozen Whipped Topping (Extra Creamy, Fat Free, Regular), Real Whipped Cream (Lite, Regular)

**Kraft -**

Aerosol (Extra Creamy, Lite, Regular)

Cool Whip Topping (Extra Creamy, Fat Free, Lite, Regular, Sugar Free)

Dips (Chocolate, Stawberry Crème)

**Kroger Brand**

**Laura Lynn -** Frozen Whipped Topping, Whipping Cream

**Lowes Foods Brand -** Frozen Whipped Topping (Fat Free, Lite, Regular), Whipping Cream (Heavy, Light, Regular)

**Lucerne -** Aerosol Whipping Cream (Light, Non Dairy), Whipping Cream (Heavy, Light, Regular), Whipped Topping (Fat Free, Lite, Original)

**Meijer Brand -**

Frozen Whipped Topping (Fat Free, Lite, Original)

Ultra Pasteurized (Heavy Whipping Cream, Whipped Cream Aerosol (Non Dairy, Regular))

**Organic Valley -** Heavy Whipping Cream (Pasteurized, Ultra Pasteurized)

**Prairie Farms -** Half & Half (Fat Free, Heavy Whipping, Regular, Ultra Pasteurized), Ultra Pasteurized Heavy Whipping Cream, Whipped Cream Aerosol

**Publix -** Heavy Whipping Cream, Whipped Cream (Heavy, Light), Whipped Topping (Fat Free), Whipping Cream

**Reddi -Wip -** Extra Creamy, Fat Free, Original

**Safeway Brand -** Light, Non Dairy, Regular

**Shamrock Farms -** Fresh Whipping, Gourmet Heavy Cream

**Spartan Brand** - Frozen Whipped Topping (Light, Regular)

**Stop & Shop Brand** - Whipped Topping (Fat Free, French Vanilla, Lite, Non Dairy, Regular)

**Wegmans Brand** - Fresh (Extra Creamy, Fat Free, Lite, Regular, Whipped Light Cream), Frozen Whipped Topping (Fat Free, Lite, Regular)

**Woodstock Farms** - Organic Whipping Cream

Whiskey... *All **Distilled** Alcohol Is **Gluten-Free** [2]

Wine... *All Wine Made **In The USA** Is Gluten-Free [2]

Wing Sauce

**Butcher's Cut** - Jazz N Spicy Buffalo Wing Sauce

**Di Lusso** - Buffalo Wing Sauce

**Frank's RedHot** - Buffalo Wing (Hot, Regular), Sweet Heat BBQ

**Ken's Steak House** - Buffalo Wing Sauce

**Moore's Marinade** - Buffalo Wing, Honey BBQ Wing

**Mr. Spice Organic** - Salt Free Hot Wing! Sauce & Marinade

**Texas Pete** - Buffalo Wing

**Wingo** - Wing Sauce

Wings... *All **Fresh** Chicken Is **Gluten-Free (Non-Marinated, Unseasoned)**

**Jennie-O Turkey Store** - Smoked Turkey Wings & Drumsticks

**Stop & Shop Brand** - Wings (Buffalo Style, Honey BBQ)

**Trader Joe's** - Chicken Wings

**Wegmans** - Chicken Wings, Jumbo Buffalo Style

Worcestershire Sauce

**Food Club Brand**

**French's**

**Hannaford Brand**

**Hargis House**

**Heinz**

**Kurtz**

**Lea & Perrins** - Original

**W**

**X**

**Y**

Lowes Foods Brand
Meijer Brand
Safeway Brand
Spartan Brand
The Wizard's - Organic CF/GF Vegan Worcestershire
Winn & Lovett

# X

Xanthan Gum
  Authentic Foods
  Bob's Red Mill▲
  Ener-G▲
  Gluten-Free Essentials▲ ●
  Kinnikinnick▲

# Y

Yams... *All **Fresh** Fruits & Vegetables Are **Gluten-Free***
  Food Club Brand - Canned
  S&W - All Canned Vegetables
  Spartan Brand - Yams
Yeast
  Bakipan - Active Dry, Bread Machine, Fast Rising Instant
  Bob's Red Mill▲ - Yeast (Active Dry, Nutritional T6635)
  Fleischmann's - All Varieties
  Gayelord Hauser - 100% Natural Brewer's Yeast
  Hodgson Mill▲ - Active Dry, Fast Rise
  Kroger Brand - Yeast Packets
  Red Star - Active Dry, Bread Machine, Cake, Quick Rise
  SAF - Bread Machine, Gourmet Perfect Rise, Traditional Active Dry

## Yogurt

**Y**

**Albertsons** - All Flavors (Blended, Fruit On Bottom, Light, Low Fat, Non Fat)

**Brown Cow Yogurt** -

Low Fat (Black Cherry●, Blueberry●, Boysenberry●, Lemon Twist●, Maple●, Peach●, Plain 32●, Strawberry●, Vanilla 32●, Vanilla Bean●)

Nonfat (Apricot Mango●, Blueberry●, Chocolate●, Lemon●, Plain●, Raspberry●, Strawberry●, Vanilla●, Vanilla 32●)

Whole Milk Yogurt (Apricot/Mango●, Blueberry●, Blueberry Cream Top●, Cherry/Vanilla●, Chocolate●, Coffee●, Maple●, Maple 32●, Peach●, Plain●, Plain 32●, Raspberry●, Strawberry●, Vanilla●, Vanilla 32●)

**Cascade Fresh** - All Varieties

**Coburn Farms** - Lite, Low Fat

**Dannon** - Plain (Activia 24oz. Container, Low Fat, Natural, Nonfat)

**Food Club Brand -** All Varieties

**Great Value Brand (Wal-Mart)** - Light Yogurt (Banana Cream Pie, Black Cherry, Blueberry, Mixed Berry, Peach, Strawberry, Strawberry Banana, Vanilla)

**Horizon Organic** - All Varieties

**Hy-Vee** -

Fat Free Plain

Hy Active (Blueberry, Peach, Strawberry, Vanilla)

Light (Banana Cream, Blueberry, Cherry, Lemon Chiffon, Peach, Raspberry, Strawberry, Strawberry Banana, Vanilla)

Low Fat (Black Cherry, Blueberry, Cherry Vanilla, Lemon, Mixed Berry, Plain, Raspberry, Strawberry, Strawberry Banana)

**Kemps -** All Varieties

**Laura Lynn** - Low Fat, Nonfat

**Lifeway** - All Varieties

**Lowes Foods Brand** -

Drinkable Yogurts (Mixed Berry, Strawberry, Strawberry Banana)

**Y**

Lite (Black Cherry, Blueberry, Key Lime, Lemon Chiffon, Peach, Raspberry, Strawberry, Vanilla)

Low Fat Vanilla

Non Fat Plain

Regular (Blueberry, Mixed Berry, Peach, Strawberry, Strawberry Banana)

**Lucerne** - All Varieties (Fat Free, Pre Stirred Low Fat)

**Meijer Brand** -

Blended (Boysenberry, Strawberry, Strawberry Banana, Tropical Fruit)

Fruit On The Bottom (Blueberry, Peach, Raspberry, Strawberry)

Lite (Banana Crème, Black Cherry, Blueberry, Cherry Vanilla, Coconut Cream, Lemon Chiffon, Mint Chocolate, Peach, Raspberry, Strawberry, Strawberry Banana, Vanilla)

Low Fat Blended (Blueberry, Cherry, Mixed Berry, Peach, Pina Colada, Raspberry)

Low Fat Vanilla

Tube Yo Lar (Strawberry Banana, Strawberry Blueberry, Tropical Punch Raspberry)

**Nancy's** - All Varieties

**Nogurt** - Organic (Banana Cinnamon, Blueberry, Chocolate, Orange, Pomegranate)

**O Organics** - All Flavors

**Prairie Farms** -

Fat Free

Banana Crème Pie

Black Cherry

Blueberry

Cherry Vanilla

Keylime Pie

Mixed Berry

Orange Crème

Peach

    Raspberry

    Strawberry

    Vanilla

  Low Fat

    Apricot

    Black Cherry

    Blackberry

    Blueberry

    Cherry Vanilla

    Peach

    Pineapple

    Raspberry

    Strawberry (Banana, Regular)

**Publix** -

  Creamy Blends (Black Cherry, Blueberry, Peach, Regular, Strawberry, Vanilla)

  Fat Free (Plain, Strawberry Orange)

  Fat Free Active (Peach, Strawberry, Vanilla)

  Fat Free Light (Banana Crème, Blackberry, Blueberry, Blueberry Pomegranate, Cappuccino, Caramel Crème, Cherry, Coconut Crème, Key Lime, Lemon Chiffon, Mandarin Orange, Peach, Raspberry, Strawberry, Strawberry Banana, Strawberry Orange, Vanilla, Wild Berry Crumb Cake)

  Fruit On The Bottom (Banana, Black Cherry, Blackberry, Blueberry, Cherry, Guava, Honey, Mango, Mixed Berry, Peach, Pineapple, Raspberry, Strawberry, Strawberry Banana, Tropical Blend)

  Just 4 Kidz (Blue Raspberry & Cotton Candy, Strawberry & Blueberry, Strawberry Banana & Cherry)

  Multi Packs

    Creamy Blends (Black Cherry & Mixed Berry, Blueberry & Strawberry Banana, Peach & Strawberry)

**Y**

No Sugar Added (Blueberry, Cranberry Raspberry, Peach, Strawberry, Vanilla)

**Silk Live!** - All Varieties

**Spartan Brand** - Banana Cream, Blackberry Pie, Blueberry, Boysenberry, Cherry, Cherry Vanilla, Mixed Berry, Peach, Peach Mango, Pineapple, Raspberry, Strawberry, Strawberry Banana, Strawberry Kiwi, Vanilla

**So Delicious** - Coconut Milk (Blueberry, Chocolate, Passionate Mango, Plain, Pina Colada, Raspberry, Strawberry, Strawberry Banana, Vanilla)

**Sol Cuisine** - Organic Solgurt (Lowfat Blueberry, Lowfat Strawberry, Lowfat Vanilla, Unsweetened Natural)

**Stonyfield Farm** - All Smoothies●, Soy Yogurts●, Yogurts● *(Except YoBaby Plus Fruit & Cereal, YoKids Squeezers, Oikos Greek Yogurt, Frozen Yogurt)*

**Stop & Shop Brand** -

Grab'ums Yogurt To Go (Cotton Candy Melon, Strawberry Blueberry, Tropical Punch Raspberry)

Low Fat Blended (Blueberry, Peach, Raspberry, Strawberry, Vanilla)

Low Fat Fruit On The Bottom (Blueberry, Peach, Raspberry, Strawberry, Strawberry Banana)

Nonfat Light (Banana, Blueberry, Cherry, Cherry Vanilla, Coffee, Peach, Raspberry, Strawberry, Strawberry Banana, Vanilla)

Nonfat Plain Yogurt

**Tillamook** - All Yogurts & Yogurt Smoothies

**Trader Joe's** -

All Varieties

Soy Yogurt (All Varieties)

**Wegmans Brand** -

Blended Low Fat (Blueberry, Cherry, Coffee, Key Lime, Lemon, Mixed Berry, Orange Cream, Peach, Raspberry, Strawberry, Vanilla)

Blended Strawberry Banana

**Y**

Fruit On The Bottom

Fat Free (Black Cherry, Blueberry, Lemon, Mixed Berry, Peach, Raspberry, Strawberry, Strawberry Banana)

Low Fat (Apricot Mango, Blueberry, Cherry (Regular, Vanilla), Lemon, Mixed Berry, Peach, Pina Colada, Pineapple, Plain, Raspberry, Strawberry (Banana, Kiwi, Regular), Vanilla)

Light Blended Nonfat (Blueberry, Keylime, Mixed Berry, Orange Cream, Peach, Raspberry, Strawberry (Banana, Regular), Vanilla

Nonfat Plain Yogurt

Organic Super Yogurt (Blueberry, Peach, Plain, Raspberry, Strawberry, Vanilla)

**WholeSoy & Co.** - All Products (Frozen Yogurts, Smoothies, Yogurts)

**Wild Wood Organics** - All Varieties

**Winn Dixie** -

Fat Free (Banana Cream Pie, Black Cherry, Blueberry, Key Lime, Mixed Berry, Peach, Pina Colada, Raspberry, Strawberry, Strawberry Banana, Vanilla)

Low Fat (Blueberry, Peach, Pineapple, Pineapple Cherry, Plain, Raspberry, Strawberry, Vanilla)

No Sugar Added Strawberry

**Yoplait** -

Kids 25 % Less Sugar

Strawberry Banana/Peach

Strawberry Vanilla/Strawberry

Vanilla/Banana

Light

Apple Turnover

Banana Cream Pie

Blackberry

Blueberry

Boston Cream Pie

Lemon Cream Pie

**Y**
Orange Crème
Pineapple Upside Down Cake
Raspberry Cheesecake
Red Raspberry
Strawberry (Banana, Shortcake)
Very (Cherry, Vanilla)
White Chocolate Strawberry
Light Thick & Creamy
  Key Lime Pie
  Lemon Meringue
  Mixed Berry
  Peaches 'N Cream
  Strawberry
Original
  Blackberry Harvest
  French Vanilla
  Harvest Peach
  Mixed Berry
  Mountain Blueberrry
  Orange Crème
  Pina Colada
  Red Raspberry
  Strawberry (Banana, Cheesecake, Regular)
Thick & Creamy
  Blackberry Harvest
  Peaches 'N Cream
  Royal Raspberry
  Strawberry (Banana, Regular)
  Vanilla

# Z                                                                    Z

**Zucchini...** *All **Fresh** Fruits & Vegetables Are **Gluten-Free***
   **Del Monte -** Zucchini w/Italian Style Tomato Sauce
   **Stop & Shop Brand**

# Gluten-Free
# Over The Counter (OTC)
# Pharmacy Guide

# Rx

## After Shave/Shaving Gel

**Arbonne** - NutriMinC RE9 Resurface Shave Gel
**Avon** -
    Black Suede After Shave
    Blue Rush After Shave Conditioner
    Christian Lacroix Noir After Shave Conditioner
    Derek Jeter Driven After Shave Balm
    Derek Jeter Driven Black After Shave Conditioner
    Derek Jeter Driven Ultimate Shave Gel
    Perceive for Men After Shave Conditioner
    Pro Sport Daily Performance Sleek Glide Shave Gel
    R.P.M. After Shave Conditioner
    Tomorrow For Men After Shave Conditioner
    Wild Country After Shave
    Wild Country After Shave Conditioner
**Burt's Bees** -
    Men's Natural Aftershave
    Men's Natural Shave Cream

## Allergy/Sinus/Cold/Flu Relief

**Actifed** - Tablets
**Afrin** - Nasal Spray
**Airborne** - Lemon Lime, On The Go Lemon Lime, Original, Pink Grapefruit, Very Berry
**Children's Motrin** - Cold Suspension (Berry, Dye Free, Grape)

## allergy/sinus/cold/flu relief

**Children's Tylenol** -                                                **Rx**

    Cold Suspension Grape

    Plus (Cold & Cough Chewable Tablets Cherry, Cold & Cough
        Suspension Cherry, Cold Chewable Tablets)

**Claritin** - D12, D24, Ready Tabs, Regular

**Cold-Eeze** - Cold Remedy Lozenges (All Flavors)

**Dayquil** - All Liquid Varieties

**Diabetic** - Tussin (All Varieties)

**Halls** - All Varieties

**Infant's Tylenol** - Drops Plus Cold

**Meijer** -

    Apap

        Cold Child Suspension Grape

        Cough Cold (Child Suspension Cherry, Infant Drops Cherry)

        PE Allergy Sinus Caplets

        PE Cold Flu Day Cool Caplets

        PE Cold Severe Congestion Caplets

        XC PM Caplets

    Daytime 6hr (Liquid, Liquid Gels)

    Dibromm (DM Grape Elixir, Grape Elixir)

    Diphedryl (Capsules, Cherry Elixir, Tablets)

    Effervescent Cold Tablets

    Ibuprofen Sinus (Brown Caplets)

    Loratadine (Allergy Daily Tablets, Allergy QD Tablets, D 24hr
        Tablets)

    Naproxen Sodium Sinus Cold Caplets

    Nasal Spray (Extra Moist Liquid, Liquid, Multi Symptom Liquid, No
        Drip Pump Liquid)

    Nitetime 6 hr (Cherry Liquid, Liquid Gels, Original Liquid)

    Nitetime Cough 6 hr (Cherry Liquid)

    Pedia Cough Decongestion Drops

**Rx**  Pseudoephedrine Tablets

Tri Acting Nitetime Grape Liquid

Tussin (CF Liquid, CS Liquid, Cough Cold Softgels, DM Clear Liquid, DM Liquid, Pedia Cough Cold Liquid)

XP Day/Nite 6hr Original Liquid

**Motrin** - Cold & Sinus Caplets

**Nyquil** - All Liquid Varieties

**PediaCare** - Children's Decongestant (Liquid), Gentle Vapors, Long Acting Cough

**Primatene** - Mist, Tablets

**Safeway Select** -

24 Hour Allergy Relief (Regular, w/Loratadine)

Allergy Diphenhydramine Hydrochloride Antihistamine

Allergy Relief

Benehist Allergy

Children's Elixir Cough & Cold

Children's Elixir Nasal Decongestant

Cough & Cold Decongestant

Day Time Cold & Cough

Maximum Strength Suphedrine

Mucous Relief (DM & PE)

Multi Symptom Nasal Spray

Night Time Cold Medicine (Liquid)

Non Aspirin Cold (Non Drowsy)

Suphedrine

Tussin

**Simply Cough** - Liquid

**Simply Stuffy** - Liquid

**Theraflu** -

Hot Liquids (Cold & Cough, Cold & Sore Throat, Daytime Severe Cold & Cough, Flu & Sore Throat, Nightime Severe Cold & Cough, Sugar Free Nightime Severe Cold & Cough)

Thin Strips (Daytime Cold & Cough, Multi Symptom, Nightime Cold & Cough)

Warming Relief Syrups (Cold & Chest Congestion, Daytime, Flu & Sore Throat, Nightime)

**Topcare** -

All Day Allergy Tablets

Allergy Capsules

Allergy Multi Symptom Tablets

Allergy Relief Tablets (Non Drowsy, Regular)

Chest & Sinus Congestion Tablets

Children's Allergy Liquid

Children's Cold & Allergy Elixir

Children's Cold & Cough Elixir

Children's Cough & Sore Throat

Children's Mucous Relief

Cold/Flu Liquid (Daytime, Nitetime)

Cold/Flu Softgels (Daytime, Nitetime)

Head Congestion

Pain Relief & Severe Congestion Tablets

Nasal Decongestant PE Tablets

Sinus & Allergy PE Tablets

Sinus Congestion & Pain Tablets

Sinus Tablets (Day, Nitetime)

Tussin CF

Tussin DM

**Tylenol** -

Allergy Complete Caplets

Cold (Day Non Drowsy Caplet, Severe Cold & Flu Liquid, Severe Congestion Caplets)

Sinus (Day Caplets, Severe Congestion)

**Wal-Act** - Tablets

**Rx**

**Rx**<sup>Wal-Dryl</sup> -

    Allergy Sinus Headache Caplets

    Capsules

    Minitabs

**Wal-Finate** - Allergy Tablets

**Wal-Finate D** - Tablets

**Wal-Flu** - Night Time Gelcaps

**Wal-Phed** -

    Cold & Allergy Tablets

    Tablets

**Walgreens** -

    Allergy (Tablets Maximum Strength)

    Allergy Sinus (Maximum Strength Caplets)

    Apap Cold (Caplets, Child Suspension Grape, Infant Drops
      Bubblegum, Severe Congestion Caplets)

    Apap Flu (Child Suspension Bubblegum)

    Cold Tablets

    Comfort Gelcaps

    Cough FM Decongestant Liquid

    Day/Night Cold Relief

    Dayhist Allergy Tablet

    Daytime (Liqui gels, Liquid)

    Dibromm Grape Elixir

    Diphedryl (Cherry Elixir)

    Effervescent Cold Tablets

    Flu (Maximum Strength Non Drowsy Gelcaps, Maximum Strength
      Non Drowsy Pouch, Maximum Strength Tablets, Regular Strength
      Pouch Tablets)

    Loratadine D 24 Hour Tablets

    Maximum Strength Non Aspirin Allergy Sinus Gelcaps

    Maximum Strength Non Drowsy Sinus (Caplets, Gelcaps)

Cecelia's Marketplace Gluten-Free Grocery Shopping Guide

Multi Symptom Cold (Cold Relief Tablets, Complete Caplets)     **Rx**

Nasal Spray Multi Symptom Liquid

Nitetime Cough Cherry Liquid

Nitetime Liquid (Cherry, Child Cherry)

Nose Drops Decongestant Liquid

Pedia CC Liquid

Pedia Cough Decongestant Drops

Pseudoephedrine (12 hr Tablets, Child Decongestant Liquid, Severe
    Cold Non Drowsy Caplets, Sinus Maximum Strength Non Drowsy
    Tablets)

Tri Acting Cold Allergy (Liquid, Nitetime Grape Liquid)

Tussin (CC Maximum Strength Liquid, CF Liquid, CS Liquid, DM
    Clear Liquid, DM Liquid, Pedia CC Liquid)

**Vicks** - All Products


# Antacids

**Children's Mylanta** - Tablets Bubblegum

**Digestive Advantage** - All Varieties *(Except Gas Defense)*

**Lactaid** - Dietary Supplement (Fast Act Caplets, Fast Act Chewables,
    Original Strength Caplets)

**Meijer** -

Antacid Calcium (Peppermint Chewables, Ultra Fruit Chewables,
    XS Berry Chewables, XS Chewables, XS Fruit Chewables, XS
    Tropical Chewables, XS Wintergreen Chewables)

Antacid Fast Acting Liquid (Maximum Strength Cherry, Maximum
    Strength Original, Regular Strength Original)

Cimetidine Tablets

Dairy Digestive (Extra Strength Caplets, Regular Strength, Ultra
    Caplets)

Effervescent Antacid Pain Tablets

**Rx** Famotidine Tablets

Milk Of Magnesia (Cherry Liquid, Mint Liquid, Original Liquid)

Pink Bismuth (Chewables, Maximum Strength Liquid, Regular Strength Liquid)

Ranitidine

**Mylanta** - Maximum Strength Liquid Original Flavor, Regular Strength Liquid Original Flavor, Ultra Tablets Cool Mint

**Pepcid AC** - 10 mg Tablets, Complete Chewable Mint Tablets

**Pepto Bismol** - All Varieties

**Rolaids** - All Tablets *(Softchews Are NOT Gluten-Free)*

**Safeway Select** -

Antacid Plus (Double Strength)

Antacid Tablets (Fruit Flavored, Peppermint, Wintergreen)

Effervescent Antacid Tablets

Famotidine Tablets

Milk Of Magnesia (Mint)

Stomach Relief

Ultra Dairy Digestive

**Tagamet HB**

**Tums** -

Dual Action (Berry, Mint)

EX 750 (Assorted Berries, Assorted Fruit, Assorted Tropical Fruit, Wintergreen)

EX Sugar Free (Orange Cream)

Quik Pak (Berry Instant Dissolving Powder)

Regular Strength (Assorted Fruit, Peppermint) *(Kids Cherry Blast Is NOT Gluten Free)*

Smoothies (Assorted Tropical Fruit, Cocoa & Crème, Peppermint) *(Assorted Fruit Smoothies, Berry Fusion Smoothies Are NOT Gluten Free)*

Ultra 1000 (Assorted (Berries, Fruit, Tropical Fruit), Peppermint)

## antibiotic/analgesic ointment & spray

**Walgreens -** **Rx**

Antacid Fast Acting Regular Strength Liquid (Mint, Original)

Antacid Tablets (Extra Strength Fruit, Extra Strength Tropical, Extra Strength Wintergreen, Fruit, Fruit Assorted, Original, Peppermint)

Dairy Digestive (Regular Strength Caplets, Ultra Caplets)

Effervescent Antacid Pain Tab

Milk Of Magnesia (Mint Liquid, Original Liquid, Tablets)

Pink Bismuth (Maximum Strength Liquid, Regular Strength Liquid)

# Antibiotic/Analgesic Ointment & Spray

**Cortaid -** All Varieties

**Hy-Vee -**

First Aid (Allergy Creme 2%, Antibiotic Ointment, Hydrocortisone Cream 1%)

Isopropyl Alcohol

Petroleum Jelly

Triple Antibiotic Ointment Plus

**Top Care -**

Anti Itch Cream 2%

Antibiotic Cream & Pain Relief

Bacitracin Zinc Ointment

Burn Relief Spray

First Aid Spray

Hydrocortisone 1% (Cream, Cream with Aloe, Ointment)

Triple Antibiotic Ointment

Triple Antibiotic Ointment & Pain Relief

**Rx**                    Anti-Diarrhea

**Digestive Advantage** - All Varieties *(Except Gas Defense)*
**Imodium** - AD Caplets, Advanced Chewable Tablets
**Lactaid** - Dietary Supplement (Fast Act Caplets, Fast Act Chewables, Original Strength)
**Meijer** -
   Loperamide (Caplets, Liquid, NCRC Caplet)
   Pink Bismuth (Chewables, Maximum Strength Liquid, Regular Strength Liquid)
**Pepto Bismol** - All Varieties
**Safeway Select** - Anti Diarrheal Tablets, Stomach Relief, Ultra Dairy Digestive
**Walgreens** -
   Loperamide (Caplets, Liquid)
   Pink Bismuth (Maximum Strength Liquid, Regular Strength Liquid)


## Anti-Fungal

**AZO** - Yeast Tablet (Maximum Strength, Standard)
**Avon** - Footworks (Antifungal Foot (Cream, Spray), Odor Neutralizing Foot Spray, Tropical Coconut Cooling Foot Spray)
**Hy-Vee** - Foot Care/Antifungal Creme
**Meijer** -
   Miconazole 2% Foot Spray Liquid
   Miconazole Cream (3 Day Preapp. Combo, 3 Day Disapp. Combo, 7 Day Disapp., 7 Day Reapp.)
   Tioconazole 1 Day Ointment (Disapp.)
   Tolnaftate 1% Foot Spray (Liquid, Powder)
**Walgreens** - Tioconazole 1 Day Ointment (Disapp.)

# Anti-Gas                                           **Rx**

**Digestive Advantage** - All Varieties *(Except Gas Defense)*

**Infant's Mylicon** - Drops Non Staining

**Lactaid** - Dietary Supplement (Fast Act Caplets, Fast Act Chewables, Original Strength)

**Meijer** - Gas Relief Ultra Softgels, Simethicone Nonstaining Drops

**Mylanta** - Maximum Strength Gas Mint Tablets

**Phazyme** - Ultra Strength Softgels

**Top-Care** - Infant Gas Relief

**Walgreens** - Dairy Digestive Caplets (Regular, Ultra)

# Body Spray

**Avon** -

Naturals Body Spray (Apricot & Sunflower, Cucumber Melon, Gardenia, Lavender & Chamomile, Mandarin & Jasmine, Peach, Plum & Nectarine, Raspberry, Strawberry & Guava, Vanilla)

Self Sanctuary Lemon Sugar Scent Mist

# Cosmetics

**Afterglow Cosmetics ▲** - All Products

**Arbonne-**

About Face

Blusher

Brow Wax

Cream Concealer

**Rx**  Eye Pencil

Eye Shadow

Line Defiance Liquid Foundation SPF 15

Lip Pencil

Mineral Powder Foundation SPF 15

Sheer Shine

Translucent Powder (Loose, Pressed)

Wipe Out Eye Makeup Remover

Before Sun No Sun Intended Bronzing Powder

**Avon** -

8-in-1 Eye Palette

Anew

Beauty Age (Transforming Compact Makeup SPF 15, Transforming Pressed Powder SPF 15)

Beauty Eye Lifting Serum Shadow

Clinical Plump & Smooth Lip System

Be Blushed Cheek Color

Beyond Color

Line Softening Mousse Foundation

Plumping Lip Color SPF 15 w/Double The Retinol

Plumping Lip Conditioner SPF 15 w/Double The Retinol

Radiant Lifting Eyeshadow

Skin Smoothing Compact Foundation

Big Color (Eye Pencil, Lip Pencil)

Daring Curves (Mascara, Waterproof Mascara)

Daring Definition Mousse Mascara

Dramatic Focus Kohl Eye Liner

Feeling Fine Ultra Thin Eye Liner

Glazewear (Diamonds Eye Color, Lip Liner, Lipstick, Liquid Lip Color)

Glimmersticks (Brow Definer, Eye Liner, Lip Liner, Waterproof Eye Liner)

Heavenly Soft Eyeshadow Trio

## cosmetics

Hydra Cool Bronzing Stick

**Rx**

Ideal Shade
- Concealer Stick
- Cream To Powder Foundation SPF 10
- Fresh and Light Foundation
- Liquid Foundation SPF 10
- Loose Powder
- Pressed Powder
- Smooth Mineral Makeup

In A Wink Instant Eyeshadow Sheets

Jillian Dempsey For Avon
- Horizon Blush
- Professional Eyeshadow
- Professional Kohl Eye Liner
- Professional Mascara
- Retro Rouge

Let It Glow Powder Bronzer

Line N' Design Eye Duo

Lip Swirls Gloss

Look Alert Eye Brightener

Luster Glow Lip Shine

MagiX Face Perfector SPF 20

Mark
- Bronze Pro Bronzing Powder
- C Thru U Beautifying Sheer Tint
- Comb Out Lash Lifting Mascara
- Crystal Shimmer Hook Up Powder
- Custom Pick Eye Shadow
- Dew Drenched Moisturlicious Lip Color
- Eyemarker Color On Line
- Face Xpert Flawless Touch Makeup

**Rx**

Flip For It Fall 2008 For Eyes Lips Cheeks

Gleamstick Hook Up Lip Color

Glossblossom Ripening Lip Tint

Glow Baby Glow Hook Up Lip Gloss

Glow Xpert Face Shimmer

Good (Glowing Custom Pick Powder Blush, Glowing Mosaic Blush Custom Color Palette)

Gorgeous Eye Trio

Hooked On Glamour Kits

I Glimmer Illuminating Eye Color

I Sheer Hook Up Creamy Eye Shadow

Invisible Touch Perfecting Concealer

Juice Gems

Just Pinched Instant Blush Tint

Kiss Dry Goodbye Lip Smoother

Kiss Therapy Super Soothing Lip Balm (Regular, SPF)

Lip Gloss Triangles

Make It Big Lash Plumping Mascara

Mini Mark It Stick For Lips

On The Edge Hook Up Liquid Eyeliner

Pop In Color (Eye Shadow, Eyeliner, Lip Gloss)

Powder Buff Natural Skin Foundation

Powder Matic Go Anywhere Loose Powder

Pro Glimmer Hook Up Powder

Pro Gloss Hook Up Plumping Lip Shine

Pure Body Soufflé

Scanda Lash Hook Up Mascara

Sheenstick Hook Up Lip Balm

Shimmer Bars

Shimmer Cubes Lip Gloss

Shimmer Tubes Hook Up Gel Blush

**Rx**

Shine Tubes Hook Up Lip Gloss
Speedway Do Everything Makeup
Tinted Sheenstick Hook Up Lip Balm
Winkstick Hook Up Eye Shadow Stick
Mattenificent Oil Absorbing Powder
Metalluscious Lip Cream Hook Up
Mini Wash Off Waterproof Mascara
Mistake Proof Mascara
Moisture Effective Eye Makeup Remover Lotion
Perfect Wear
  All Day Comfort Lipstick SPF 12
  Extralasting Liquid Foundation SPF 15
  Extralasting Powder Eyeshadow
  Eyewriter Liquid Eye Liner
Perfectly Paired Dual Ended (Lipstick, Shadow Stick)
Perfectly Portable Liquid Eye Liner
Personal Match Loose Powder
Plump Pout Lip Gloss
Pro To Go Lipstick
Satin Deluxe (Blush, Eyeshadow Duo)
Smoky Lines Eye Liner
Smoldering Pastels (Blush Duo, Eyeshadow Duo)
Smooth Mineral (Blush, Eyeshadow)
Smooth Over Eye Definer
Spring Delights Lip Balm
Super Full Mascara
Supershock Mascara
Tahitian Holiday (All Over Bronzer, Liquid Lip Balm SPF 15)
Triple Threat Cream Eyeshadow
True Color (Blush, Eyeshadow Quad, Eyeshadow Single)
Truffle Delights Lip Gloss

**Rx**
Ultra Color Rich (Lip Conditioner, Lip Exfoliator, Lipstick, Lipstick in Sparkling Shades, Mousse Lipstick)

Ultra Luxury (Brow Liner, Eye Liner, Lip Liner)

Uplifting Mascara

Wash Off Waterproof Mascara

# Cough Drops/Sore Throat Spray/Lozenges

**Cold-Eeze** - Cold Remedy Lozenges (All Flavors)

**Halls** - All Varieties

**Health Market** - Zinc Lozenges w/Vitamin C & B6

**Hy-Vee** - Cherry Eucalyptus Flavor Drops, Honey Lemon Cough Drops, Sugar Free Black Cherry Drops

**Meijer** - Cherry Sore Throat Spray

**Organix** - Organic Cough & Sore Throat Drops (Golden Honey Lemon, Orchard Cherry)

**Safeway Select** -

Cough Drops (Cherry, Honey Lemon, Vitamin C Citrus)

Sore Throat Spray (Menthol)

Triacting Sore Throat Formula

**Top Care** -

Cough Drops (Cherry, Eucalyptus, Honey Lemon, Iced Blue, Sugar Free Cherry)

Pectin Throat Drops

Sore Throat Spray

**Vicks** - Formula 44 Sore Throat (Lozenges, Spray)

**Walgreens** -

Cough Drops (Cherry, Dad's Rootbeer, Herbal, Honey Lemon, Honey Lemon Tea, Ice Blue, Menthol, Orange Crush w/Vitamin C, Strawberry, Sugar Free Black Cherry, Sugar Free Menthol)

Soothe Chewable Tablets
Sore Throat Spray Liquid (Cherry, Menthol)
Throat Lozenges (Black Cherry, Cherry, Menthol)

**Rx**

# Deodorant

**Avon** -
Black Suede Roll On Anti Perspirant Deodorant
Blue Rush Roll On Anti Perspirant Deodorant
Derek Jeter Driven Anti Perspirant Deodorant
Mesmerize Roll On Anti Perspirant Deodorant
On Duty Roll On Anti Perspirant Deodorant
Perceive Roll On Anti Perspirant Deodorant
R.P.M. Roll On Anti Perspirant Deodorant
Skin So Soft Soft & Sensual Roll On Anti Perspirant Deodorant
Tomorrow For Him Roll On Anti Perspirant Deodorant
Wild Country Roll On Anti Perspirant Deodorant
**Burt's Bees** - Herbal Deodorant
**Tom's Of Maine** -
Natural Long Lasting Deodorant (Roll On, Stick)
Natural Original Deodorant Stick
Natural Sensitive Care Deodorant Stick

# Diabetic Products

**Diabetic** - Tussin (All Varieties)
**DiabetiDerm** - Cream (All Varieties)

**Rx** DiabetiSweet - Sugar Substitute
Diachrome
**Enterex** - Diabetic (Chocolate, Strawberry, Vanilla)
**Glucerna** -
    Shakes (All Varieties)
    Snack Shakes (All Varieties)
**Glucoburst** - Drink (Vanilla), Gel
**Health Market** - Glucose Tablets (Orange, Raspberry)
**Multi-Betic** - Diabetic Multi Vitamin
**Walgreens** - Orange Glucose Tablets

# Eye Care

**Top Care** -
    Eye Drops (Advanced Relief, Original, Seasonal Relief)
    Multi Purpose Solution (Contacts)
**Visine** - A, AC, Advanced Relief, For Contacts, L.R., Multi Symptom
    Relief, Original, Pure Tears Singles, Tears Dry Eye Relief, Tears Long
    Lasting Dry Eye Relief, Total Eye Soothing Wipes

# Hair Care

**Aquaphor** - Baby Gentle Wash & Shampoo
**Arbonne** - Sea Source Detox Spa Fortifying Hair Mask
**Avon**-
    2 In 1 Anti Dandruff Shampoo & Conditioner
    Advance Techniques
        Anti Frizz Capsules
        Cello Shine Treatment

## hair care

**Rx**

Color Protection
    Lock In Treatment For Color Treated Hair
    Restorative Mask For Color Treated Hair
Color Reviving (Conditioner, Shampoo)
Curl Defining Liquid Gel
Dry Ends Serum
Grey Root Touch Up
Hair Spray
Mirror Shine Spray
Purifying Treatment Shampoo
Salon
    Curl Refreshing Spray
    Luminous Anti Brassiness Spray
    Skinny Serum
Shaping Gel
Smoothing (Conditioner, Shampoo)
Sun Dimension Highlight Builder for Blonde Highlights
Super Straight Smoothing Balm
Volumizing Mousse
Hannah Montana 2 In 1 Shampoo
Mark
  Curl Goddess
    Curl and Wave Defining Gel w/Conditioning Sunflower
    Curling Mist w/Conditioning Sunflower
    Silkening Serum
    Styling Cream w/Conditioning Sunflower
  Mega Volume
    Hair Spray w/Soothing Geranium
    Next Day Spray
    Root Lifting Spray w/Soothing Geranium
    Spray Gel w/Soothing Geranium

**Rx**      Salon Straight
   Anti Frizz Serum w/Invigorating Orange
   Pre Style Protector
   Shine Spray w/Invigorating Orange
   Smoothing Balm w/Invigorating Orange
  Planet Spa Mediterranean Olive Oil Conditioning Hair Mask

**Burt's Bees** -
  Color Keeper (Conditioner, Shampoo)
  Deep Repair Conditioner
  Super Shiny Grapefruit (Conditioner, Shampoo)
  Volumizing (Conditioner, Shampoo)

**California Baby** -
  Calendula Hair Conditioner
  Calendula Shampoo & Bodywash
  Calming Hair Conditioner
  Calming Hair Detangler
  Calming Shampoo & Body Wash
  Super Sensitive Hair Conditioner
  Super Sensitive Shampoo & Bodywash
  Swimmer's Defense Shampoo & Body Wash
  Tea Tree & Lavender Shampoo & Body Wash

**Dessert Essence Organics** -
  Conditioner (Fragrance Free, Green Apple & Ginger, Italian Red
   Grape, Lemon Tea Tree, Red Raspberry)
  Shampoo (Fragrance Free, Green Apple & Ginger, Italian Red
   Grape, Lemon Tea Tree, Red Raspberry)

**Fleurish Beauty** - Premium Conditioner, Premium Shampoo
**Gluten-Free Savonnerie** ▲ - All Products
**Hy-Vee** -
  Baby Shampoo
  Extra Body Shampoo Plus Conditioner

Le Techniq (Silk Shiny & Smooth Pro Vitamin, Truly Clean Pro Vitamin Conditioner, Truly Clean Pro Vitamin Shampoo, Truly Clean Vitamin Shampoo & Conditioner)

Lice Killing Shampoo

Lice Shampoo & Cream Rinse

Lice Treatment Kit

Normal Vitamin Shampoo & Conditioner

**Johnson's** - Baby Shampoo

**Keys** - All Products

**Meijer** - Minoxidil 5% Liquid (30 Day, 90 Day)

**Pantene Pro-V** - All Shampoos & Conditioners

**Safeway Select** - Baby Shampoo (Conditioning, Regular)

**Rx**

## Laxatives/Hemorrhoidal Relief

**Citrucel** - Fiber Therapy Powder (Orange Regular, Orange Sugar Free)

**Dulcolax** - Bisacodyl Tablets

**Ensure** - All Fiber Shakes

**Fleet** - Fiber Gummies

**Konsyl** - All Fiber Products

**Meijer** -

Fiber Therapy Caplets

Hemorrhoidal (Cream, Ointment, Suppository)

Laxative Tablets (Natural MS, Senna, Womens)

NVP (Capsules, Original Orange Powder, Original Regular Powder, Smooth Orange Powder, Sugar Free Smooth Orange Powder)

**Metamucil** - All Capsules, All Powders

**Pedia-Lax** - All Varieties

**Rx** **Safeway Select** - Fiber (Supplement, Fiber Therapy, Fiber Therapy Capsules)

**Tucks** - Hydrocortisone Anti Itch Ointment, Medicated Pads, Hemorrhoidal Ointment, Take Alongs Medicated Pads

**Walgreens** -

Fiber Laxative

Fiber Therapy Orange Powder

Gentle Laxative

Hemorrhoidal (Cream, Ointment, Suppositories)

Laxative Pills

Maximum Strength Laxative Pills

Women's Laxative

# Lip Care

**Arbonne** -

Bio Nutria Herbal Lip Ointment

Bio Nutria Lip Service Dietary Supplement

F.Y.I. It Shines Lip Gloss

Before Sun Lip Saver SPF 30

**Avon** -

Hannah Montana Lip Balm

High School Musical Lip Balm

Kiss Therapy Super Soothing Lip Balm (Regular, SPF)

Moisture Therapy Moisturizing Lip Treatment SPF 15

Naturals Lip Balm

Sheenstick Hook Up Lip Balm (Regular, Tinted)

**Blistex** -

Clear Advance

Complete Moisture

**Rx**

DCT SPF 20
Deep Renewal
Fruit Smoothies (Berry Explosion, Melon Medley, Triple Tropical)
Gentle Sense
Herbal Answer Gel
Lip Balm (Berry, Medicated, Mint)
Lip Infusions (Cherry Splash, Moisture Splash, Soothing Splash)
Lip Medex
Lip Ointment
Lip Revitalizer
Lip Tone
Raspberry Lemonade Blast
Silk & Shine
Ultra Protection

**Burt's Bees** -
Lip Balm (All Varieties) *(Except Rescue SPF 15)*
Lip Gloss (All Shades)
Lipshimmer (All Shades)

**Desert Essence Organics** - Lip Tints (Coconut, Italian Red Grape, Red Raspberry, Vanilla Chai)

**Safeway Select** - Lip Balm

**Whole Foods** - Lip Balm (Peppermint, Tangerine)

# Misc. Products

**Avon** -
Healthy Remedies Detox Patches
Healthy Remedies Green Tea Extract
Healthy Remedies Headache Relief
Kids Bath Time Body Paints

**Rx** **Band-Aid** - Flexible Fabric
**Burt's Bees** -
    Bug Bite Relief
    Herbal Blemish Stick
    Insect Repellent
    Therapeutic Bath Crystals
**Elmer's** - All Products *(Except Finger Paints)*
**Nature's Baby Organics** - All Purpose Deodorizer
**Safeway Select** - Foam Adhesive Bandages, Sam E

## Motion Sickness

**Meijer** - Anti Nausea Liquid
**Wal-Dram** - II Less Drowsy Tablets, Tablets

## Oral Hygiene

**3M** - All Dental Materials *(at the dentist)*
**Aquafresh** - All Toothpaste Varieties
**Biotene Oral Balance** - All Products
**Colgate** - All Toothpaste Varieties
**Crest** - All Mouthrinses, All Toothpaste Varieties, All Whitestrips
**Day White** - Take Home Whitening Gel *(at the dentist)*
**Efferdent** - Denture Cleanser
**Effergrip** - Denture Adhesive Cream
**Enamel Pro** -
    Fluoride Topical Gel (Bubblegum, Cherry, Orange, Strawberry) *(at the dentist)*
    Prophy Paste (All Flavors)*(at the dentist)*

**Glide - Floss**

**Rx**

**Glitter** - Prophy Paste (All Flavors)*(at the dentist)*

**Hy-Vee** -

    Antiseptic Mouthwash/Rinse (Blue Mint, Mint, Mint Anti Cavity Fluoride, Mint Trial Size, Peppermint, Spring Mint)

    Anti Plaque Rinse (Mint, Regular)

    Dental Floss (Hi Tech, Unwaxed, Waxed, Waxed Mint)

    Effervescent Denture Tabs

    Mint Denture Cleanser

**Kirkman** - Toothpaste Gel

**Kolorz** - Prophy Paste (All Flavors) *(at the dentist)*

**Listerine** -

    Agent Cool Blue Tinting Rinse

    Antiseptic Mouthwash (All Varieties)

    Pocket Paks Oral Care Strips (All Varieties)

    Tooth Defense Anticavity Fluoride Rinse

    Totalcare Anticavity Mouthwash

    Whitening Pen

    Whitening Pre Brush Rinse

    Whitening Quick Dissolving Strips

    Whitening Vibrant White Rinse

**Nite White** - Take Home Whitening Gel *(at the dentist)*

**Nupro** - Prophy Paste *(at the dentist)*

**Oasis** - Moisturizing Mouthwash

**Peridex** - Chlorhexidine Gluconate Oral Rinse

**Plax** - Advanced Formula Plaque Loosening Rinse (Original, Soft Mint)

**Polident** - Denture Cleanser

**Premier** - All Prophy Pastes, All Topical Gels *(at the dentist)*

**Safeway Select** - Waxed Dental Floss (Mint)

**Scope** - Mouthwash (All Varieties)

**Sensodyne** - Pronamel Toothpaste

**Rx** **Sparkle** - Prophy Paste (All Flavors) *(at the dentist)*
**Sparkle Free** - Prophy Paste (All Flavors) *(at the dentist)*
**Tom's Of Maine** -
Children's Natural Anticavity Fluoride Toothpaste
Children's Natural Fluoride Free Toothpaste
Floss Antiplaque Flat
Floss Antiplaque Round
Maximum Strength Sensitive Fluoride Toothpaste
Natural Anticavity Fluoride Mouthwash
Natural Anticavity Fluoride Toothpaste
Natural Antiplaque Fluoride Free Toothpaste w/Propolis & Myrrh
Natural Antiplaque Plus Whitening Gel Fluoride Free Toothpaste
Natural Antiplaque Tartar Control & Whitening Fluoride Free
Toothpaste
Natural Clean & Gentle Care SLS Free Anticavity Plus Dry Mouth
Soother Fluoride Toothpaste
Natural Clean & Gentle Care SLS Free Anticavity Plus Whitening
Fluoride Toothpaste
Natural Clean & Gentle Care SLS Free Antiplaque Plus Whitening
Fluoride Free Toothpaste
Natural Cleansing Mouthwash
Natural Sensitive Toothpaste
Natural Tartar Control Mouthwash
Natural Whole Care Toothpaste
Natural Whole Care Toothpaste Gel
Sensitive Care SLS Free
**Top Care** -
Antiseptic Rinse (Amber, Blue Mint, Citrus, Iceburg Blue, Spring
Mint)
Mouthwash (Fluoride Rinse, Gargle Mint, Gargle Peppermint, Mint,
Pre Brushing)

**Rx**

**Topex** - Prep and Polish Paste *(at the dentist)*
**Topicale** - Topical Gel (Original, Xtra) *(at the dentist)*
**Uni-Pro** - Prophy Paste *(at the dentist)*
**Ziroxide** - Prophy Paste *(at the dentist)*
**ZOOM** - Whitening Gel *(at the dentist)*

# Pain Relief

**Bengay** - Pain Relieving Cream (Arthritis Formula, Greaseless, Ultra Strength), Vanishing Scent Gel
**Children's Motrin** - Chewables Grape, Chewables Orange, Suspension Berry, Suspension Bubblegum, Suspension Dye Free, Suspension Grape
**Children's Tylenol** -
Flavor Packets (Apple, Bubblegum, Chocolate, Strawberry)
Meltaways (Bubblegum Burst, Grape Punch, Wacky Watermelon)
Suspension (Bubblegum, Cherry Blast, Grape, Strawberry)
**Infant's Motrin** - Drops (Dye Free, Regular)
**Infant's Tylenol** - Drops (Cherry, Grape)
**Junior Tylenol** - Meltaways (Bubblegum Burst, Grape Punch)
**Meijer** -
Apap (Caplet, Cool Caplet, ER Caplet Red, ER Caplet White, ETS Tablet, Gelcap, Geltab, Tablet)
Apap Child (Bubblegum Suspension, Cherry Suspension, Grape Suspension)
Apap Infant Cherry Suspension
Aspirin (Adult Orange Chewables, Child Orange Chewables, Coated Tablets, Coated Yellow Tablets)
Aspirin Enteric Coated (Tablet, Yellow Tablet)

**Rx**  Headache Tablets

Ibuprofen (Caplets Brown, Caplets Orange, Child Suspension Bubblegum, Junior Caplets, Junior Chewables Orange, Tablets Brown, Tablets Orange)

Migraine Caplets

Naproxen Sodium (Caplets, NCRC Caplets, Tablets)

**Motrin IB** - Caplets, Gelcaps, Tablets

**Safeway Select** -

Acetaminophen

Acetaminophen Extra Strength Rapid Release Gelcaps

Arthritis Pain Formula Caplets

Aspirin (Enteric Coated, Low Strength, Micro Coated, Regular Strength)

Children's Ibuprofen Grape Oral Suspension

Children's Non Aspirin Chewables (Fruit, Grape)

Ibuprofen (Caplets Brown, Liquid Softgels, Tablets)

Migraine Relief Capsules

Naproxen Sodium Tablets

Non Aspirin Extra Strength (Capsules, Gel Capsules)

Pain Reliever Fever Reducer Tablets

Rapid Release Acetaminophen Gel Tabs Pain Relief

**St. Joseph** - Aspirin (Adult Chewable Tablets, Enteric Coated Tablets)

**Top Care** -

Children's Ibuprofen Tablets

Children's Pain Reliever (Grape, Bubble Gum)

Infant Ibuprofen Drops

Infant Pain Reliever Oral Drops (Cherry, Grape)

Ibuprofen Oral Suspension

Multi Symptom Tablets

**Tylenol** - 8hr Caplets, 8hr Geltabs, Arthritis Pain Relief Caplets, Extra Strength Caplets, Extra Strength Geltabs, Extra Strength Tablets, Rapid Release Gels, Regular Strength Tablets

**Walgreens** -                                                            **Rx**

Apap Children's (Suspension Bubblegum, Suspension Cherry, Suspension Grape)

Apap Infant Drops (Cherry, Grape)

Arthritis (Extra Strength Caplets)

Aspirin (Children's Tablets Cherry, Children's Tablets Orange, Enteric Coated Tablets, Extra Strength Caplets, Low Strength Enteric Tablets, Maximum Strength Enteric Tablets, Plus Tablets, Tablets)

Backache Relief Caplets

Children's Non Aspirin Soft Chews (Bubblegum, Fruit, Grape)

Headache Relief Extra Strength (Tablets)

Ibuprofen (Gelcaps, Orange Caplets, Orange Tablets)

Ibuprofen Child Suspension (Berry, Bubblegum, Fruit, Grape)

Ibuprofen Infant Berry Drops

Junior Strength Non Aspirin Soft Chews (Grape, Fruit)

Menstrual Relief Maximum Strength (Caplets, Gelcaps)

Migraine Caplets

Naproxen Sodium (Caplets, Tablets)

Non Aspirin (Extra Strength Caplets, Extra Strength Gelcaps, Extra Strength Tablets, Regular Strength Tablets)

Tri Buffered Aspirin Tablets

Women's Menstrual Capletes

**Wal-Profen** - Caplets, Tablets, Twin Tabs

# Pet Food

**Eukanuba**

Adult (Chicken Formula, Indoor Hairball Relief, Indoor Weight Control, Lamb & Rice)

Kitten (Chicken Formula)

**Rx** Nutro -
>    Natural Choice Dry Food Adult Dog (Lamb Meal & Rice)
>    Natural Choice Dry Food Puppy (Lamb Meal & Rice)

**Purina One**
>    Adult Cat (Hairball & Healthy Weight Formula, Healthy Weight Formula, Salmon & Tuna Flavor)

**Royal Canin -**
>    Adult Cat Indoor Intense Hairball 34
>    Baby Cat 34
>    Chihuahua 28
>    Maxi German Shepherd 24
>    Medium Bulldog 24
>    Veterinary Diets Canine (Hypoallergenic, Potato & Duck, Potato & Rabbit, Potato & Venison, Potato & Whitefish)
>    Veterinary Diets Feline (Hypoallergenic, Green Peas & Duck, Green Peas & Lamb, Green Peas & Rabbit, Green Peas & Venison)

**Science Diet**
>    Adult Cat (Active Longevitiy, Hairball Control, Indoor, Optimal Care (Oceanfish, Original), Oral Care, Sensitive Skin, Sensitive Stomach)
>    Kitten (Healthy Development (Oceanfish, Original), Indoor)

# Play Dough

**Aroma Dough** - All Natural Playing Dough

**BlueDominoes** - Organic Activity Dough●

**Crayola** - Air Dry Clay, Model Magic, Model Magic Fusion, Modeling Clay *(Crayola Dough is NOT Gluten Free)*

**Dokedo** - Play Putty (Scented, Unscented)

**Max's Mud** - Organic Sculpting Dough

# Skin Care

**Rx**

**Aquaphor** - Baby Healing Ointment, Healing Ointment
**Arbonne** -
 ABC Baby Care (Body Oil, Herbal Diaper Rash Cream)
 Aromassentials
  Awaken Sea Salt Scrub 16 oz.
  Unwind Bath Salts
  Unwind Massage Oil
 Bio Nutria
  Herbal Muscle Massage Gel
  Herbal Vapor Rub
  Leg Vein Formula
 Clear Advantage
  Acne Lotion
  Refining Toner
  Skin Support Supplement
  Spot Treatment
 FC5
  Exfoliating New Cell Scrub
  Hydrating Eye Crème
  Moisturizing Night Crème
  Nurturing Day Lotion w/SPF 20
  Oil Absorbing Day Lotion w/SPF 20
  Purifying Cleanser + Toner
  Skin Conditioning Oil
  Ultra Hydrating Hand Crème
 F.Y.I.
  Body Better Body Cream
  Eye Q Cream Eye Shadow

**Rx**    Get Even Tinted Moisturizer SPF 15
Sugar Slush Body Scrub

Figure 8
Vanish Pre Shower Cellulite Scrub
Vanish Water Relief Treatment Serum

NutriMinC RE9
Regain Illuminating Enzyme Peel
Retaliate Wrinkle Filler

Revelâge
Age Spot Brightening Day Cream w/SPF 30
Age Spot Brightening Hand Therapy w/SPF 30
Concentrated Age Spot Minimizer
Intensive Pro Brightening Night Serum

SeaSource Detox Spa
5 In 1 Essential Massage Oil
Foaming Sea Salt Scrub
Purifying Sea Soak
Remineralizing Body Lotion 24 Hr.
Renewing Body Gelée
Sea Mud Face and Body Mask

**Avon** -
Always Body Moisture
Anew
Advanced All In One Max SPF 15 UVA/UVB (Cream, Lotion)
Alternative (Clearly C 10% Vitamin C Serum, Intensive Age
Treatment PM, Photo Radiance Treatment SPF 15)
Clarifying Essence
Clinical (Advanced Dermabrasion System, Advanced
Retexturizing Peel, Eye Lift , Lift and Tuck Professional Body
Shaper, Professional Stretch Mark Smoother, Spider Vein
Therapy SPF 15 UVA/UVB)

**Rx**

Force Extra Triple Lifting Day Cream SPF

Rejuvenate (24 Hour Eye Moisturizer SPF 25, Dial A Glow Anti Aging Moisturizer SPF 15, Night Revitalizing Cream)

Retroactive+ (Youth Extending Cream Night, Youth Extending Cream SPF 25 Day)

Ultimate Age Repair (Day Cream SPF 25, Elixir, Night Cream)

Ultimate (Contouring Eye System, Transforming Hand & Nail Cream SPF 15)

Christian Lacroix Rouge Body Lotion

Crystal Aura Body Lotion

Far Away Body Lotion

Flower By Cynthia Rowley Body Lotion

Foot Works

Berry Mint (Foot Scrub, Moisturizing Foot Cream)

Citrus Mint Cooling Foot Lotion

Corn & Callus Softening Balm

Creamy Powder Lotion

Deep Moisture Cream

Deodorizing Foot Powder

Intensive Callus Cream

Invisible Silicone Sock Cream

Overnight Renewing Foot Cream

Pedi Peel

Therapeutic (Corn & Callus Remover, Cracked Heel Relief Cream)

Triple Duty Cream

Tropical Coconut Foot Lotion

Watermelon Cooling Foot Lotion

Haiku Body Lotion

Hannah Montana Hand Cream

High School Musical Hand Cream

**Rx**

Hydra Radiance Rapid Rescue Mask

Hydrofirming Drench Recovery Mask

Imari

    Body Lotion

    Seduction Body Lotion

Liiv

    Botanicals Vital Day Cream with SPF 20

    Botanicals Vital Night Moisturizer

Mark

    For Goodness Face Antioxidant Skin Moisturizing Lotion SPF 30

    Get Clearance Anti Acne Blemish Treatment Gel

    Instant Vacation Caribbean Self Tanner For (Body, Face)

    Jewel Body Cream

    Light Bright Lighten & Depuff Eye Gel

    Matte Chance Mattifying Lotion

    Mist Opportunity Multi Tasking Refresher

    Need A Shrink? Pore Minimizer Lotion

    Sassy Mark Dry Oil Mist

    See Things Clearly Brightening Moisturizer

    Self Sanctuary Chocolate Orchid (Body Butter, Dry Oil Mist, Moisture Milk)

    Self Sanctuary Honey Jasmine (Body Butter, Dry Oil Mist, Moisture Milk)

    Self Sanctuary Lemon Sugar (Body Butter, Dry Oil Mist, Moisture Milk)

Moisture Therapy

    ACE Provitamin Complex (Body Lotion, Hand Cream)

    Intensive (Body Lotion, Extra Strength Cream, Mini Hand Cream)

    Restorative Rescue Balm

Naturals

    Apricot & Sunflower (Refreshing Body Lotion, Soothing Cool Jelly Moisturizer)

## skin care

**Rx**

Banana & Coconut Milk Body Lotion

Cucumber Melon (Body Lotion, Hand & Body Lotion)

Gardenia Body Lotion

Lavender & Chamomile Body Lotion

Mandarin & Jasmine Body Lotion

Mango & Passion Fruit Body Lotion

Peach (Body Lotion, Cool Jelly Moisturizer, Hand Cream)

Plum & Nectarine (Moisturizing Hand and Body Lotion, Moisturizing Milk)

Raspberry Lotion

Strawberry & Guava Body Lotion

Vanilla (Body Lotion, Hand and Body Lotion, Hand Cream)

Planet Spa

African Shea Butter (Foot & Elbow Cream w/AHA, Hand & Cuticle Cream, Whipped Body Balm)

Hawaiian Thermal Volcano (Massaging Body Lotion, Paraffin Hand & Foot Treatment, Warming Face Mask)

Mediterranean Olive Oil (Firming Neck & Chest Serum, Whipped Body Cream)

Rare Gold Body Lotion

Rare Pearls Body Lotion

Skin So Soft

Bug Guard Plus

IR3535 Cool 'N Fabulous Disappearing Color SPF 30 Sunscreen Lotion

IR3535 Expedition Pump Spray

IR3535 Expedition SPF 30 Aerosol Spray

IR3535 Gentle Breeze SPF 30 Sunscreen Lotion

Picardin Spray (Aerosol, Pump, Towelettes)

Fresh & Smooth

Facial Hair Removal Cream

**Rx**

Hair Removal Cream (In Tropical Fruity Scent, Regular)
Hair Removal Microwave Wax For Face and Body
Post Hair Removal Soothing Gel

Fusions Soft & Nourish
  Dual Softening Body Oil

Fusions Soft & Replenish
  Dual Softening Body Moisturizer
  Dual Softening Body Oil

Fusions Soft & Sensual
  Dual Softening Body Moisturizer
  Dual Softening Body Oil

Original
  Bath Oil
  Bath Oil Spray
  Gelled Body Oil
  Replenishing Body Lotion
  Whipped Body Oil

Renew & Refresh Age Defying
  Corrective Neck & Chest Treatment
  Renewing Body Moisturizer

Satin Glow
  Body Firming Moisturizer For Fair Skin Tones
  Body Firming Moisturizer For Medium Skin Tones
  Continuous Mist Airbrush Spray For Fair Skin Tones
  Continuous Mist Airbrush Spray For Medium Skin Tones

Sensual Shape Targeted Firming Treatment

Soft & Relaxed
  Night Body Cream

Soft & Sensual
  Foaming Oil Body Moisturizer
  Gelled Body Oil

**Rx**

Replenishing Bath Oil
Replenishing Body Lotion
Replenishing Hand Cream
Whipped Body Oil
Summer Soft
Cooling Gel Moisturizer
Revitalizing Body Spray Lotion
Wintersoft
Hand Cream
Solutions
Ageless Results (Nightly Nutrient Peel, Overnight Renewing Cream PM, Renewing Day Cream SPF 15, Renewing Eye Cream)
Ageless Results Intensive (Line Filler SPF 15, A Line Treatment)
Banishing Cream Skin Discoloration Improver
Botanisource Comforting Cream
Bust Sculpt Contouring Cream
Dramatic Firming Cream
Hydra Radiance (Continuous Glow Daily Moisturizer, Moisturizing Day Lotion SPF 15, Moisturizing Night Cream)
Hydrofirming (Eye Cream, Night Cream)
Lighten Up Plus Eye Cream
Moisture 24 Long Lasting Hydrating Cream
Nurtura Replenishing Cream
Re Fine Stretch Mark Smoother
Super Shape Anti Cellulite & Stretch Mark Cream
True Pore Fection (Oil Free Skin Clearing Lotion, Skin Refining Toner)
Surreal Body Lotion
Tahitian Holiday Shimmering Glow Body Lotion
Today Body Moisture

**Rx**  Tomorrow Body Moisture

True Glow Body Lotion

Wish of Happiness Body Lotion

**Burt's Bees** -

After Sun Soother

Almond Milk Hand Crème

Baby Bee (Buttermilk Bath, Crème, Diaper Ointment, Dusting Powder, Lotion)

Banana Hand Crème

Beeswax Moist (Day Creme, Night Crème)

Carrot Nutritive Body Lotion

Carrot Seed Complexion Mist

Deep Clean Cleanser

Deep Pore Scrub

Garden Tomato Toner

Ginger Citrus Body Wash

Hand Salve

Hand Sanitizer

Healing Body Butter

Healthy Treatment (Evening Primrose Crème, Marshmallow Crème, Pore Refining Mask, Royal Jelly Eye Crème, Shea Butter Hand Repair, Toner)

Lemon Butter Cuticle Crème

Lemon Poppy Seed

Milk & Honey Lotion

Naturally Ageless (Day Cream, Eye Cream, Night Cream)

Radiance Body Lotion

Radiance (Day Cream, Eye Cream)

Soothingly Sensitive Lotion

Thoroughly Therapeutic (Body Butter, Foot Cream, Hand Cream, Lotion)

## skin care

**Rx**

**California Baby** -
  Aloe Vera Cream
  Botanical Moisturizing Cream
  Calendula (Cream, Everyday Lotion)
  Calming (Everyday Lotion, Diaper Rash Cream, Massage Oil, Non Talc Powder, Soothing & Healing Spray)
  Citronella (SPF 30+ Sunscreen Lotion, Summer Lotion)
  Colds & Flu Massage Oil
  Everyday/Year Round SPF 30 (Sunblock Stick, Sunscreen Lotion)
  I Love You Aromatherapy Massage Oil
  No Fragrance Sunblock Stick (SPF 30+)
  No Fragrance Sunscreen Lotion (SPF 18, SPF 30+)
  Overtired & Cranky Massage Oil
  Sunblock Stick SPF 30 (No Fragrance)
  Sunscreen SPF 30 (Citronella, No Fragrance)
  Super Sensitive (Everyday Lotion, Massage Oil)
**Clean & Clear** - Foaming Facial Cleaner (Oil Free, Sensitive Skin)
**Coppertone** - All Varieties (Continuous Spray, Kids, Oil Free, Pure & Simple, Sport, Sunless, Tanning, UltraGuard, Water Babies)
**Dessert Essence Organics** -
  Age Reversal Pomegranate (Eye Serum, Face Serum)
  Age Reversal SPF 30 Mineral Sunscreen
  Almond Hand & Body Lotion
  Bulgarian Lavender Hand & Body Lotion
  Coconut Hand & Body Lotion
  Pistachio Foot Repair Cream
  Pumpkin Hand Repair Cream
  Spicy Citrus Hand & Body Lotion
  Vanilla Chai Hand & Body Lotion
**Eucerin** - Original Lotion

**Rx** **Fleurish Beauty** - Luxe Lotion

**Gluten-Free Savonnerie▲** - All Products

**Hy-Vee** -

Skin Cream

Therapeutic Skin Lotion

**Johnson's** - Head To Toe Fragrance Free Baby Lotion

**Keys** - All Products

**Lubriderm** - Daily Moisture Lotion (Advanced Therapy, Fragrance Free, Regular, Sensitive Skin, w/ SPF 15, w/Sea Kelp Extract, w/Shea & Cocoa Butters)

**Nature's Baby Organics** - Ah Choo Chest Rub, Baby Oil, Diaper Cream, Face & Body Moisturizer, Silky Dusting Powder, Soothing Stick

**Safeway Select** - Lotion Moisturizing Replenishment

# Sleep Aids

**Meijer** - Sleep Aid Nitetime (Caplets, Tablets)

**Safeway Select** - PM Pain Reliever

**Simply Sleep** - Caplets

**Tylenol** - PM Caplets

**Walgreens** -

Nightime Sleep Aid Mini Caplets

Non Aspirin Pain Reliever PM Tablets

Sleep II Tablets

Sleep Aid Tablets

**Wal-Nadol** - Caplets, Non Aspirin (PM Caplets, PM Gelcaps, PM Tablets), PM Extra Strength Caplets, Tablets

# Soap

**Aquaphor** - Baby Gentle Wash & Shampoo
**Arbonne** -
   Aromassentials
     Awaken Sea Salt Scrub 16 oz.
     Unwind Bath Salts
   Bio Nutria Herbal Vapor Soak
   Clear Advantage
     Acne Wash
     Refining Toner
   FC5
     Exfoliating New Cell Scrub
     Purifying Cleanser + Toner
   F.Y.I. Sugar Slush Body Scrub
   Figure 8 Vanish Pre Shower Cellulite Scrub
   SeaSource Detox Spa
     Detoxifying Rescue Wash
     Foaming Sea Salt Scrub
     Purifying Sea Soak
**Avon** -
   Always Body Rinse
   Anew
     Daily Resurfacing Cleanser
     Ultra Cream Cleanser
     Retroactive+ 2 In 1 Cleanser
   Black Suede Hair and Body Wash
   Blue Rush Hair and Body Wash
   Bubble Bath

**Rx** Clearskin

    Cleansing Pads

    Invigorating Cleansing Scrub

    Purifying Astringent Blackhead Clearing Formula

Christian Lacroix (Noir Shower Gel, Rouge Shower Gel)

Crystal Aura Pearlized Shower Gel

Derek Jeter Driven

    Black Body Wash

    Body Wash

    Foaming Face Scrub

    Oil Control Face Wash

Far Away Pearlized Shower Gel

Flower By Cynthia Rowley Shower Gel

Footworks

    Exfoliating Bar Soap

    Tropical Coconut Sea Salt Foot Scrub

    Watermelon Effervescent Foot Tablets

    Watermelon Exfoliating Foot Scrub

Goddess Pearlized Shower Gel

Haiku Shower Gel

Hannah Montana Shower Gel

Healthy Remedies Antibacterial Hand Gel

High School Musical Bubble Bath

His Story Hair and Body Wash

Imari (Bath and Shower Gel, Seduction Shower Gel)

Liiv Botanicals Rejuvenating Facial Cleanser

Mark

    Self Sanctuary Shower Wash (Chocolate Orchid, Honey Jasmine, Lemon Sugar, Violet Berry)

    That's Deep Purifying Gel Cleanser

Mesmerize For Men Hair and Body Wash

Naturals                                                                  **Rx**
  Antibacterial Hand Gel (Cucumber, Gardenia, Peach, Sea, Vanilla)
  Cucumber Melon Antibacterial Liquid Soap
  Lavender & Chamomile Shower Gel
  Mandarin & Jasmine Shower Gel
  Peach (Antibacterial Liquid Soap, Creamy Yogurt Body Wash,
    Shower Gel)
  Plum & Nectarine Moisturizing Shower Gel
  Strawberry & Guava Shower Gel
  Vanilla (Antibacterial Liquid Soap, Creamy Yogurt Body Wash,
    Shower Gel)
Planet Spa
  African Shea Butter Brown Sugar Body Scrub
  Mediterranean Olive Oil Hydrating Body Wash
Perceive For Men Hair and Body Wash
R.P.M. Hair and Body Wash
Rare Gold Shower Gel
Skin So Soft
  Fresh & Smooth Silky Stay Shave Gel
  Fusions Soft & Nourish Dual Softening Body Wash
  Fusions Soft & Replenish Dual Softening Body Wash
  Fusions Soft & Sensual Dual Softening Body Wash
  Original Creamy Body Wash
  Original Moisturizing Shower Gel
  Renew & Refresh Age Defying Rejuvenating Body Cleanser
  Soft & Relaxed Night Bath Soak
  Soft & Sensual
    Creamy Body Wash
    Foaming Oil Body Wash
    Moisturizing Shower Gel
  Summer Soft Refreshing Body Wash

**Rx**   Wintersoft
>  Hand Wash
>  Intense Concentrate

Solutions
>  Completely Clean (Anti Aging Thermal Cleanser, Cleansing Cloths, Micro Exfoliating Cushions)

Surreal Shower Gel

Today Body Rinse

Tomorrow (Body Rinse, For Men Hair and Body Wash)

True Glow Shower Gel

Wild Country Hair and Body Wash

Wish of Happiness Shower Gel

**Burts Bees** -

All In One Wash

Baby Bee Shampoo & Body Wash

Bay Rum Bar Soap

Carrot Complexion Soap

Carrot Soap

Citrus & Ginger Bar Soap

Citrus & Ginger Body Wash

Citrus & Ginger Hand Soap

Green Tea & Lemongrass Hand Soap

Men's Natural Bar Soap

Men's Natural Body Wash

Peppermint & Rosemary Body Wash

Tomato Soap

**California Baby** -

Bubble Bath (Calendula, Calming, Chamomile & Herbs, Colds & Flu, I Love You, Light & Happy, Overtired & Cranky, Party, Super Sensitive)

Calendula Shampoo & Body Wash

## soap

**Rx**

Calming Shampoo & Body Wash

Diaper Area Wash

Handwash (First Aid Moisturizing, Natural Antibacterial Blend Moisturizing, Super Sensitive)

Natural Pregnancy Body Wash

Swimmer's Defense Shampoo & Body Wash

Tea Tree & Lavender Shampoo & Body Wash

**Dessert Essence Organics** -

Age Reversal Pomegranate Facial Cleansing Gel

Almond Body Wash

Bulgarian Lavender Body Wash

Coconut Body Wash

Fragrance Free Body Wash

Green Apple & Ginger Body Wash

Italian Red Grape Body Wash

Red Raspberry Body Wash

Vanilla Chai Body Wash

**Dial** - Liquid Hand Soap

**Fleurish Beauty** - Aloe & Shea Body Wash, Bar Soap (Ambrosia, Cassia Clove, Lavender, Lemongrass, Patchouli, Peppermint, Sandalwood)

**Gluten-Free Savonnerie ▲** - All Products

**Hy-Vee** -

Antibacterial Dish Detergent (Green Apple, Original)

Original Ultra Dish Detergent

Oxygen Cleaner & Stain Remover

Sparkly Clean Detergent (Fresh Scent, Lemon Scent)

Sparkly Clean Dishwasher Detergent (Fresh Scent, Lemon Scent)

Ultra All Fabric Bleach Powder

Ultra Liquid Laundry Detergent w/Bleach Alternative

**Johnson's Soothing Naturals** - Hair & Body Wash

**Keys** - All Products

**Rx** **Nature's Baby Organics** - Bubble Bath
   **Safeway Select** - Baby Wash
   **Tom's Of Maine** - Body Bar (Natural Clear, Natural Deodorant, Natural Moisturizing)

## Stay Awake

**Meijer** - Stay Awake Tablets
**Ultra Pep-Back**
**Vivarin** - Tablets
**Walgreens** - Awake Caffeine Caplets, Maximum Strength Awake Tablets

## Supplements

**Aqua Flow** - Enzymatic Therapy
**Arbonne** - Smart Nutritional Hybrids Daily Nutritional Chews For Teens, Smart Nutritional Hybrids Daily Power Punch For Kids
**Avon** - VitAdvance Flat Stomach, VitAdvance Purified Fish Oil
**Blaine MagOX 400**
**Carlson** - All Supplements
**Country Life** - All Supplements●
**Ensure** - All Shakes
**Ferro Sequels** - High Potency Iron supplement (Tablets)
**Flex A Min** - Complete, Regular Tablets, Triple Strength
**Freed** - All Supplements●
**Giant Eagle Brand** -
   Acerola C
   Acidophilus Capsules
   Beta Carotene

## supplements

**Rx**

Chondroitin Complex Caps
Coenzyme Q10 Softgels
Cranberry
Deodorized Garlic Caps
EPA Fish Oil Softgels
Echinacea
Echinacea/Goldenseal Capsules
Ester C 500 mg
Ferrous Sulfate
Fish Oil
Flaxseed Oil
Folic Acid
Garlic Odorless
Garlic/Parsley Softgels
Ginkgo Biloba
Ginseng Softgels
Ginseng w/Royal Jelly
Green Tea
Lecithin
Lysine Tablets
Magnesium
Maximum Strength Glucosamine/Chondroitin
Melatonin Tablets
Milk Thistle
Odor Free Garlic
Oyster Shell Calcium w/Vitamin D
Oystercal
Potassium Caplets
Saw Palmetto Softgels
St. John's Wort
Stress Tablets

**Rx** **Ginkoba** - Memory

**Ginsana** - Energy

**GlutaSolve** - Powdered Glutamine Supplement (Packets)

**Health Market** -

Ace Antioxidant

Acidophilus

Alpha Lipoic Acid

Beauty Gelatin

Bilberry

Biotin

Black Cohosh w/Soy

Chitosan

Chromium Picolinate

Co Q10

Cranberry Extract

DHEA

Daily Amino Acid

Echinacea Extract

Evening Primrose Oil

Ferrous Sulfate

Flaxseed (Meal, Oil)

Folic Acid

Garlic Extract (Odorless)

Garlic Oil Naturals Softgels

Ginkgo Biloba Extract

Ginseng Extract

Glucosamine

Glucosamine & Chondroitin (Maximum, Regular, TRP)

Grape Seed Extract

Hair & Skin & Nails

Healthy Eyes Extra Vision

## supplements

Herbal Energizer

**Rx**

L Arginine

L Lysine

Lecithin

Lutein

Lycopene

MSM

Melatonin

Milk Thistle Extract

Norwegian Cod Liver Oil

Olive Leaf Extract

Omega 3 Fish Oil Enteric Coated

Omega Complex 3-6-9 (Enteric Coated Triple)

Omega Softgels

Oyster Shell Calcium (Regular, w/Vitamin D)

Papaya Enzymes Chewable

Saw Palmetto Extract

Soy Isoflavones

St. John's Wort Extract

Stress (B w/Zinc, Form Plus Iron Tablets, Tablets)

Valerian Extract

**Iceland Health** - Advanced Memory Formula, Joint Relief Advanced
Formula

**Indigene** -

Memoryl (Capsules)

Pre Tense (Tablets)

Relaxane (Tablets)

**Kirkman** -

Acetyl L Carnitine

Acidophilus Powder

Alpha Ketoglutaric Acid

**Rx**  Alpha Lipoic Acid

Amino Support (Capsules, Powder)

Beta Glucan

Bifido Complex (Advanced Formula, Regular)

Bio Core Dairy

Buffered Magnesium (Glycinate Bio Max Series Powder, Oxide)

Carb Digest w/Isogest

Chromium

Cod Liver Oil (Lemon Lime Liquid, Regular Liquid, w/Vitamins A & D)

Coenzyme Q10 (Capsules, Chewable Tablets, Tablets)

Colostrum Gold (Flavored, Unflavored)

Creatine (Capsules)

DMAE (Capsules, Chewable Wafers)

DMG (Capsules, Capsules w/Folic Acid & B12, Capsules w/Folinic Acid & B12, Liquid, Maximum Strength, w/B12 & Folinic Acid Liquid)

DPP IV Forte

DRN (Detoxification Booster Capsules, Lithium, Vitamin/Mineral Basic Supplement Powder, Vitamin/Mineral LDA Basic Supplement)

Detox Aid Advanced Formula

Detoxification Aid Pro Support II

EFA Powder

EnZymAid Multi Enzyme Complex

EnZym Complete DPP IV II (Regular, w/Isogest)

Everyday Multi Vitamin (Regular, w/o Vitamins A & D)

Five Recipe Cookie Base

Folic Acid (Chewable Tablets, w/B12 Capsules, w/B12 Liquid)

Folinic Acid (Capsules, w/B12 Liquid)

GABA (Plain, w/Niacinamide & Inositol)

Gastro Support

Gastromune AI Support

## supplements

Ginkgo Biloba

**Rx**

Glucosamine Sulfate

Glycine

Grape Extract

Grapefruit Seed Extract

Idebenone

Immuno Aid

Inositol Pure Soluble Powder

Iron Bio Max Series (Capsules, Liquid)

L Glutamine

L Taurine

Lactobacillus Acidophilus

Lactobacillus Duo

MSM Powder (Flavored, Unflavored)

Magnesium Citrate Soluble Powder

Magnesium Glycinate Bio Max Series

Magnesium Malate

Magnesium Sulfate Cream

Maximum Spectrum Enzyme Complete/DPP IV Fruit Free
w/Isogest

Melatonin (Chewables, Plus Magnesium, Slow Release Tablets)

Methyl Aid

Methylcobalamin Concentrated Powder

Milk Thistle

Minerall

Mito Cell Support

Molybdenum

Multi Enzyme Formula

Multi Flora Spectrum

N Acetyl Cysteine

Nordic (Berries, Omega 3 Gummies)

**Rx** Nordic Naturals (Arctic Cod Liver Oil Liquid (Orange, Peach, Regular), Balanced Omega Combination, Cod Liver Oil Soft Gels, DHA Junior Strawberry, ProDHA, ProEFA Capsules, ProEFA Soft Gels, ProEPA, ProOmega Soft Gels)

Nu Thera (Everyday, Everyday Companion, w/P5P, w/o Vitamins A & D)

P5P (Regular, w/Magnesium Glycinate)

Peptidase Complete

Phenol Assist (Companion, Regular)

Pro Bio (Chewable Wafers, Defense, Gold, Inulin Free)

Pro Culture Gold

Pro EFA Junior

Pro Immune Support

Reduced L Glatathione (Capsules, Lotion)

Saccharomyces Boulardii

Selenium

Spectrum Complete (Capsules, Powder Flavored, Powder Regular)

Super Cranberry Extract (Capsules, Chewables)

Super NuThera (Caplets, Capsules, Challenge Powders, Lemon Lime Liquid, New Improved Powder, Powder, Raspberry Flavored Concentrate, Tropical Fruit Liquid, w/P5P Caplets, w/P5P Lemon Lime Flavored Concentrate, w/P5P Liquid, w/P5P New Improved Powder, w/P5P Powder, w/o Vitamins A & D (Cherry Liquid, Regular, Tropical Fruit Liquid))

Super Pro Bio (Bio Max Series)

TMG (Capsules, Capsules w/Folic Acid & B12, Liquid w/Folinic Acid & B12, Powder w/Folic Acid & B12, w/Folic Acid & B12, w/Folinic Acid & B12, w/Folinic Acid & Methyl B12)

Thera Response

Threelac

Vanadium

Yeast Aid (Capsules, Powder)

**Knox For Nails**

## supplements

**Meijer** - 

**Rx**

Acidophilus Bifido RS

Antioxidant

Antioxidant (Natural Caplets, w/Zinc Tablets)

Astaxanthin

Beta Carotene Natural Softgels

Biocosinol

CLA (Conjugated Linolenic Acid)

Chromium Picolinate

Cinnamon Capsules

Cod Liver Oil

CoQ10 (Capsules, Softgels)

Cranberry Caplets

Cranmax

DHA

EPA (Eicosapentaenoic Acid)

Echinacea Caplets

Estroplus Extra Strength

Evening Primrose Oil Softgels

Ferrous Gluconate Tablets

Fish Oil (Concentrate, Enteric Coated, Enteric Softgels, Extra Strength, Extra Strength Enteric Coated, Hi Potency Softgels, Softgels, w/CoQ10)

Flax Seed Oil Softgels

Focus Smart

Folic Natural Tablets

GLA (Gamma Linolenic Acid)

Garlic Hi Potency Odorless Tablets

Glucosamine & Collagen & HA

Glucosamine Chondroitin (3X, All Day Double Strength Tablets, Double Strength Capsules, Extra Strength, Plus MSM, Regular,

**Rx**     Regular Strength Caplets, SOD Free Caplet, w/HA Tablet, w/MSM Double Strength Caplet, w/MSM HLA Caplet)

Glucosamine Complex Caplets

Glucosamine HCL Tablets

Glucosamine Sulfate Caplets

Green Tea

Ginkgo Biloba Caplets

Ginseng Softgels

Hair Skin Nail

Lecithin Softgels

Lutein (Capsules, Softgels)

Lycopene Capsules

Memory & Mood Supplement

Menopause Complex AM PM

Odorfree Garlic

Omega Super Softgels

Panax Ginseng

Papaya Enzyme

Phytosterol Esters

Policosanol Capsules

Potassium Natural Caplets

Saw Palmetto Softgels

Soy IsoflAvones

St. John's Wort Caplets

Super Omega

Vision Formula w/Lutein

Vitamin Mineral Herb Menopause Supplement

**Member's Mark (Sam's Club) -**

Cholesterol Support Complete

Cranberry Extract

CoQ10

Fish Oil

## supplements

**Rx**

Flaxseed Oil

Garlic

Gingko Biloba

Glucosamine +MSM

Glucosamine HCL

Glucosamine Chondroitin

Lutein

Omega 3-6-9

Saw Palmetto

**Natrol** - All Products *(Except Acai Berry Diet, Broccoli Festiv, Carb Intercept Sprinkles, Digest Support, Juice Festiv, Melatonin Liquid, MFM Original, MFM Prime, Oat Bran Tablets, Papaya Enzyme, Probiotic Intestinal Max Care)*

**Nature Made** - All Products *(Except Chewable Vitamin C)*

**Nature's Basket (Giant Eagle)** -

Acidophilus

Beta Carotene

Brain Formula

Cardio Support Softgels

Cholesterol Complex

Chromium Picolinate

Echinacea

Enzyme Complex

Eye Formula Veg Caps

Flaxseed Oil

Folic Acid

Garlic Caps

Ginkgo Biloba

Glucosamine

Kitfit Tigers

Maximum One

**Rx**   Mega Magnesium

Melatonin

Milk Thistle

Non GMO Soy Protein Powder

Potassium

Prostate Formula

Selenomax Selenium

Soft Gel Multi

Vegetarian Mu

Whey Protein Chocolate Powder

Whey Protein Powder

Zinc

**Nature's Bounty** -

Glucosamine Chondroitin Complex Xtra Strength

**Novasource** - Renal High Calorie Supplement Pack (Vanilla)

**NutraJoint** - All Varieties

**Nutrition Now** - All Varieties

**Os-Cal** - Calcium Supplement (500+ D, 500 + Extra D, 500 + Extra D Chewable, Ultra)

**Osteo Bi-Flex** - (Double Strength Softgels, Double Strength Tablets, Plus MSM, Triple Strength Tablets)

**Safeway Select** -

Acidophilus Plus

Docusate Sodium

Focus Smart

Glucosamine Chondroitin

Glucosamine Sulfate

Mineral Oil

Super Omega

Vision Formula

**Schiff** - Probiotics Acidophilus (Tablets)

## supplements

**Schiff Move Free** -

**Rx**

    Advanced

    Advanced Plus MSM (Tablets)

**Simplexity Health** -

    Acidophilus

    Alpha Sun (Capsules, Tablets)

    Bifidus

    ImmuSun

    Omega Sun (Capsules, Tablets)

    OsteoSun

    SBG Zyme

    SBG Zymes Plus

    Simply SBGA

    Spectrabiotic

    StemPlex

    Super Q10

    Super Sun Smoothie

**Top Care** -

    Calcium (Citrate, Regular, w/Vitamin D)

    Glucosamine Chondroitin

**Walgreens** -

    Chromium Picolinate

    Cod Liver Oil

    Ferrous Gluconate

    Ferrous Sulfate

    Fish Oil Softgels

    Flax Seed Oil Softgels

    Folic Acid

    Garlic (Hi Potency, Oil)

    Garlic & Parsley

    Gelatin

**supplements**

**Rx**   Ginkgo Memory
     Ginseng
     Golden Seal C Caplets
     Melatonin
     Papaya Enzyme
     Selenium
     Stress w/Zinc
**Viactiv** - Soft Calcium Chews

## Vitamins & Minerals

**Carlson** - All Vitamins
**Country Life** - All Vitamins●
**Freed** - All Vitamins●
**Giant Eagle Brand** -
    ABC Plus w/Lutein & Lycopene
    ABC Senior w/Lutein
    B Complex & C Time Release Tablets
    B Complex w/Vitamin C
    Calcium 600 Plus D
    Calcium 600 Tablets
    Calcium & Magnesium
    Calcium Magnesium & Zinc
    Calcium Plus D
    Children's Chewable
    Children's Chewable w/Iron
    Multi Day
    Multi Day Calcium/Iron/Zinc
    Multi Day w/Iron
    Vitamin A

## vitamins & minerals

Vitamin B **Rx**

Vitamin B6

Vitamin B12 Tablets

Vitamin C (Chewable, Tablets)

Vitamin C & E Softgels

Vitamin C Time Release Tabs

Vitamin C w/Rose Hips

Vitamin D Tablets

Vitamin E (Natural, Softgels)

Vitamin E Softgels

Vitamin E Water Dispersible

Zinc

### Health Market -

Antioxidant Vitamins

Calcium (Citrate, Citrate Plus D, Coral, Hi Potency Plus, Liquid Plus D, Plus, Plus D, Plus D Super Sized, Regular)

Calcium & Magnesium & Zinc Plus D

Children's Vitamins (Animal Shapes, Animal Shapes Plus Vitamin C, Animal Shapes w/Extra C, Animal Shapes w/Iron, Complete Animal Shapes, Complete Chewables, Sour Citrus Flavored Gummi Bears, Sour Fruit Flavored Gummi Bunnies)

Essential Multiple Vitamin Tablets

Iron

Magnesium

Maximum Multiple Vitamin Tablets

Multiple Vitamins (50 Plus, Mega Men's, Mega Women's, Men's, Women's)

Niacin

One Daily (Active Vitamins, Maximum, Men's, Weight Control, Women's)

Potassium

Prenatal Vitamins (NBE Stuart Prenatal, Regular)

**Rx**   Sentry (Performance, Senior, Senior Vitamins)

Smart Kids Omega 3 Fruit Flavored Gummi Drops

Therapeutic M Vitamins

Vitamin A

Vitamin B (B1, B6, B12, Balanced B)

Vitamin C (Chewables, Regular, Synthetic, Time Released, w/Rose Hips)

Vitamin D

Vitamin E (Blended, Water Soluble)

Zinc Gluconate

**Health Market Natural -**

B Complex w/ Vitamin C

Balanced B

Beta Carotene

Chewable Vitamin C w/Rose Hips

Niacin

Potassium Gluconate

Selenium/Yeast

Vitamin C w/Rose Hips

Vitamin E (DL/AL)

**Kirkman -**

Advanced Adult Multi Vitamin

Advanced Mineral Support

B Complex w/CoEnzymes Pro Support (Capsules, Powder)

Calcium Bio Max Series

Calcium Magnesium Liquid

Calcium w/Vitamin D (Chewable Tablets, Powder Unflavored)

Calcium w/o Vitamin D Bio Max Series

Children's Chewable Multi Vitamin/Mineral (Capsules, Wafers)

Buffered Vitamin C Powder

D Biotin

## vitamins & minerals

Multi Mineral Complex Pro Support

**Rx**

Multi Vitamin Pro Support

MultiVite

Mycellized Vitamin A Liquid

Perry Prenatal

Vitamin B6 (Magnesium Vitamin/Mineral Chewable Wafers, Regular)

Vitamin C (Bio Max Series Buffered Powder Flavored, Bio Max Series Buffered Powder Unflavored, Capsules, Chewables, Tablets)

Vitamin D

Vitamin D3

Vitamin E

Zinc (Bio Max Series, Liquid, Sulfate, w/Vitamin C & Slippery Elm Lozenges)

**Meijer -**

50 Plus w/Ester C

A Shaped (Gummy Chewables, w/Iron Chewables)

Advanced Formula w/Ester C

Calcium (All Day w/Vitamin D, Citrate Chewable, Citrate w/Vitamin D Caplets, Coral, Magnesium + D, Magnesium Zinc Caplet, Natural Oyster Shell Tablet, Phosphorus Plus D, Plus D, Tablets, w/D Chewables, w/D Mineral Tablets, w/Soy Tablets)

Central Vitamin Select

Daily Energy Multi Caplet

Ester C

Ferrous Sulfate (Green Tablets, TR Tablets)

Multivitamin (Bone Health, Cardio Caplet, Century Advantage, Century Mature Tablets, Century Tablets, Hi Potency Men, Hi Potency Women, Inov., Inov. Complete, Inov. Prenatal, Prenatal Tablets, RDI Cholesterol Caplets, RDI Diet Tablets, RDI Men Tablets, RDI Tablets, SNR Tablets, Super Kid Chewables, Thera M Caplets)

**Rx**  Niacin Tablets

One Daily Plus (Mens Tablets, Womens Tablets)

Slow Release Iron

Teen Multi Caplets

Vitamin A

Vitamin B (Natural Tablets, Complex w/Iron)

Vitamin B12 Tablets

Vitamin C (Caplets, Fruit Chewables, Natural w/Rosehips Caplet, Synthetic Orange Chewables, Synthetic Tablets)

Vitamin E (Blended Softgels, Natural Softgels, Oil, Synthetic Softgels, Regular, w/Fish Oil, w/Vitamin C)

Zinc Natural Caplets

**Member's Mark (Sam's Club)** -

Calcium Liquid Gels w/Vitamin D

Chewable Multi Complete

Children's Multivitamin Gummies

Complete Multivitamin

Iron Slow Release

Niacin

One Daily Women's

Potassium

Super B Complex w/Vitamin C

Vitamin B12

Vitamin B Complex w/Vitamin C

Vitamin C w/Natural Rose Hips

Vitamin D3

Vitamin E Natural D Alpha 400 IU

**Natrol** - All Products *(Except Acai Berry Diet, Broccoli Festiv, Carb Intercept Sprinkles, Digest Support, Juice Festiv, Melatonin Liquid, MFM Original, MFM Prime, Oat Bran Tablets, Papaya Enzyme, Probiotic Intestinal Max Care)*

**Nature Made** - All Products *(Except Chewable Vitamin C)*

## vitamins & minerals

**Nature's Basket (Giant Eagle)** -                                    **Rx**
  B12
  B Complex
  One Daily
  Prenatal Complete
  Womens/ Mens Multi Food
  Womens/ Mens 45+
**Nature's Bounty** - Cider Vinegar Tablets, Glucosamine Chondroitin
  Complex Extra Strength
**Nutrition Now** - All Varieties
**Ocuvite** - Lutein Forte
**Pioneer** - Nutritional Formulas (All Varieties)
**Safeway Select** -
  B Complex
  Calcium
  Calcium (Coral Tablets, Plus D 600, W/ Vitamin D)
  Calcium & Magnesium & Zinc
  Central Vite (Multi Card, Senior Formula, Multi Vitamin, w/Lutein)
  Children's Chewable Vitamins (All)
  Iron
  Natural Zinc
  One Tablet Daily Vitamin
  Prenatal Vitamins
  Super Men's Multi Vitamin
  Vitamin C
  Woman's One Tablet Daily
**Schiff** - Niacin Flush Free (Tablets)
**Slice of Life** - Gummy Vitamins For Adults (All Varieties)
**Top Care** -
  Century Advanced Vitamins
  Century Advantage Vitamins

## vitamins & minerals

**Rx**
Century Cardio Health Vitamins
Childrens Gummi Vitamins
Mens Multi Vitamins
Multi Vitamins (High Potency, Max)
PreNatal Vitamins
Womens Multi Vitamins

**Viactiv** - Calcium Soft Chews
**Vitaball** - Vitamin Gumballs
**Walgreens** -
A Thru Z (Advantage Tablets, Hi Potency Caplets, Select Caplets)
Calcium (Citrate Tablet, Citrate Plus Magnesium +D, Citrate w/D, Magnesium + Soy, Tablet, w/D Tablet, w/Minerals Tablet)
Natural B (100, 50, 6)
Natural Beta Carotene
Natural Magnesium
Natural Zinc
Niacin
One Daily Vitamins (50 Plus Formula, Healthy Weight, Mens Formula, Today Women, Women's Way Multi)
Potassium
Super Aytinal (50 Plus, PRR)
Vitamin A (Regular, w/Vitamin D)
Vitamin B Complex w/Vitamin C
Vitamin B1
Vitamin B6 (Synthetic)
Vitamin B12 Time Released Tablets
Vitamin B100 (Time Released)
Vitamin C (Caplets, Chewable Orange, Ester, Orange Tablets, Synthetic, Tablets, Time Released Synthetic, Time Released w/Rose Hips, w/Echinacea, w/Rose Hips)
Vitamin E Softgels

## weight loss

**Rx**

**Walgreens Finest** -
    Calcium Citrate w/ Vitamin D (Tablets)
    Calcium/Magnesium (Tablets)
    Calcium/Magnesium/Zinc (Tablets)
    Calcium Tablets
    Calcium w/Vitamin D (Tablets)
    Coral Calcium (Capsules, Softgels)
    Ester C (Caplets, Tablets)
    Natural Source Calcium Tablets
    Vitamin C Chewable Tablets
    Vitamin C w/Rose Hips (Tablets, Time Released Caplets, Time
      Released Tablets)
    Vitamin E (Blend Softgels, Natural Softgels)
**Yummi Bears** - All Varieties (Organic, Regular)

# Weight Loss

**Alli**

**Arbonne** - Figure 8 On the Go! Weight Loss Chews (Berry Burst,
    Chocolate, Creamy Caramel, Peanut Butter)

**Celebrity Low Carb Diet** - Juice (Original, Wildberry)

**CitriMax Plus**

**CortiSlim** - Original

**Hoodia** - Concentrate, Extract

**Pure CitriMax**

# Index

# index

# index

# index

# index

## Gluten-Free OTC Pharmacy

# NOTES

# NOTES

# NOTES

# NOTES

# NOTES

# Making Gluten-Free Living Easy!

## Cecelia's Marketplace

Kalamazoo, Michigan

www.CeceliasMarketplace.com

# Quick Order Form

**Online Orders:** www.CeceliasMarketplace.com

**Mail Orders:** Kal-Haven Publishing
P.O. Box 20383
Kalamazoo, MI  49019
U.S.A.

| **Cecelia's Marketplace** | Quantity | Price | Total |
|---|---|---|---|
| ***Gluten-Free***<br>Grocery Shopping Guide | _____ | (x $24.95) = | _____ |
| ***Gluten/Casein Free***<br>Grocery Shopping Guide | _____ | (x $24.95) = | _____ |
| ***Gluten/Casein/Soy Free***<br>Grocery Shopping Guide | _____ | (x $24.95) = | _____ |

**Sales Tax:** Michigan residents please add 6% sales tax          _____

**Sub Total:**          _____

**Shipping:**  (quantities 1-2 add $5.25)
(quantities 3-6 add $9.95)          _____

**Total:**          _____

*Please make check or money order payable to Kal-Haven Publishing

Name:_____

Address:_____

City:_____State:_____Zip:_____

Email address:_____

# Making Gluten-Free Living Easy!

## Cecelia's Marketplace

Kalamazoo, Michigan

www.CeceliasMarketplace.com

# Quick Order Form

 **Online Orders:** www.CeceliasMarketplace.com

✉ **Mail Orders:** Kal-Haven Publishing
P.O. Box 20383
Kalamazoo, MI  49019
U.S.A.

| Cecelia's Marketplace | Quantity | Price | Total |
|---|---|---|---|

**Gluten-Free**
Grocery Shopping Guide     _____  (x $24.95) =  _____

**Gluten/Casein Free**
Grocery Shopping Guide     _____  (x $24.95) =  _____

**Gluten/Casein/Soy Free**
Grocery Shopping Guide     _____  (x $24.95) =  _____

**Sales Tax:** Michigan residents please add 6% sales tax     _____

**Sub Total:**     _____

**Shipping:**     (quantities 1-2 add $5.25)
(quantities 3-6 add $9.95)     _____

**Total:**     _____

*Please make check or money order payable to Kal-Haven Publishing

Name: _____

Address:_____

City:_____State:_____Zip:_____

Email address:_____

# Making Gluten-Free Living Easy!

**Cecelia's Marketplace**

Kalamazoo, Michigan

www.CeceliasMarketplace.com

# Quick Order Form

 **Online Orders:** www.CeceliasMarketplace.com

✉ **Mail Orders:** Kal-Haven Publishing
P.O. Box 20383
Kalamazoo, MI 49019
U.S.A.

| Cecelia's Marketplace | Quantity | Price | Total |
|---|---|---|---|
| **Gluten-Free**<br>Grocery Shopping Guide | _____ | (x $24.95) = | _____ |
| **Gluten/Casein Free**<br>Grocery Shopping Guide | _____ | (x $24.95) = | _____ |
| **Gluten/Casein/Soy Free**<br>Grocery Shopping Guide | _____ | (x $24.95) = | _____ |

| | | |
|---|---|---|
| **Sales Tax:** Michigan residents please add 6% sales tax | _____ |
| **Sub Total:** | _____ |
| **Shipping:** (quantities 1-2 add $5.25)<br>(quantities 3-6 add $9.95) | _____ |
| **Total:** | _____ |

*Please make check or money order payable to Kal-Haven Publishing

Name: _____

Address: _____

City: _____ State: _____ Zip: _____

Email address: _____

# Making Gluten-Free Living Easy!

## Cecelia's Marketplace

Kalamazoo, Michigan

www.CeceliasMarketplace.com

# Quick Order Form

 **Online Orders:** www.CeceliasMarketplace.com

✉ **Mail Orders:** Kal-Haven Publishing
P.O. Box 20383
Kalamazoo, MI  49019
U.S.A.

| **Cecelia's Marketplace** | Quantity | Price | Total |
|---|---|---|---|
| ***Gluten-Free***<br>Grocery Shopping Guide | _____ | (x $24.95) = | _____ |
| ***Gluten/Casein Free***<br>Grocery Shopping Guide | _____ | (x $24.95) = | _____ |
| ***Gluten/Casein/Soy Free***<br>Grocery Shopping Guide | _____ | (x $24.95) = | _____ |

**Sales Tax:** Michigan residents please add 6% sales tax    _____

**Sub Total:**    _____

**Shipping:**    (quantities 1-2 add $5.25)
(quantities 3-6 add $9.95)    _____

**Total:**    _____

*Please make check or money order payable to Kal-Haven Publishing

Name: _____

Address: _____

City: _____State: _____Zip: _____

Email address: _____